Rudie

FISHES OF THE MALDIVES

INDIAN OCEAN

Published by:	Atoll Editions, Cairns, Australia. First edition published as Photo Guide to Fishes of the Maldives, 1998. Second edition, Fishes of the Maldives *Indian Ocean*, 2014. Reprinted with scientific name updates 2018. Cover Design by Joe Calvert.

Citation:	KUITER, R. H. 2014. *Fishes of the Maldives: Indian Ocean*, Cairns, Australia, Atoll Editions.

Front Cover photos:	Main photo: Whale Shark *Rhincodon typus* – Melody Sky, www.melodysky.com
	Bottom photos, left to right: Powder-blue Surgeonfish *Acanthurus leucoster*, Clown Triggerfish *Balistoides conspicillum*, Coral Beauty *Centropyge bispinosa* - Rudie Kuiter; Scalloped Hammerhead Shark *Sphyrna lewini* - Patrick Van Moer.
Title Page photo:	McCosker's Wrasse *Paracheilinus mccoskeri* (p207). An extended ray on the dorsal fin readily identifies males.
Back Cover photos:	Top to bottom: Big-nose Unicornfish *Naso vlamingii*, Threadfin Basslet *Nemanthias carberryi*, Leopard Blenny *Exallias brevis* - Rudie Kuiter, Zebra Shark *Stegostoma fasciatum* – Guy Stevens.

ISBN:	Soft cover edition: 978-1-876410-25-4 Hard back edition: 978-1-876410-97-1
Available from:	Atoll Editions. www.atolleditions.com.au www.fishesofthemaldives.com

Table of Contents

FOREWORD

This is the second edition of the book that was originally published as Photo Guide to Fishes of the Maldives, by Rudie H Kuiter, in 1998. Fishes of the Maldives *Indian Ocean* has been fully revised and substantially expanded to include, for the first time, all the sharks and rays of the Maldives known within a divers depth range. In the present volume, changes have been made to the scientific Latin name of 80 bony fishes. Around 25% of all fish photographs have been replaced and fish text has been fully revised and updated to reflect new information on life history, habitat, distribution and identification. Text also includes notes on regional and local endemic species, doubtful records and new discoveries for the Maldives. This book also differentiates between Maldives forms and other forms that occur elsewhere, making it a versatile fish guide for other regions in the Indian Ocean.

The first edition of this book has enjoyed remarkable success as a comprehensive photo guide for snorkellers, divers, anglers and aquarists and this new edition will fill an important gap in current knowledge with the inclusion of a comprehensive section on sharks and rays of the Maldives.

This book serves primarily as an identification guide, however selected photos highlight not only colouration and key identification features, but also the varied and unique habitat in which they live. I sincerely hope this edition will assist all who use it and provide a new generation of marine scientists, educators and researchers with a critical resource in which to better understand the life history and habitats of fishes, sharks and rays of the Maldives and Indian Ocean region.

Tim Godfrey,
Publisher.
January 2014.

The role of taxonomy in understanding and managing marine ecosystems is pivotal. Taxonomy provides basic and fundamental understanding of ecosystem components and units (biodiversity) that are important in its functioning, its maintenance and sustainable use. Without this understanding it is very difficult to conserve species through targeted management intervention. The loss of global marine biodiversity at an alarming rate means that difficult but important decisions have to be made now to protect species and their habitats. Consequently, accurate species identification in the field would allow more people to understand and appreciate coral reef fish. This Guide is a fundamental step forward in understanding and managing coral reef fish species of the Maldives.

Ameer Abdulla, PhD
Senior Advisor, Marine Biodiversity and Conservation Science
IUCN Global Marine and Polar Program

Senior Research Fellow
Centre for Biodiversity and Conservation Science
University of Queensland, Australia

ACKNOWLEDGEMENTS

The generosity of many people who have contributed to this book in various ways has been overwhelming. Firstly, I would like to thank those who played a major role in the production of the first edition of the book itself *Photo Guide to Fishes of the Maldives*. Tim Godfrey, thanks for asking me to do the book, and also for organising the photographic expeditions. Thanks to the participants of the original expeditions, Toshi Kozawa, Junko Maruoka and Neville Coleman for their natural ability to work with species, which resulted in, not only a more efficient distribution of the work-load, but lively discussions after dives. I greatly appreciate the contributions made by Jörg Aebi, Mustag Hussain, Roger Steene, Charles Anderson, Jack Randall, Jerry Allen, Scott Michael, Helmut Debelius and Herwarth Voigtmann. Also thanks to those people in Malé for their hospitality and for additional diving by Gert-Jan van Weert of Sea Explorers; and to his wife Shaheena for convincing me that seahorses exist in the Maldives. Thank you to Charles and Sue Anderson for the fun dive-trip during my first visit to the Maldives and for putting me up.

Rudie H. Kuiter

I am thankful to Rudie Kuiter for agreeing to include a sharks and rays section to Fishes of the Maldives *Indian Ocean* and for providing the initial text and photos to support it. I am grateful to Ameer Abdulla, senior marine advisor of the IUCN, and sponsors Global Blue and USAID for their support and funding to drive greater research in this area. I'm appreciative of designer Dave Saed who provided patient and reliable service from the other side of the globe and also Joe Calvert for his diligence and pre-press preparation of files. The basis for research of sharks was from papers published in the early 1990's by Charles Anderson, Ahmed Hafiz, and others in Marine Research Section, Male'. Important contributions of unpublished photos, provided additional confirmation of species, especially of the rays, and further observations by divers with many years of experience in the Maldives, provided additional text beyond what is available in the general literature. Where possible, all photos included were taken in the Maldives and I would especially like to thank Guy Stevens, who made his library of exceptional photographs available, and give credit to Marc Zaalberg, and the many other individual photographers who generously provided their photos for use in this section. Taxonomy, choice of common English species names and mode of reproduction often create energetic debates and I'm grateful to Rudie Kuiter, Anne-Marie Kitchen-Wheeler, Guy Stevens, Richard Rees, Pascal Geraghty, Ed Roberts, Nick Graham and Colin Simpfendorfer for their contributions and clarifications in this field.

Tim Godfrey

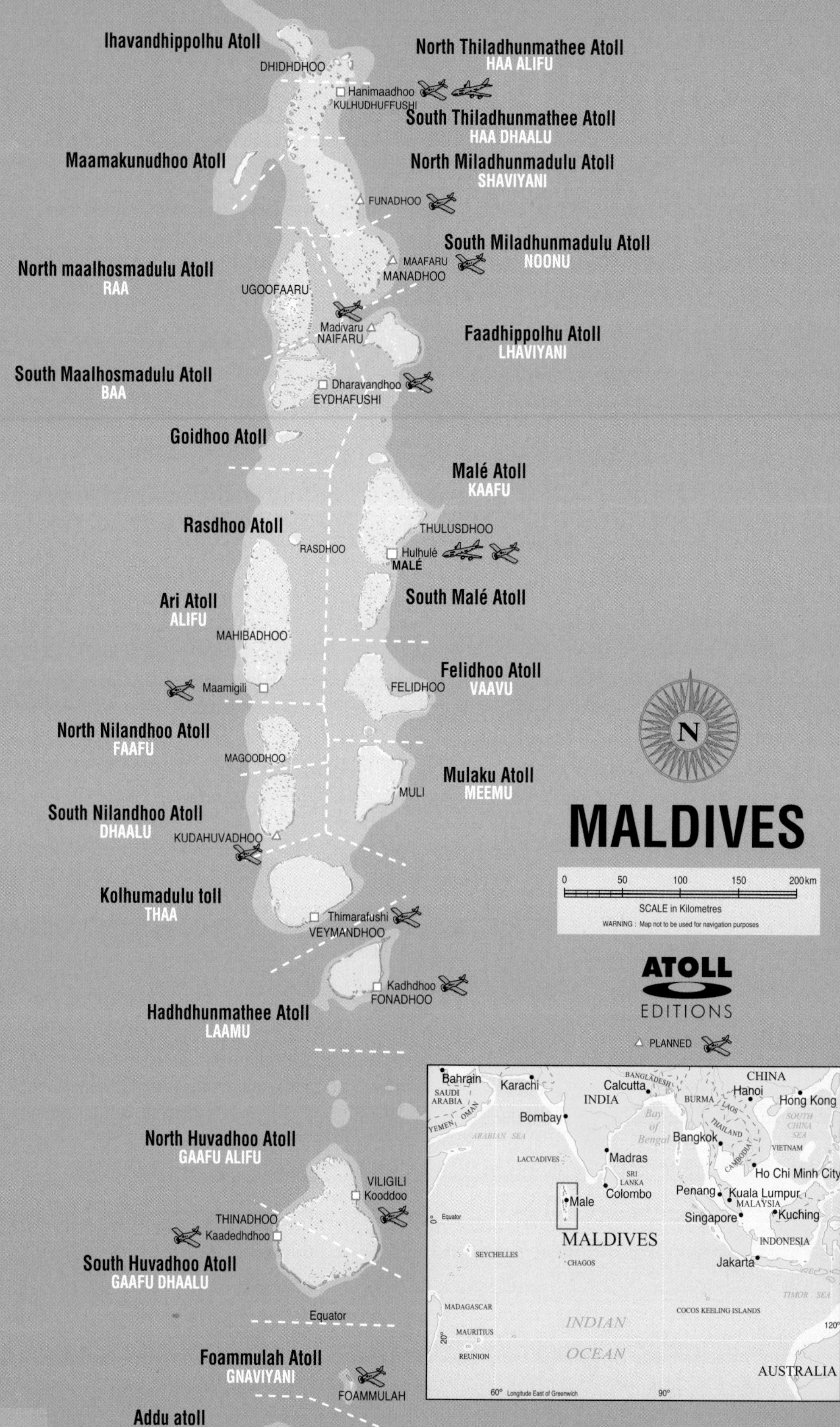

Ihavandhippolhu Atoll
DHIDHDHOO
North Thiladhunmathee Atoll
HAA ALIFU
Hanimaadhoo
KULHUDHUFFUSHI
South Thiladhunmathee Atoll
HAA DHAALU
Maamakunudhoo Atoll
North Miladhunmadulu Atoll
SHAVIYANI
FUNADHOO
South Miladhunmadulu Atoll
NOONU
MAAFARU
MANADHOO
North maalhosmadulu Atoll
RAA
UGOOFAARU
Madivaru
NAIFARU
Faadhippolhu Atoll
LHAVIYANI
South Maalhosmadulu Atoll
BAA
Dharavandhoo
EYDHAFUSHI
Goidhoo Atoll
Malé Atoll
KAAFU
Rasdhoo Atoll
THULUSDHOO
RASDHOO
Hulhulé
MALÉ
Ari Atoll
ALIFU
South Malé Atoll
MAHIBADHOO
Felidhoo Atoll
VAAVU
Maamigili
FELIDHOO
North Nilandhoo Atoll
FAAFU
MAGOODHOO
Mulaku Atoll
MEEMU
MULI
South Nilandhoo Atoll
DHAALU
KUDAHUVADHOO
MALDIVES
0
50
100
150
200 km
SCALE in Kilometres
WARNING : Map not to be used for navigation purposes
Kolhumadulu toll
THAA
Thimarafushi
VEYMANDHOO
ATOLL
EDITIONS
Kadhdhoo
FONADHOO
Hadhdhunmathee Atoll
LAAMU
PLANNED
North Huvadhoo Atoll
GAAFU ALIFU
VILIGILI
Kooddoo
THINADHOO
Kaadedhdhoo
South Huvadhoo Atoll
GAAFU DHAALU
Equator
Foammulah Atoll
GNAVIYANI
FOAMMULAH
Addu atoll
SEENU
HITHADHOO
Gan
Bahrain
SAUDI ARABIA
OMAN
YEMEN
Karachi
Calcutta
BANGLADESH
INDIA
Bombay
ARABIAN SEA
Bay of Bengal
LACCADIVES
Madras
SRI LANKA
Colombo
Male
MALDIVES
SEYCHELLES
CHAGOS
MADAGASCAR
MAURITIUS
REUNION
INDIAN
OCEAN
CHINA
Hanoi
Hong Kong
BURMA
LAOS
THAILAND
SOUTH CHINA SEA
VIETNAM
Bangkok
CAMBODIA
Ho Chi Minh City
Penang
Kuala Lumpur
MALAYSIA
Kuching
Singapore
INDONESIA
Jakarta
TIMOR SEA
COCOS KEELING ISLANDS
AUSTRALIA
0°
Equator
20°
60°
Longitude East of Greenwich
90°
120°

ABOUT THE MALDIVES by Tim Godfrey

Geography

The Republic of the Maldives lies to the southwest of Sri Lanka stretching over 868 kms between 7° 6' 30" N to just south of the equator 0° 42' 30" S, and between longitudes 72° 32' 30" E and 73° 46' 15" E.

The Maldives consists of some 1200 islands and cays grouped into 25 carbonate atolls separated by depths of 200 meters or more and surrounded by a steep sea floor 2500 – 3000 m deep to the east and 2800 – 4200 m deep to the west. The archipelago comprises a total area of approximately 21,370 km2 of which coral reefs, lagoons and islands make up to 21% of the total area (Naseer and Hatcher, 2004). An estimated 0.5 % is dry land. The atolls vary in size from the tiny atoll of Thoddoo with a diameter of 2.5 kms and only one island, to the great Huvadhoo Atoll with a length of 82 kms, a width of 67 kms and comprising 244 islands. Most of the north and central part of the Maldives is made up of two separate chains of atolls separated by an "inner sea", a submerged plateau with depths ranging between 300 m and 500 m. In the south, the atolls form a single chain and are separated by wider and deeper channels. The widest channel, Huvadhoo Kandu, otherwise known as the One and Half Degree Channel is 96 km across with depths reaching 900 m.

Reef geomorphology

The Maldives archipelago lies on a volcanic basement at a depth of about 2000 m and makes up the central part of a submarine ridge between the Laccadives and Chagos Bank. The ridge was formed by basalt outpourings from a volcanic hotspot under the island of Réunion and the northward migration of the Indian Plate during the Cretaceous and early Cenozoic times. During the Quaternary, as many as 27 glacial sea level cycles with eustatic sea levels fluctuating by more than 120 m at various times have been recorded, resulting in many 'karst-induced' coral reef formations and geomorphological structures.

Reef geomorphology differs considerably between the north and south of the Maldives. Most atoll lagoons have an inward sloping floor with lagoon depths greater than the atoll rim. In the north, atoll lagoons are shallower at around 30 m, while in the south lagoons are up to 90 m in depth. Woodroffe (1992) suggested rainfall, monsoonal reversal and storms have a major influence on the lagoon depth, continuity of atoll rim, reef growth and island formation. The strength and dominance of the south-west monsoon (April to November) over the north-east monsoon (November to April) may result in greater surface runoff and solutional erosion occurring in the south of the atolls.

Weather

The weather in the Maldives is determined to a large extent by the monsoon circulation. Each year there are two monsoon seasons, the north-east monsoon, Iruvaa, and the south-west monsoon, Hulhagu. The prevailing winds can become quite strong and are from the N-NE-E during the north-east monsoon and the SW-W-NW during the south-west monsoon. The south-west monsoon typically brings much more rain, cloud cover and reduced visibility with rougher seas, while the north-east monsoon usually brings blue skies and exceptionally clear waters for much of the time. The monsoonal influence is greater in the north of the Maldives than the south, which is more influenced by the equatorial currents. Mean annual rainfall of 2390 mm in the south is substantially greater than the 1650 mm in the north.

According to the traditional Maldivian calendar, Nakaiy, the Iruvaa begins on December 10 with typically strong, unsettled winds and rough seas that gradually travel down the Maldives from the north. It is divided into nine 'Nakaiy', or periods, with the last Nakaiy finishing on April 7. The Iruvaa brings the driest period – the air having a comparatively short sea track compared with that during the remainder of the year.

The Hulhagu begins on April 8 and starts with a storm and rain moving up from the south. It is followed by a brief period of calm winds. The Hulhagu has 18 Nakaiy with the last one finishing on December 9. The hot season is in March and April, while the wet season is from June to September. Gales and moderate to rough seas are common during the wet season and cloudy days are more frequent. There is considerable variation in climate between the northern and southern atolls in the Maldives. In the south the rainfall is greater and temperatures are less extreme, as the seasons are less evident close to the equator.

Ocean water temperatures rarely vary beyond 27 – 30° C, although a thermocline can sometimes be experienced at depths below 20 metres. During hot periods, water temperatures inside the lagoons increases measurably, influencing water temperatures inside the atolls.

Currents

The exposure of the Maldives to the vast Indian Ocean ensures that an immense body of water is constantly flowing across the plateau on which these atolls are built. Oceanic currents are largely influenced by the direction of the trade winds. These currents create deep-water upwelling around the atolls, bringing nutrient rich waters to the surface, heralding the start of life in the atoll food chain. The nutrient-rich currents flow from the NE to the SW during the Iruvaa and from the SW to the NE during the Hulhagu. By the time they reach the lee of the atoll, primary productivity is at its peak and zooplankton is supporting large populations of manta rays, whale sharks and other marine life. Currents can be of great strength and in the channels near Malé, speeds of four knots or more have been recorded. Tidal currents flow according to the height of the tide and the direction of the prevailing winds and are said to be much weaker than oceanic currents, though they cause velocity variations in the flow. At atoll passages, current streams can be quite irregular due to the islands, reefs and sandy shoals.

Cross section of a coral reef in the Maldives

The outer reef slope of the atolls are generally distinguished by greater depths and increased clarity of water. The visibility may exceed 50 metres. Looking down the reef slope, coral and fish communities change rapidly with increasing depth. At depths greater than 20 metres, wave surge is non-existent and extensive coral growth may occur to depths of 50 metres and more. Light availability is the main factor limiting the range of the coral here. The upper parts of the outer reef slope may be affected by wave action, restricting the growth of more delicate plate coral. Coral growth can be wiped out in a single freak storm in this zone. In areas less exposed to wave action, extensive stands of staghorn corals can dominate. A great variety of fish life occurs among the coral in this zone.

The reef front is the part of the reef which takes the full force of the ocean swells. The coral here tends to

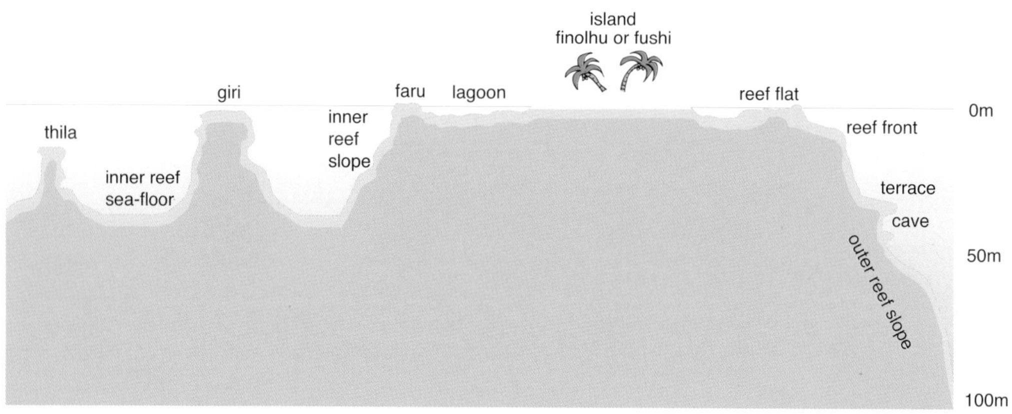

Hurasdhoo, Alifu Dhaalu. Photo: Sigurd Schjoett

be gnarled and stunted as a result of the pounding by waves. The reef flats can range in width from a few metres to a few kilometres. Rainwater can damage or completely destroy the coral in this zone if heavy or cyclonic rainfall coincides with very low tides. Lagoons with good circulation of water may have large stands of branching corals growing on the sand. Lagoons can trap many fish varieties as the tide recedes. On the inner reef slope, coral growth may be rich if the slope is not too steep. Steep or vertical slopes may be bare. Many interesting caves, overhangs and gullies can occur in this zone. Rising from the floor are separate coral reefs or coral patches, known as giris and thilas. The giris nearly reach the surface, whereas the thilas lay below at depths between five and 15 metres.

There are many words in Dhivehi, the local language, used to describe islands and reefs. A fushi is a big island usually on the outside reef of the atoll and a finolhu is an island with few or no coconut trees. Dhoo and Huraa are other words for an island. Reefs are usually called farus or falhus. A faru, is a reef partially exposed at low tide and a falhu is often a reef encircling a lagoon, sometimes with one or more islands inside. Gaa and haa are other words used to describe coral reefs.

Further Reading

Naseer, A & Hatcher, B 2004, 'Inventory of the Maldives' coral reefs using morphometrics generated from Landsat ETM+ imagery', *Coral Reefs*, vol. 23, pp. 161–168.

Woodroffe, CD 1992, 'Morphology and evolution of reef islands in the Maldives', *Proc 7th Int Coral Reef Symp, Guam*, 2:1, pp. 217–1226.

INTRODUCTION

Maldives reefs are exceptionally rich with fish life, with schools often filling the water column between the surface and the reef edge. Divers visiting tropical reefs for the first time can be overwhelmed by the myriad of colours and movement when watching fish. The abundant fish in the water column and brightly coloured individuals amongst the corals, provide many opportunities for fish-watching or photographing them. Photography has become one of the most popular pastimes with the tourist diver and nowadays almost every diver has a camera. For the majority of divers, fish are their main subjects and for some it is the largest fish, such as the Whale Shark, that is targeted while for others, it is the smaller but interesting goby. Many divers are taking more and more notice of the smaller species that live in the reefs, with the added excitement of finding new species. In the Maldives, shooting fish is with a camera only, as spear guns are not allowed.

This book encompasses all bony and cartilaginous fishes known from the Maldives Archipelago likely to be noticed by divers, including the smallest species. In all, over one thousand different fishes are known from the area, including sharks and pelagic fishes that occasionally visit reefs and more will undoubtedly turn up as time goes by. Numerous photographic books on diving and marine life in the Maldives have been published by diver-photographers, but they often include underwater pictures taken elsewhere. Such photographs may show fish species that are not known from the Maldives. The most reliable source on Maldives fishes was published by Randall & Anderson in 1993, based on specimens and positive sighting or photographs from the actual area of the Maldives, including notes on doubtfully recorded species. This list formed the basis for this book, but many new records have been added since. Much of the Maldives Archipelago remains unexplored by fish experts and new areas visited usually results in several new records. Many of the photographs taken for this book represent new records for the Maldives. In all, about 1200 photographs were used, illustrating over 730 species.

Oceanic locations, such as the Maldives, support fewer habitats compared to large continental land masses and as a result, species diversity is usually less. Generally, the more remote the less diverse, but the Maldives stretches over a large area from north to south, crossing the equator, supporting a rich ecology that balances out the lack of diversity with abundance of particular species. The colourful species are especially noted when schooling in massive numbers, forming a spectacular sight rarely seen elsewhere and is a major attraction to divers from all over the world.

Fig. 1. The Maldives is noted for the abundance of particular species, such as this school of Black Tail Barracuda *Sphyraena genie*. Photo: Damien Perry.

ABOUT THE BOOK

This book serves primarily as a photographic identification guide for divers. Of course, it is of interest to aquarists and everybody else interested in fishes, sharks and rays. Many species have geographical variations, meaning that a particular species looks slightly different between different areas, and this particularly applies in the Maldives. Some of such species may even prove to be valid species. For this reason, pictures for this book were taken in the Maldives as much as possible, giving additional value to the book. A photograph taken in a particular locality represents a record, even if the scientific name changes in the future. The entire book is a collection of photographs that show species in living colours, which is very useful for taxonomists who often work with preserved material. Photographs taken outside the Maldives are captioned with their locality. Almost every picture was taken in the wild, only a few in aquariums. The book includes the work of some other contributing photographers and they are credited with each of their pictures.

Species order (classification)

Species are arranged in an order generally accepted by fish taxonomists: starting with the ones considered the most primitive, and ending with those most advanced, in evolutionary terms. However, as this book serves mainly as a photo guide and images are the main tool to identify particular species, some compromises were made to put more similar species closer together to make comparison easier. This book is not about systematics and family is the highest level, with each containing genera, and each genera containing species. Each level or group, family, genus, species, etc, is called a taxon, and scientists working these groups are called taxonomists. A particular species is a life form that reproduces itself and keeps its distinctive identity. Those species that have evolved most recently, separately from a common ancestor, are known as sibling species. They can be very similar and often there is some debate about

Fig. 2. Swimming as a pair in Bali, Indonesia *Chaetodon trifasciatus* and its Pacific sibling *C. lunulatus*. Several sibling butterflyfishes overlap in range, but usually form pairs between their own kind. Mixed pairs are rare and may produce infertile offspring.

them being a valid species in their own right, a subspecies, or merely a geographical variation. It is generally accepted that when two such forms occur together and maintain their identity they are regarded as good species. Sometimes sibling species occur in mixed pairs and may produce infertile hybrids (Fig. 2.).

Siblings are very closely related and always placed in the same genus. Those that share key characteristics or certain diagnostic features are also closely related and belong to the same genus. When there are a number of similar species in a genus, that derived from a common ancestor, they are referred to as a species-complex. Species that have evolved with other strong features that typify them are usually placed in their own genus, but like species level, the genus level is sometimes difficult to determine with intermediate forms. You can't simply draw a line between levels. Each species is given a scientific name that consists of two parts, the first is the genus, and the second the species. If a particular genus comprises a number of species, the first or genus name is repeated for each species and followed by a different second or species name. Scientific names are always written in italics. The genera start with a capital letter, while species always start in lower case.

EVOLUTION
SPECIES CREATION

General
Creatures change over time, but not without reason. In general, each species is perfectly suited to a particular environment, 'in tune' as often stated. In a stable environment there is no need to change and species can remain the same for numerous generations with perhaps some 'fine tuning' that may be reflected in slight colour variations or aspects of behaviour that makes life a little easier.

When a stable environment is interrupted by some natural cause, such as temperature and/or sea-level alterations, the habitat and its creatures change or move accordingly to suit new conditions. Changes versus time are variable, from gradual over millions of years or relatively fast, taking a few thousand years. The rate of change determines the adaptability of life forms. If changes are gradual, then species can adapt more easily compared to fast rates. Fast changing habitat causes a species dropout, or creates highly adaptable new species. The evolution process is more related to change in the environment than time. Changes may happen regularly or after long stable times and can come in various forms. It could be a single impact event that could have little to enormous consequences, depending on the severity and duration of the event, and whether it stabilises or continues with fluctuations or change at various rates. A volcanic eruption and an ice age could be viewed as opposite extremes of evolutionary change: the first being very short but drastic and probably killing many animals but not effecting evolution; the second more gradual and causing slow modifications of faunas where species can adapt.

At great depths in the sea, where temperatures and conditions are very stable, fishes are the most primitive and are like living fossils. In the shallows, where temperatures and conditions greatly fluctuate, fishes are the most evolved and highly diversified. Continental drift over tens of millions of years, making land rise and sink, has shaped the world as we know it. Oceanic currents have changed, influencing the weather and altering land and sea environments. Global change continues to occur, seemingly at the same slow pace, and so will evolution.

Adaptation
Nature always experiments and offspring receive something extra from their parents, but with many variations distributed throughout their brood. A slightly longer snout or some colour modification in a few individuals may give them the edge to survive better than the rest. The survivors will reproduce and maintain the advantage that made them more successful with added variations, amplifying the best features to be more successful with each next generation. Particular features will develop in different habitats, and given enough time such species become so different from their original form, that they are no longer compatible. Species change with the environment, resulting in additional or separate species, and sometimes in a complex of new species between different environments, depending on circumstances.

Humans have created ornamental forms of particular fish-species in relatively short periods by selective breeding over a few hundred years. Naturally (in situ), such changes are much slower, probably taking thousands to millions of years, depending on many factors such as lifespans and environmental changes, or dispersal possibilities during environmental changes. The larger species that usually live much longer than the smaller ones are clearly at a disadvantage by having fewer generations over time. The larger species are less numerous and live in more stable and deeper habitats. The small species are most specious in shallow tropical zones.

Faunas dividing

Continental drift causes land to move slowly across the earth surface. Like Noahs Ark, entire faunas, including the surrounding sea, were taken on a journey that began millions of years ago. During that time habitats changed in various ways or to degrees between different areas, regardless of distance or time. Where areas were split, drifting in opposite directions, we can find parallel-zones far apart, in which parts of the fauna have changed the least, and closely represent the ancestral fauna. Zones of particular interest include subtropical waters such as in Japan and Australia, where common fauna are found, indicating separation a long time ago.

Separations of faunas between Indian and Pacific Oceans appear to be relatively recent, and are more related to changes in the environment than continental drift. Temperatures and sea-levels fluctuated during ice-ages, causing faunas to slowly shift geographically. The species changed slightly between the different areas, resulting in sub-species and many closely related siblings. Some of the most recent ones have returned to their ancestral ground and can be found together in the areas of Java or Bali, Indonesia. Those that dispersed earlier are geographically much further separated, but the siblings remain remarkably similar. Faunas that moved and followed the same conditions changed little, but those left behind often changed dramatically. If a species survived in the changed area, it would change accordingly, whilst those migrating away would change only slightly by comparison. The resulting three forms are usually isolated and can be geographical variations, subspecies, or valid species. There are many such examples in the Indo-Pacific. The most changed species occupy the area of Indonesia, the least changed occurs in two very similar forms, one to the west in the Red Sea and east in Hawaii; or north in Japan and south in Australia.

When a particular species becomes separated into isolated populations for whatever reason, with each having its own environmental pressures, several developments can take place. Firstly, the entire fauna, including plants, corals and fish amongst others, gradually travels in a certain direction, staying in touch with conditions that requires the least change and species are under no pressure to change. When the faunas are split under those conditions, migration is usually in opposite directions and can travel a great distance with time, resulting in some very similar species in geographically distant locations. Migration of faunas have occurred over millions of years and still show remarkable similarities in the make up of species between different areas, some of which are so similar that many scientists have problems understanding this phenomena. The best approach appears to be to treat an entire fauna as a specific entity.

Usually many species show individuality to various degrees, from clearly being good species to those difficult to separate into species in their own right. Techniques for determining a species is generally based on physical features, with some limitations, and differences are not easily seen. Modern techniques such as electrophoresis or DNA can be useful, but don't always give results. The lumping of similar forms into single species has the potential of endangering a species. Different looking populations should be treated as separate species until shown without doubt to be the same, rather than the other way around. With loss of habitat, especially estuarine ones that are taken over by human development, populations could vanish.

The more species have evolved and are different at higher degrees, the more the above analyses becomes obvious, including at higher taxon levels. In general, the most similar species are the furthest apart, geographically speaking. Secondly, as the fauna changes or migrates away from an area, those left behind, such as in land-locked situations, have to adapt and change the most to suit new the conditions or vanish. In some cases marine environments were cut-off from the sea and gradually turned into freshwater lakes. Some species were able to adapt, even sharks. Isolation can just as well be in the sea itself. If one imagines a small island with quickly changing conditions and nowhere to go, the only options for species is adapting to changes to survive, or alternatively vanish. In most stable environments of recent

Fig. 3. Left, the Exquisite Wrasse *Cirrhilabrus exquisites* is only found in the Indian Ocean. Right, its Pacific sibling going under the same name, even though it is totally different and should be recognised as a species in its own right. Juveniles and females of sibling wrasse species are often similar, but fully coloured males, as shown in these pictures, should erase any doubt.

times, the species diversity is the greatest, and often genera have numerous species. The greatest diversity is found near the largest land masses, but especially where numerous strings of islands form extensions over great distances, such as the Indo-Malay region where island hopping of larval fishes can influence speciation. When speciation occurred earlier in time, the diversity was at different levels now, and this shows in the various eco-systems. For instance, in temperate shallow seas diversity shows at genus level, whilst in deep water with the more primitive fishes, this is at family levels.

When recent separation of faunas occurred, different species are the most similar. Such species are mainly divided between Indian and Pacific Oceans, the sibling species. In many cases there are colour variations that are seen as geographical forms, and this is particularly relative to Maldives fishes. However, in future I expect that most of such variations will be recognised as species in their own right.

Scientific and common names

With many languages and many localised names used for numerous creatures or plants, a scientific framework of taxons to overcome this problem began about 200 years ago. Now we can apply an international name to a fish, the scientific name, so everybody knows what fish we are talking about. Similarly, to a family such as LABRIDAE that represents a particular group of fishes known under various names or in different languages, they are known as wrasses in English. Fish taxonomy has some way to go yet to get itself sorted out. On the one hand, new species are still being found; and on the other hand, the same species may have been given different names by different people. The first name has priority and later names are synonyms. As literature research continues, and original specimens are examined in collections held by institutions, an older name than the present one may be found, and the name is changed accordingly.

Sometimes species placed in different genera are found to be generically the same, so the oldest genus is recognised. This may cause a minor change to the actual species name. The genus has a certain gender that can be feminine, masculine or neutral, and this is reflected in the species name as well. Masculine names of species often end in "us" and equivalent feminine names ends in "a". As the various revisions or studies iron out problems, scientific names remain unstable among some groups. Not everybody agrees to what is a species. Usually someone who specialises in a particular group will find some differences, but is often biased towards wanting to find this. Some scientists are determined in calling something a new species, going to great lengths to point out minor differences, whilst others lump different ones together, only pointing out the similarities.

In the process of producing this book, several species received name changes, and even some genera among gobies were changed at the last minute. Several species names are questionable and marked as such. Sp. is the abbreviation of a single species and spp. is of multiple species.

Common names used in the Maldives are a combination of local and introduced names from visitors from all parts of the globe. The common name in English in this book doesn't necessarily represent the local name, but one that is more suitable to most visitor-divers. However, alternative names are included in some cases. Most countries use similar names, except Americans who often mix-up similar families, or combine scientific names with common names.

Even though, the information world is shrinking at a fast rate, names will always remain a point of discussion. Fishermen use different names from aquarists and divers often have yet another version. Fisheries departments will claim that theirs is the 'official' one, but again that remains debatable as these market names are often wrong from an international point of view. For this book I have used names preferred by divers or aquarists, or relevant to the particular species itself.

Fig. 4. The Head-band Butterflyfish *Chaetodon collare* is one of the most common butterflyfishes in the Maldives, often seen in large schools on shallow coral reefs. Being a distinctive species, the scientific name has never been an issue and the name *collare* refers to the white head band. As often is the case, vernacular names are often more than one when a species occurs in different regions or has a different usage. It is known as the Pakistani Butterflyfish in Pakistan and in the aquarium trade it is best known as the Red-tailed Butterflyfish.

FISHES OF THE MALDIVES

All the fishes in this book belong in the Superclass PISCES, which represents fishes that possess jaws and paired fins. PISCES comprises two main groups: Class CHONDRICHTHYES, the cartilaginous fishes that includes sharks, rays, skates and chimaeras (ghostsharks); and Class OSTEICHTHYES, the bony fishes that includes eels, scorpionfishes, pipefishes, perch-like fishes and pufferfishes. The main difference between the two groups is that bony fishes have a skeleton made of bone, whereas the chondrichthyans have a cartilaginous skeleton without true bone. Other obvious features that distinguish chondrichthyans from bony fishes include the presence of small tooth-like scales called dermal denticles, which make the skin feel rough when stroked from the tail to head, a mouth and nostrils usually on the underside of the head, pelvic claspers on males, and teeth that are continuously being replaced or that are fused into plates that grow with the animal. Modern day cartilaginous fishes first appeared in the era of the dinosaurs, and they now inhabit all major marine habitats, from shallow coastal waters to the deepest sea. Today, more than 1200 species of cartilaginous fishes live in the oceans and freshwater and estuarine systems of the world. Sharks and rays belong to the Elasmobranchii, a subclass of Chondrichthyes and are hence collectively known as elasmobranchs. There are no chimaeroids in the tropical marine systems, so in this book we refer only to the elasmobranchs. Elasmobranchs are a highly diverse group, which comprises around 34 families of sharks and 23 families of batoids, the skates and rays, with over 750 species worldwide. All orders of sharks (Hexanchiformes, Squaliformes, Squatiniformes, Heterodontiformes, Pristiophoriformes, Lamniformes, Orectolobiformes, and Carcharhiniformes), and batoids (order Batoidea) are represented by over 450 species in tropical marine waters.

ABOUT CARTILAGINOUS FISHES by Tim Godfrey

Traditional Shark Fishery of the Maldives

The traditional shark fishery of the Maldives targeted the large Tiger Shark *Galeocerdo cuvier*, Whale Shark *Rhincodon typus*, and Bluntnose Sixgill Shark *Hexanchus griseus*, all of which have enormous livers with high quality oil, used to soak the interior of fishing dhonis every few weeks.

Whale sharks were occasionally caught using a large hook thrust into the corner of the whale sharks mouth, sometimes with the aid of a pole. The Whale Shark was allowed to tow the fishing vessel for some time before tiring. It was then killed with a large knife thrust into the brain or spinal cord. This fishery was conducted seasonally until 1995 by at least two islands, Dhonfanu (Baa Atoll) and Manadhoo (Noonu Atoll). Whale sharks were regarded highly not just for their liver oil, but because they often aggregated live bait species used in tuna fishing, such as Silver Sprat *Sprateioides gracilis*, making it easy for them to catch tuna. Despite the ban on fishing, they are still targeted illegally by some fishermen for their fins and occasionally suffer from injury or death from propeller strike.

By the early 1960's the traditional fishing lifestyle of the people began to change following the introduction of Japanese tuna longliners into the central Indian Ocean and three main shark fisheries developed: a deepwater vertical longline fishery for Gulper Shark (Spiny Dogfish *Centrophorus* spp.) which yields high-value oil for export; an offshore longline and handline fishery for oceanic sharks, which yields fins and meat for export; and an inshore gillnet, handline and longline fishery for reef and other atoll-associated shark, which also yields fins and meat for export. Many Maldivian fishermen used to seeing an endless source of pelagic tuna had no concept of overfishing and by 1991 Gulper Shark stocks in the north of the Maldives crashed.

Motorization of the nation's fleet of sailing fishing boats, the Masdhoni, started in 1974 and was well established by 1977 and soon after shark longlining started to spread rapidly through Maldives. The shift away from a sustainable subsistence economy towards economic dependence on fossil fuels, communication and tourism was a major factor in the diversification of the fisheries sector and the exploitation of atoll-associated 'non-tuna' stocks, including shark fisheries.

Sharks of the Maldives

Around 40 species of sharks have been recorded from the Maldives of which 15 are likely to be seen by divers and snorkellers. They include the Whale Shark *Rhincodon typus* the largest shark in the ocean. Species vary from being restricted to the Maldives, to widespread in tropical regions (circumtropical), or widespread in the Indo-Pacific (found in both the Indian and Pacific Oceans). Some Maldives shark species that live mainly near the bottom, such as the small Sliteye Shark *Loxodon macrorhinus* (Fig. 5) are rarely if ever seen by divers and are therefore not included in this book. A variety of pelagic shark species previously taken by the Maldivian shark fishery may be occasionally seen by divers but are not included in this book. They include the Shortfin Mako Shark *Isurus oxyrinchus*; Common Thresher Shark *Alopias vulpinus*; Bigeye Thresher Shark *A. superciliosus*; Blue Shark *Prionace glauca*; Bignose Shark *Carcharhinus altimus*; and Blacktip Shark *Carcharhinus limbatus*. Other shark and ray species not listed here, could possibly be encountered at more isolated or largely inaccessible locations in the future.

Batoids (rays) of the Maldives

There are 16 rays known in the Maldives which are likely to be seen by divers and snorkellers. They include the Oceanic Manta Ray *Manta birostris* the largest ray. Rays are usually benthic and primarily marine, though some may enter the brackish or freshwater lagoons of mangroves. Overall, rays form a diverse group, comprising the manta rays, eagle rays, stingrays and stingarees, electric rays, shovelnose and sharkfin guitarfishes, sawfishes and skates, although not all groups are represented in the Maldives. Rays not included in this book include the Bluespotted Ribbontail Ray *Taeniura lymna* which is doubtfully recorded from the Maldives, and the Sickle-fin Devil Ray *Mobula tarapacana* a pelagic species which has been observed, but rarely seen. Another ray, the Smalleye Stingray *Dasyatis microps* is rarely seen,

Fig. 5. The Sliteye Shark, *Loxodon macrorhinus*. Rarely seen by divers as it lives near the bottom. Photo: Guy Stevens, North Malé Atoll.

but has been included, as it has been observed on several occasions in at least one location, Rasdhoo Atoll.

Identification of sharks and rays

Sharks are easily recognised by external characters, such as 5-7 paired gill openings, paired fins and a small opening posterior to the eye, called a spiracle. The various orders of sharks are generally determined by the number of paired gill slits, the presence or absence of a dorsal-fin spine or a nictitating membrane, the position of the mouth in relation to the eye, and whether the snout is pronounced or not. The most important features for identifying sharks are colour, body shape, fin size and markings and dorsal fin position. Each species of shark has distinctively shaped teeth and number, which are important characters in taxonomy. Sharks have one or two dorsal fins with or without spines, a pair of pectoral and pelvic fins and usually an anal fin, although absent in some species.

Rays differ from sharks in that their pectoral fins are fused to the side of the head and their gills are located ventrally. Rays have one or two dorsal fins, and occasionally none. They have no fin spines, a thin often whip-like tail, and no anal fin. Characters used to separate the 6 groups of rays are the various shapes (dorsally or ventrally viewed) and disc width, types of snout, presence of electric organs, type of tails or venomous spines on tails, and number of paired gill openings. The important features for identifying rays are colour, disc and tail shape, dorsal fin position and the position and shape of dermal thorns and denticles.

Some species are superficially similar to sharks. The more typical 'ray-like' species have a flattened body, virtually surrounded by large and massively expanded pectoral fins forming a disc, with eyes on top of the head and mouth ventral, except in the Mobulidae and Myliobatidae. The tail is mostly longer than the disc and is often whip-like and generally lack dorsal, anal and caudal fins; instead it sometimes has membranous skin folds on upper or lower sides of the tail and most species have one or more serrated stinging spines. Viewed from the top, shapes vary from circular to diamond and some are wider than long with a wing-like appearance.

Reproduction and development of elasmobranchs

Fertilisation in sharks and rays takes many forms but is always internal, usually with a period of courtship to entice females. The teeth marks observed on some sharks is often legacy of the male biting the female to hold her alongside while he uses one or two of his paired claspers to insert packages of sperm into the female reproductive tract. Unlike the teleost's, which evolved both pelagic eggs and viviparity (live bearing) as a reproductive strategy, epipelagic elasmobranchs have facilitated the survival of their offspring by increased protection and development of fewer offspring through internal development, often with specializations for the transfer of nutrients to the developing embryos.

Sharks have low fecundity, producing very few young, compared to other fishes, and gestation can range from three to 22 months. Around 80% of tropical marine elasmobranchs are viviparous and most of the remainder are oviparous (egg layers), while some remain unknown. Oviparous species are typically bottom-dwelling and deposit eggs externally inside a tough leathery case, laying them carefully on the bottom. There are two types of oviparity: (1) single or extended oviparity where one pair of eggs is extruded at a time and (2) multiple or retained oviparity, where eggs are retained within the reproductive tract for a period of time where some embryonic development takes place. Retained oviparity occurs in at least one Maldives species, the Zebra Shark *Stegostoma fasciatum*. In oviparous species, the developing embryos obtain all their nutrition from the yolk supply inside the egg and generally hatch externally within a year, thus eggs are lecithotrophic.

All viviparous species depend on the yolk sac as the initial source of fetal nutrition. Viviparous forms may be further subdivided into aplacental (yolk dependent/lecithotrophic), oophagic (egg eating) and aplacental (matrotrophic). Aplacental viviparous forms, which include the Whale Shark *Rhincodon typus*, do not have a placental connection between mother and offspring and are yolk fed for the majority of their development. In the past this was called ovoviviparity, a term which has now been superseded. In the Mobulidae and Dasyatidae, foetal development is augmented by maternal input of nutrients. They are fed by a milky histotroph, which is considered analogous to a placenta, hence they are termed matrotrophic, which is based on a form of viviparity. Oocytes or other embryos can also provide embryonic nourishment during gestation and often only one large well-developed embryo is produced after cannibalising its siblings. The Pelagic Thresher Shark *Alopias pelagicus* is one Maldivian species that cannibalises its siblings.

Epipelagic oceanic elasmobranchs

There are five epipelagic oceanic elasmobranchs occasionally seen in the Maldives: the Pelagic Thresher Shark *Alopias pelagicus*, Oceanic Whitetip Shark *Carcharhinus longimanus*, Silky Shark *Carcharhinus falciformis*, Whale Shark *Rhincodon typus* and Oceanic Manta Ray *Manta birostris*. Epipelagic oceanic species are mostly large with increased vagility, or dispersal ability, and have wide ranging distribution. They are highly mobile species that primarily inhabit ocean basins away from the shelf edge of landmasses, usually in the top 200 m of the water column although often descending to great depths to feed (eg. Whale Shark 1600 m). Of these species, all are circumglobal except the Pelagic Thresher Shark, which is distributed in the Indo-Pacific.

Epipelagic oceanic elasmobranchs have developed a range of morphological adaptions and behaviour to survive in the open ocean environment. All are viviparous as attaching eggs to the substrate is not an optional reproduction strategy for these species. The plankton eaters, which include the whale sharks and manta rays, exploit both depth and temperature regimes to capture their prey and take advantage of seasonal pulses in productivity to feed on dense prey concentrations near coastal waters. Whale sharks occur in both tropical and warm temperate waters and show diel behaviour, generally diving deeper during the day and more shallow at night, probably in association with prey.

The majority of oceanic sharks are predators and have streamlined, perfectly shaped bodies for high speed and long distance swimming. They feed on fish and cephalopods and various other animals, including other sharks and rays.

Tropical marine elasmobranchs

A wide variety of habitats exist within the tropical waters of the Maldives, including coral reefs, shallow lagoons, soft sediment beds, seagrass meadows, sandy channels, and mangroves. Many species of elasmobranchs will move between habitats and can show strong site fidelity. Relatively few mangrove habitats exist in the Maldives, but these are important areas for many fishes and some species of elasmobranchs. In other regions, they are important nursery areas for the Blacktip Reef Shark *Carcharhinus melanopterus* and Sicklefin Lemon Shark *Negaprion acutidens*

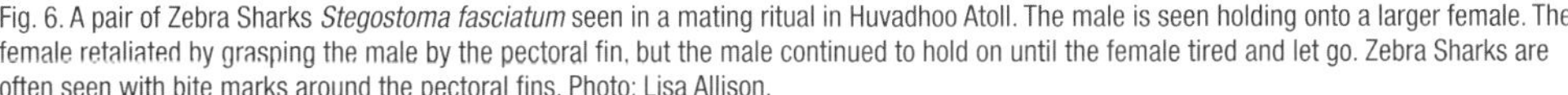
Fig. 6. A pair of Zebra Sharks *Stegostoma fasciatum* seen in a mating ritual in Huvadhoo Atoll. The male is seen holding onto a larger female. The female retaliated by grasping the male by the pectoral fin, but the male continued to hold on until the female tired and let go. Zebra Sharks are often seen with bite marks around the pectoral fins. Photo: Lisa Allison.

and are important habitats in the lifecycle of the Porcupine Ray *Urogymnus asperrimus*. Recent sightings of large numbers of juvenile rays of least two species in the mangroves in Foammulah Atoll have been reported. Off Western Australia, the Tiger Shark *Galeocerdo cuvier* makes use of seagrass beds for much of their lifecycle. In some atolls of the Maldives where there are extensive seagrass beds, such as Laamu Atoll, seagrasses are likely to play important roles in the lifecycle of sharks and rays, although there is very limited information on the role of elasmobranchs in these Maldives systems.

A large number of elasmobranchs are dependent on coral reefs. The Grey Reef Shark *Carcharhinus amblyrhynchos*, Blacktip Reef Shark *Carcharhinus melanopterus* and Whitetip Reef Shark *Triaenodon obesus* use coral reefs for resting or foraging, while the benthic Zebra Shark *Stegostoma fasciatum* and Nurse Shark *Nebrius ferrugineus* use their colour and spot patterns as camouflage against the brightly coloured reefs. Fewer batoid species use coral reefs as their primary habitat. The Blotched Fantail Ray *Taeniura meyeni* is frequently seen on coral reefs or in caves while other rays are more likely to be observed in sandy areas adjacent to reefs. Members of the Mobulidae and the Smalleye Stingray *Dasyatis microps* are observed over coral reefs at certain times. The Giant Guitarfish *Rhynchobatus djiddensis* and Bow-mouth Guitarfish *Rhina ancylostoma* are often associated with soft sandy bottoms and seen in the open or in sandy channels, although they are sometimes observed passing over reefs. The White-spotted Eagle Ray *Aetobatus narinari* feeds mainly over extensive sand-flats between the shore and reefs.

Conservation and management

The IUCN Red List of Threatened Species is a comprehensive, global approach for evaluating the conservation status of plant and animal species. IUCN Red List of shark and ray species in the Maldives include those in categories of Least concern (LC), Near threatened (NT), Vulnerable (VU), Endangered (EN) and Data deficient (DD). The status of each shark and ray species listed in this book has been included in the descriptions.

Following concerns by the tourism sector of shark fishing at major dive sites, the Government of the Maldives announced in 1995, the establishment of 15 Protected Marine Areas (PMA's) and the total protection of the Whale Shark *Rhincodon Typus*. A further nine PMA's were identified in 1999. In 1998, the government implemented a 10 year moratorium on all types of shark fishing inside and within the rim of seven major tourist atolls in the Maldives. A failure to enforce the moratorium and effectively ban fishing at PMA's, led to a total ban on all fishing, capture, killing or extraction of sharks from Maldivian waters from 15th March, 2010.

Shark and ray fisheries are more susceptible to overfishing than most other fisheries and require careful management. Commercial targeting of sharks and rays for human consumption and bycatch can quickly reduce local populations of a species to unsustainable levels. Increased demand and prices in the international shark fin trade has led to huge increases in fishing effort for most pelagic species to supply this market. International concern over shark stocks raises questions over the sustainability of the shark catch and the effect on the ecosystem. Different populations can often be distinguished by their life history parameters and information on growth, mortality rates and productivity are essential for estimating the population status of species. In general, deep water and many epipelagic oceanic species, have smaller litters, slower growth rates and later ages at maturity compared to continental shelf species; a combination that results in generally slow rates of population increase and recovery from overfishing, placing them at high risk, especially in international waters.

Pelagic sharks and rays are a major bycatch of longline, tuna purse seine and gillnet fisheries, particularly from nations with high-seas fleets, and are targeted in harpoon fisheries in parts of southeast Asia. This affects the number of individuals that can be seen in the Maldives, including the Whale Shark, Oceanic Manta Ray, Silky Shark, Oceanic Whitetip Shark, Pelagic Thresher, and others. Whale shark meat is reputed to be the most expensive shark meat. It has been heavily targeted in fisheries throughout southeast

Asia, with most available capture data coming from countries including India, Taiwan and the Philippines.

In the past, the Maldives severely depleted some elasmobranch species due to overfishing for dried meat exports, oil and shark fin. However, they retain some species that in other areas are threatened with local extinction due to overfishing, pollution and habitat removal. Species like the Tawny Nurse Shark, Zebra Shark and Sicklefin Lemon Shark prefer inshore shallow water locations and are particularly vulnerable around the main population centres of Asia.

The ecological role of elasmobranchs in regulating prey populations and community structure are critical components of the marine ecosystem. The loss of coral reefs due to natural causes and climate change, including storms, crown of thorns and coral bleaching, will affect all marine life that depend on them; however, elasmobranches are more susceptible to habitat change due to the effects of overfishing, pollution, mangrove removal and seagrass destruction than many other marine species and their loss will be felt across the whole ecosystem.

Fig 7. Vulnerable species like this manta ray and guitarfish at a fish market in Sri Lanka, have slow recovery rates and are being overfished for their meat, fins and gill-rakers. Photos: Guy Stevens.

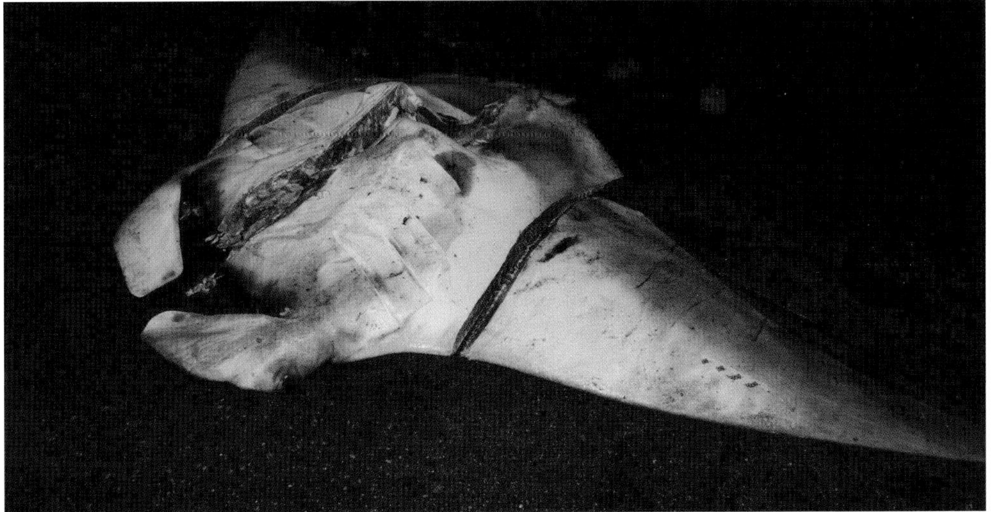

Protecting the Gentle Giants

Guy Stevens (www.mantatrust.org)

Photo: Manta gill plate, Guy Stevens.

Manta rays are world renowned for their charismatic beauty, gentle behaviour, and inquisitive, playful nature. For this reason, tourists globally spend nearly US $140 million annually ($8.2 million in the Maldives alone) to see these animals in the wild providing an important source of income to many countries. Unfortunately, in the last decade, a market has emerged in Asia for the gill plates of the *Manta* and their close relatives the *Mobula*. The rays' gill plates are used as a tonic, which has no basis in official Traditional Chinese Medicine and no proven health benefits, but it is having devastating consequences for the wild populations of these animals.

Manta rays are long lived and late maturing animals that only reproduce on average once every 2 to 5 years and only give birth to a single pup at a time. As a result of this gill plate market, populations of manta rays, which are listed as Vulnerable (VU) by the IUCN's Red List of threatened species, are becoming increasing threatened. In Bangkok, Thailand in March 2013 at the CITES (Convention on International Trade in Endangered Species of Wild Fauna and Flora) the world's nations overwhelmingly voted in favour of regulating the manta ray gill plate trade by listing *Manta* species under Appendix II of CITES. Prior to this CITES listing, the Maldives was one of just a handful of countries globally which had any protective measures in place for these species. While the future now looks a little brighter for the *Manta* populations, similar conservation measures are urgently required to protect the manta rays smaller cousins, the *Mobula*, which are equally threatened through this unsustainable and senseless trade.

Further Reading

Anderson, R., & Ahmed, H. (1993). The shark fisheries in the Maldives. MOFA, *Maldives and FAO, Rome*.

Anderson, R., Waheed, Z., & Whitevaves, H. (1999). Management of shark fisheries in the Maldives. *FAO Fisheries Technical Paper*.

Carrier, J., Pratt, H., & Castro, J. (2004). Reproductive biology of elasmobranchs. *CRC Marine Biology Series*.

Compagno, L., Dando, M., & Fowler, S. (2005). *Sharks of the World*: Princetown University Press.

Hamlett, W. C. (2005). *Reproductive biology and phylogeny of Chondrichthyes*: Science Publ.

Heithaus, M. R., & Vaudo, J. J. (2012). Predator-Prey Interactions. In J. C. Carrier, J. A. Musick & M. R. Heithaus (Eds.), *Biology of Sharks and Their Relatives* (second ed., pp. 505 – 546). Boca Raton: Taylor & Francis Group.

Randall, J., Allen, G., & Steene, R. (1997). *Fishes of the Great Barrier Reef and Coral Sea*: University of Hawaii Press.

Stevens, J. D. (2009). Epipelagic Oceanic Elasmobranchs. In: *Sharks and Their Relatives II: Physiological Adaptations, Behavior, Ecology, Conservation, and Management*, 11, 34.

White, W. (2009). Elasmobranchs of Tropical Marine Ecosystems. In: *Sharks and Their Relatives II: Physiological Adaptations, Behavior, Ecology, Conservation, and Management*, 11, 81.

STRUCTURAL FEATURES OF A GENERALISED SHARK

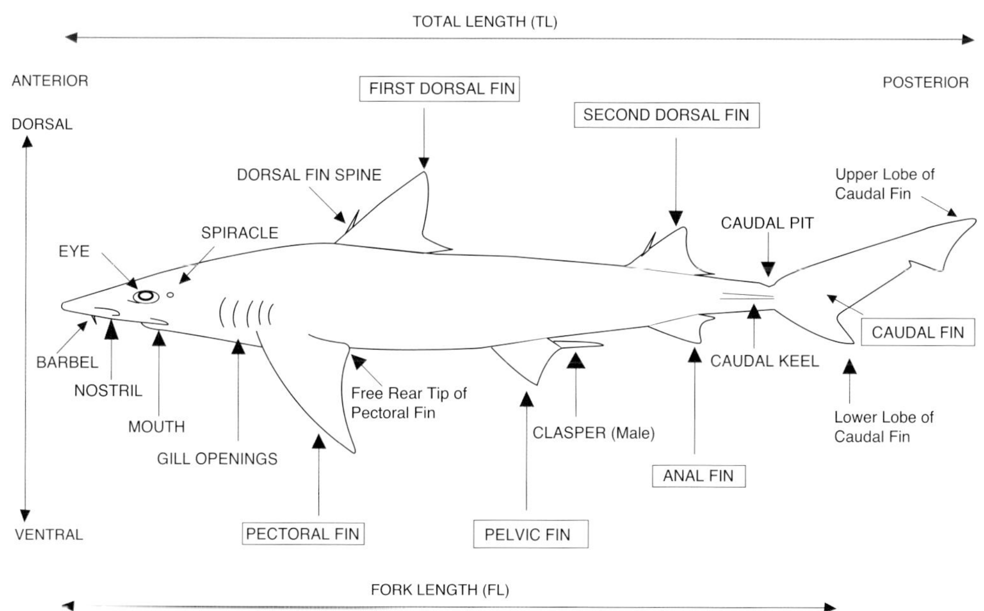

STRUCTURAL FEATURES OF A GENERALISED RAY

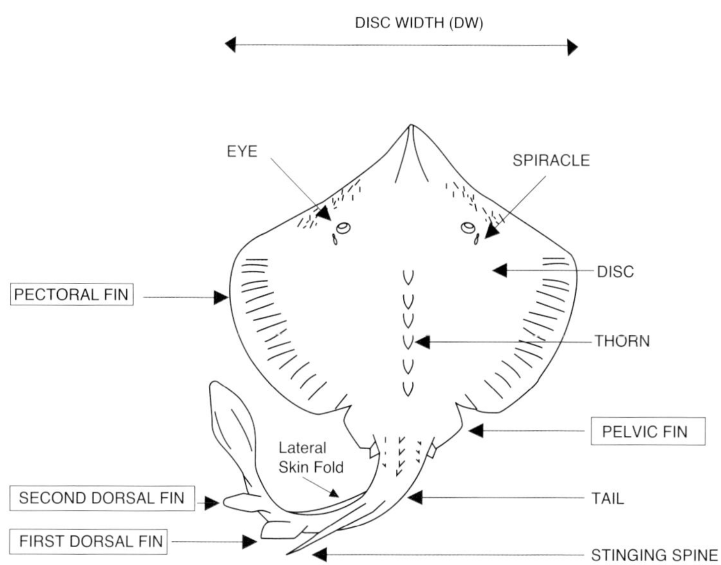

ABOUT BONY FISHES

Bony Fishes of the Maldives.

While we can admire beautifully coloured fishes, there is much to learn about their behaviour. Generalisation on aspects of behaviour is particularly dangerous, even when dealing with a single species. For instance: many butterflyfish occur in pairs in certain areas and it is often assumed that this is the case everywhere, but such fishes can school in other areas. The reason can relate directly to differences in habitat and competition. Many fishes behave differently in the Maldives from their counterparts in mainland waters. They behave more like oceanic species, as around Pacific islands, by the tendency to school compared to pairing by many identical species in continental waters. Some, that elsewhere are shallow water species, live only deep in the Maldives and that is a direct reflection of food availability, and not related to temperature as often suggested. Studying fish behaviour is not only fascinating, but always something new comes along and makes you want to know more. However, one has to be very careful in observations as we are influenced by what we read, and can easily make the wrong assumption.

Colour and camouflage

Many reef fishes have amazing colours and bolt patterns, but these are all for a particular purpose. They can serve for recognition, warning, display or confuse a potential predator. Juveniles are

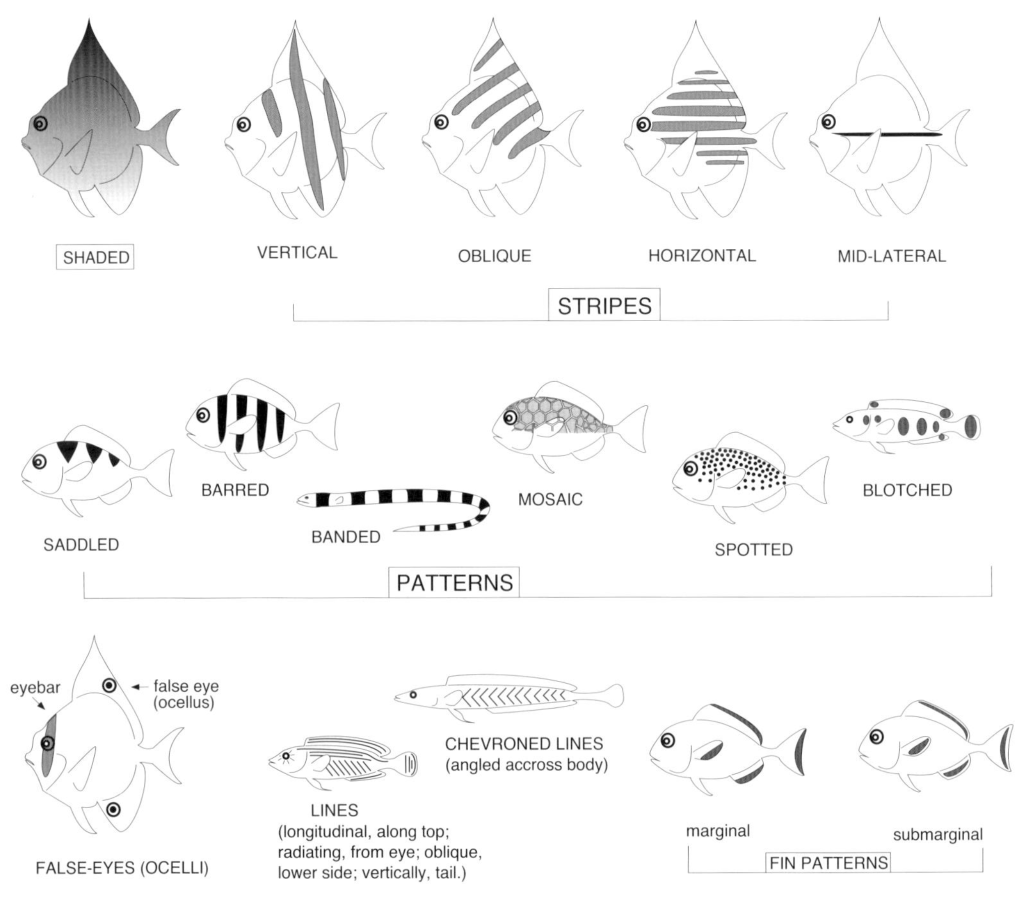

inexperienced and most vulnerable; a stage in which the process of learning to survive is most important, when survival depends on appearance. They usually have colours that are more suitable to avoid detection, confuse or put a predator off. Many species go through various colour changes with growth. Sexes are often different, especially in territorial species that live in groups with dominating males. Colour patterns often serve to break-up the body outline with stripes or bands. Some important parts, such as eyes, are often coloured the same as the immediate areas around them, whilst one or more eye-like spots, or false eyes (called ocellus, single, and ocelli, plural) somewhere else on the body confuses a predator. The real eye is camouflaged and protected, whilst a predator striking expects it to swim in another direction. Small juveniles often have several ocelli and may appear as a face of a much larger fish, when viewed side-on.

Most fishes are camouflaged in one way or another; small fishes to escape detection by predators, and the predators to get close to prey. Open water fishes are usually silvery, shaded with bluish or greenish backs that reflect their surroundings, while reef fishes are coloured to suit their surroundings and habits. Slow fishes that live in direct contact with the bottom are best camouflaged. Those on sand match the texture and colour of sand, while those on reef match the various features and combine colour and shape for camouflage. A flounder on the sand is rarely seen unless it moves, like the stonefish on the reef that is almost impossible to detect. Fishes that are more mobile make use of coverage of reefs and use camouflage to lesser extent, but some of the bright colours we see in photographs, can be for camouflage. Bright red fishes that live deep or are active at night, are actually camouflaged because red light doesn't travel far, red is like having no colour at all in natural light at depth.

Mimicry

Mimicry, meaning imitating or copying, is commonly used by fishes in various forms, some of which have evolved to amazing perfection. One of the best examples is the Mimic Filefish *Paraluteres prionurus* that is the perfect copy of the poisonous Saddled Pufferfish *Canthigaster valentini*, usually avoided by predators. Producing poison to the system requires energy and special diet, thus is expensive, but the filefish gets around by bluff, as easily as the pufferfish. They are so similar, that only a close look reveals the long dorsal and anal fin bases compared to the short ones of the pufferfish. Several similar examples are among blennies, in which harmless species look like those with a venomous bite, and juveniles of several other fish families take on similar colours of a venomous blenny until outgrowing its model.

Fishes learn quickly, especially when food is involved, and already know the easy pickings around divers. Over time, evolution has created some amazing examples, especially the cunning False Cleanerfish *Aspidontus taeniatus*, a blenny and a near perfect copy of the Cleaner Wrasse *Labroides dimidiatus*. While the wrasse removes small parasites, the blenny will bite and remove

Fig. 8. Left, Saddled Pufferfish *Canthigaster valentini* and right, Mimic Filefish *Paraluteres prionurus*.

skin or fin bits instead. Some small blennies mix with schooling planktivores and bite unexpectedly at fish swimming past.

Many predators have become very cunning in capturing prey by using a disguise, ambush, or following others for an easy meal. Some small groupers try to look like wrasses or damsels of the same size that feed on small invertebrates, enabling them to get close enough to snap up unsuspected juvenile damselfishes. Often small juveniles mimic uninteresting things, like a leaf floating on the surface or along the bottom in currents, that are of no interest to predators. Others mimic something bad-tasting or poisonous, such as a flatworm and nudibranch, that bare bright warning colours. In addition, by swimming or moving in certain ways, those that copy nature can be very convincing. Tiny post-larvae batfish are an excellent example of mimicking a leaf and when approached, they will flatten themselves against the surface. Tiny juvenile anglerfish sit openly on rocks, pretending to be a nudibranchs, and several small soles mimic flatworms on sand.

Cleaning Stations

Specialisation of fishes is evident in various ways, usually in regards to feeding, but generally is reflected in morphological features, such as a very long nose, numerous gill rakers, large mouth, and so on. A different form of specialisation has developed into a relationship between fishes themselves, helping each other by favours and rewards, whereby small fishes help the usually large ones getting rid of external parasites in return for food. The parasites are part of the diet for the small fishes, and in addition feed on food-bits stuck between teeth or filtering parts in the gills. A few fishes have almost exclusively adapted to such activities and are called cleanerfishes. The most famous of all is the Cleaner Wrasse *Labroides dimidiatus*. Cleaning activities begin from the post-larval stage and tiny juveniles are found in small caves or below overhangs of reef. Adults usually work in pairs, and are found in a particular place on the reef that has prominent features, such as a particular cave or bommie.

Such places are known as cleaning stations and visited by reef fishes as well as pelagics that come to be served at a particular time of the day. Shrimps often work together with these fishes, as they too have adapted to this behaviour in the specially established spots. The busy times are late afternoon and fishes may actually form a queue, waiting patiently for their turn. When inspected, most fishes change colour that assists in showing their problem. Parasites usually match the colour of their host, but when the host changes colour it has trouble catching-up, and with the host paling its colour, the parasite becomes readily visible. Assistance is also given by opening the mouth and gills for easy access to the cleaners. Cleaning behaviour is done by numerous fishes, sometimes juveniles only, but often is a localised behaviour. In some areas certain butterflyfishes are active cleaners and sometimes schooling bannerfishes clean large pelagic species.

Fig. 9. A juvenile Clown Anglerfish *Antennarius maculatus* photographed in Bali, Indonesia. They are typically brightly coloured and sit openly in coralline-algae reef, pretending to be a nudibranch.

Fig. 10. Surgeonfish *Acanthurus thompsoni* in a cleaning station with the Cleaner Wrasse *Labroides dimidiatus* and participating is a juvenile Diana Wrasse *Bodianus diana*, that commonly cleans when young.

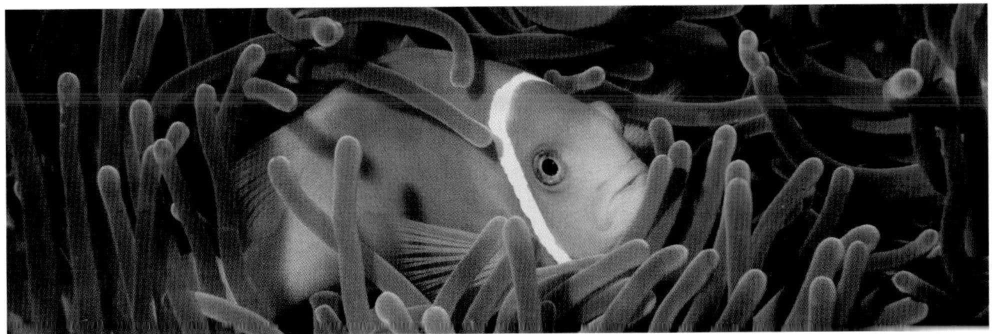

Fig. 11. Blackfoot Anemonefish *Amphiprion nigripes* in the tentacles of an anemone.

Symbiotic Relationships

When different life forms live together in a mutually dependant relationship, or partnership, it is called symbiosis. Well known are the anemone fishes, a damselfish that lives amongst the stinging tentacles of some large anemones. The anemone accepts these fishes as being part of itself; the mucus on the fish containing a compound obtained from the anemone itself, probably by rubbing all external parts against the anemone's non-stinging underside. The fish is protected from predators amongst the stinging tentacles, and in return the anemone is guarded by the fish from those that would like to eat it, such as butterflyfishes. In addition the anemone can position itself in current prone positions and feed during the day, as well as at night. Most other anemones are nocturnal and live in reef or under sand during the day. In the Maldives there is a single genus of anemonefish, *Amphiprion*, but several anemone genera. Some other fishes occur intermittently in these anemones, such as juvenile Threespot Humbugs *Dascyllus trimaculatus* and small wrasses, which sometimes swim between long tentacles. In addition some interesting crabs and shrimps share the anemones.

The other group commonly observed in partnerships are the shrimpgobies. This is a large group with several genera and many species, that live with Snapping Shrimps, *Alpheus spp.* The shrimps are excellent burrowers and make tunnels that serve the gobies as homes. The gobies stand guard at the entrances, signalling the shrimps if safe to come out or not. Sometimes a goby guides the poor-sighted shrimp from the hole, the shrimp staying in touch with the long feelers. Adult gobies usually live in pairs, together with a pair of adult shrimps. Juvenile gobies normally live with juvenile shrimps; both are small, but occasionally odd sized couples can be found.

Fig.12. Dracula Shrimp *Stonogobiops dracula* lives with the snapper shrimp *Alpheus randalli.*

Spawning and parental care

Most of the Maldives larger reef fishes are pelagic spawners, in which males and female release eggs and sperm simultaneously in surface waters. These include the major families such as wrasses, surgeons, parrots, butterflies and angelfishes, amongst many others. Eggs are usually tiny and weightless but in some cases, such as with halfbeaks, spawning is over seagrass beds where the eggs sink and stick to the seagrass leaves. Most of these fishes produce millions of eggs, depending on their size as most eggs are between 0.5 and 1 mm in diameter. Some families such as damsels and triggerfishes deposit eggs on the bottom that hatch after a relatively short period and produce pelagic larval fishes. The most advanced are the pipefishes that produce well developed young with a short pelagic stage. Fishes that take care of the eggs produce much less numerous broods but much larger eggs, as their survival rate is increased dramatically. Fishes that have no pelagic stage are not known from the Maldives. Most spawning activities are on the largest tides in phase with the moon cycle, usually near full moon. Wrasses, parrotfishes and surgeonfishes are usually active during this period on dusk, congregating in reef channels where strong currents are favourable to take the eggs as far away as possible from the reef. Eventually, the developing larvae are carried back and post-larvae settle on the various habitats on the reefs. Damselfishes lay their eggs exposed on reefs, where they can easily be seen, but are heavily guarded by the parents.

The various groups within the families use different strategies. The sergeant majors are community spawners, where a school forms individual pairs and lay the eggs in patches close to each other. The anemonefishes deposit their eggs on a solid object immediately next to the anemone. Some others clear a patch of live coral tissue to lay their eggs on its skeleton. Most gobies and some other small reef dwellers have eggs hidden in the reefs or under rocks. Large male triggerfishes prepare nesting sites on deep sand or reef flats. After eggs are laid, the sites are vigorously defended by both sexes for the few days the eggs take to hatch. The male Titan Triggerfish will readily charge at a diver that ventures into the territory, and can give a painful bite, or hit with the mouth at full speed, that is just as painful.

Fig. 13. Blackfoot Anemonefish *Amphiprion nigripes* protecting its eggs, attached to the coral-rock next to the anemone.

Cardinalfishes are mouth brooders, in which the male incubates the eggs in the mouth after spawning. The egg mass is large and the extended mouth readily visible. The brood is regularly moved to provide oxygen, almost in a rough way, spitting them partly out of the mouth and back, probably to get rid of bad eggs. Many species school, and young hatch simultaneously from numerous parents at the top of large tides.

Development and age

Pelagic eggs hatch quickly, bursting out from the crammed egg, which is less than one mm in diameter. Most larvae measure a few mm long and generally just over double the egg diameter. Their diet comprises phytoplankton and the growth rate is quick. Most species reach one or two cm in a few weeks before settling on reefs, but some grow much larger, with size depending on the family. Surgeonfishes can reach 5 cm before settling. The more developed larvae, that hatch from those species with parental care, are born large and have a much shorter pelagic stage before settling on the bottom. Larval pipefishes are often 3 or 4 cm long when settling. Most larvae are transparent, showing few melanophores. Fishes settling on the substrate following a larval stage, called post-larvae, quickly colour up, change shape and become juveniles that are more recognisable as a species.

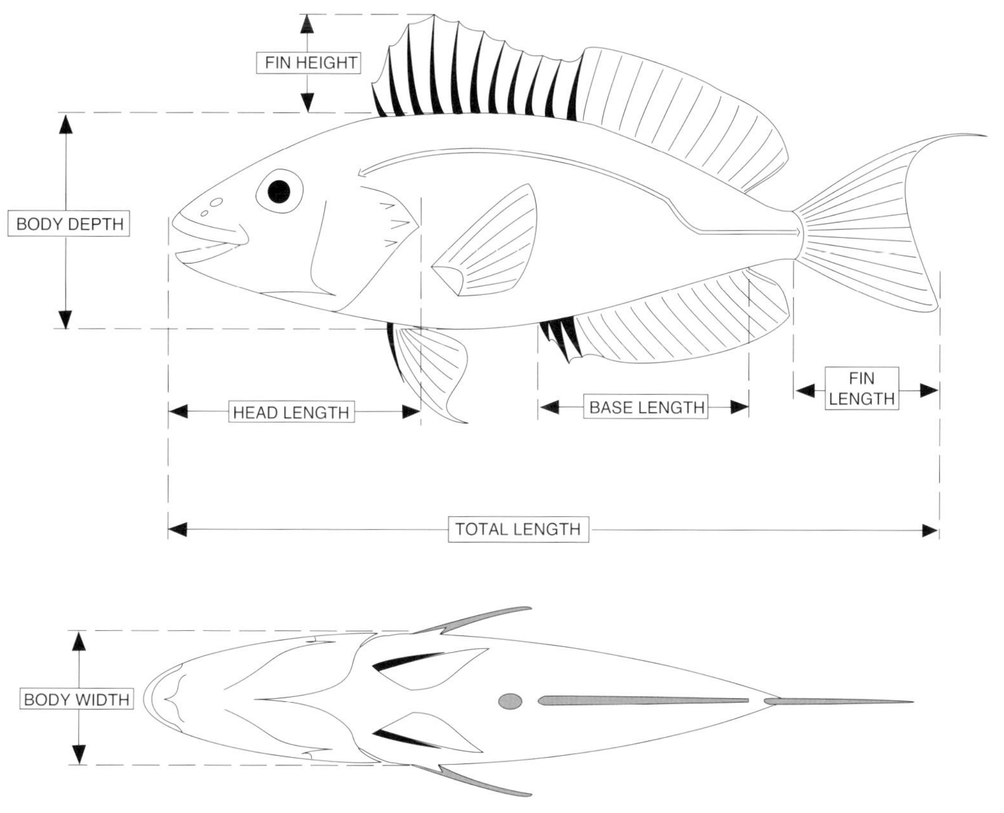

Most juveniles grow quickly in the first few weeks, usually doubling their length or more. Small species can mature in a few months but large species may take a number of years to reach full adult size. This only applies to shallow water species that are included in this book. Fishes living in very deep water, 1000 m or more, can be small and very old (100+ years) at the same time. Habitat requirements often change with growth and development of a species. The colouration of reef fishes can change dramatically at different stages. The colour pattern of a small juvenile that is often bolt, would be unsuitable at a large size, drawing unwanted attention.

Changes with growth can be gradual or in stages, depending on the species and circumstances. When mimicry is involved, the mimic often outgrows the model and quickly changes when reaching that size, sometimes not just changing colours, but also morphological features. With most fishes the changes are gradual to suit the environment, but when moving to other habitats the colour may need matching straight away. Some fishes are capable of changing almost instantly, especially those that rely on camouflage for protection. The age of fishes varies greatly with size and depths. Most reef fishes live from one year to several decades. Ghostpipefishes are thought to live annually. Some dartgobies Ptereleotris lived about ten years in an aquarium and large *Pomacentrus* angelfishes have been kept over 20 years. Deep water fishes get much older. For example, 50 cm long Orange Roughy *Hoplostethus atlanticus* living in about 1000 m depth were aged to 160 years old.

EXTERNAL FEATURES

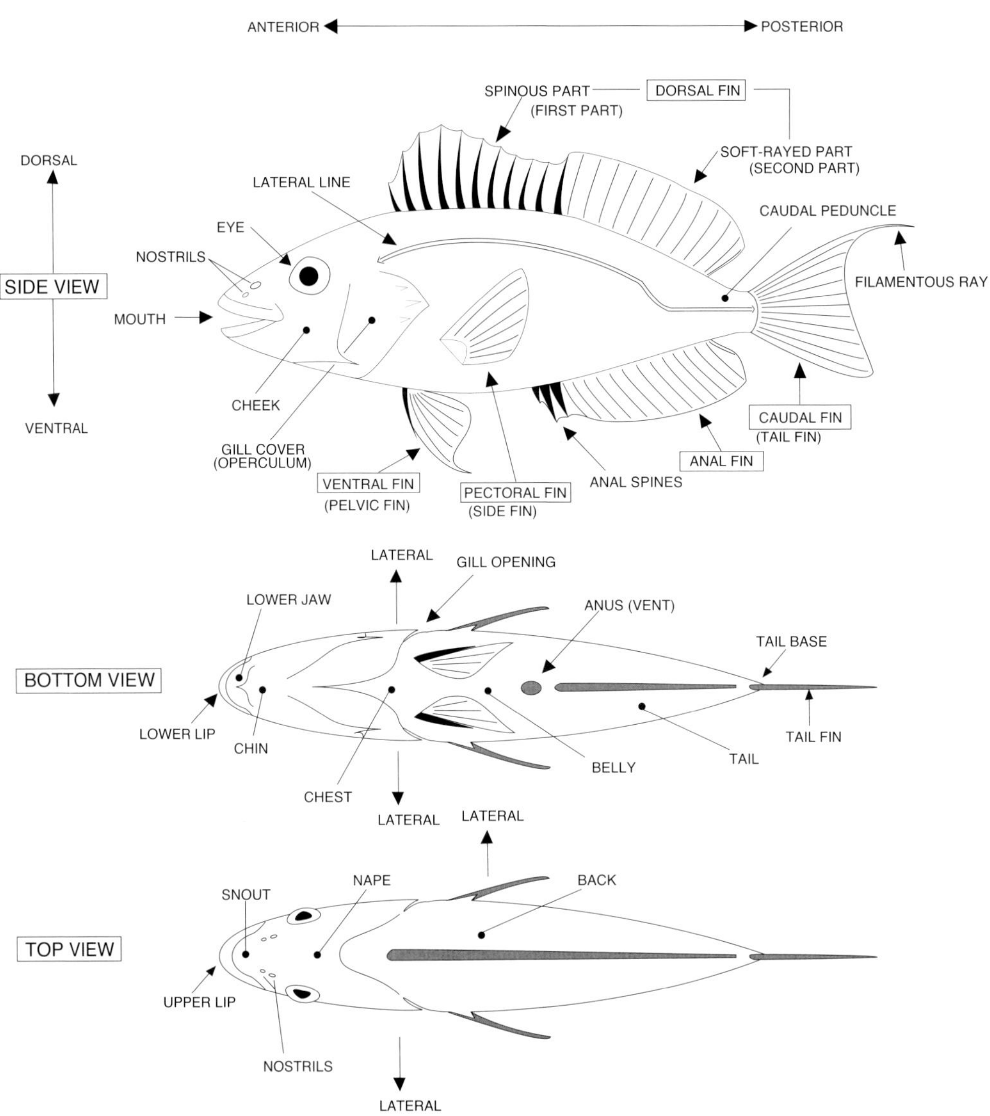

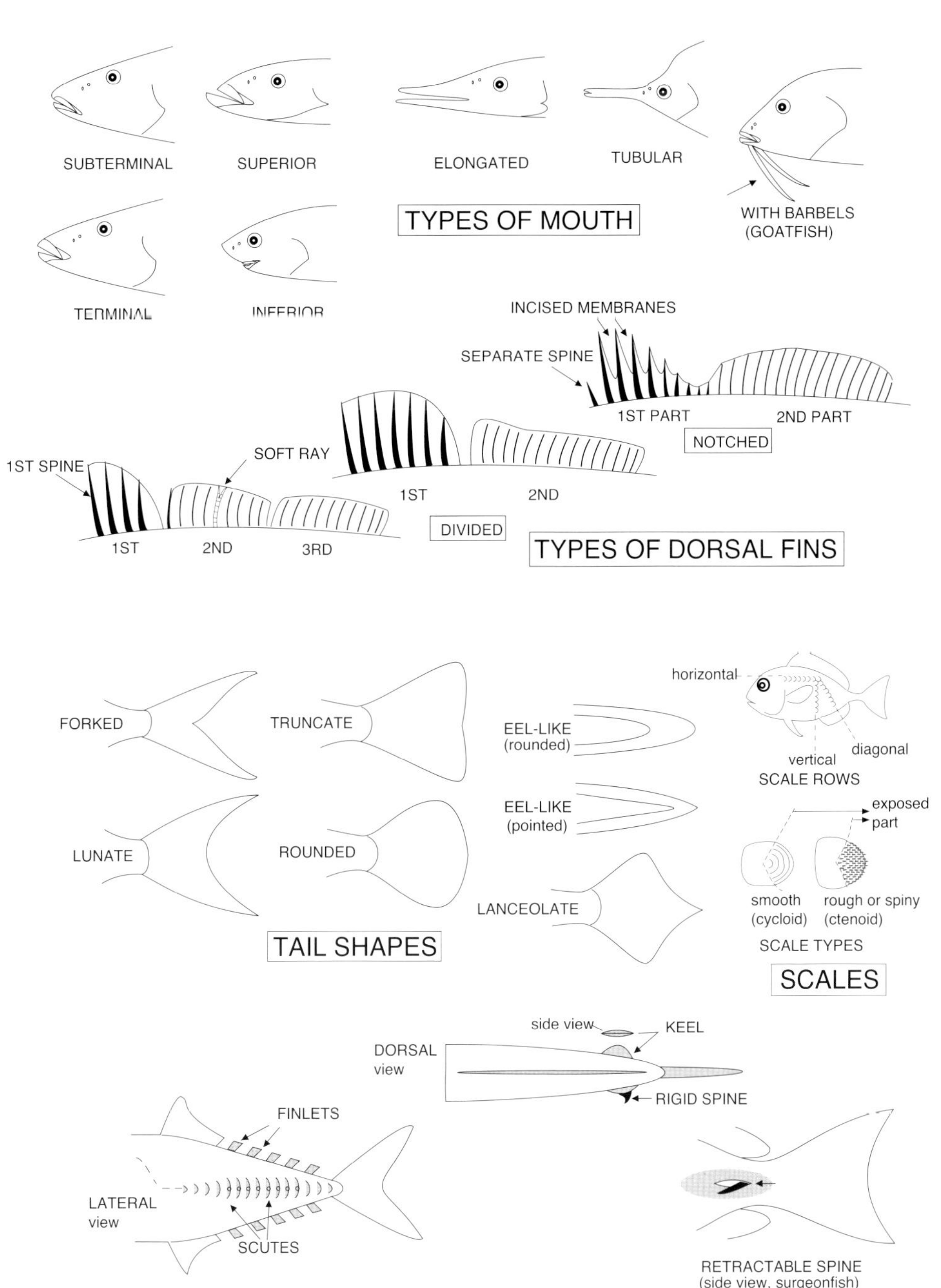

TAIL FEATURES

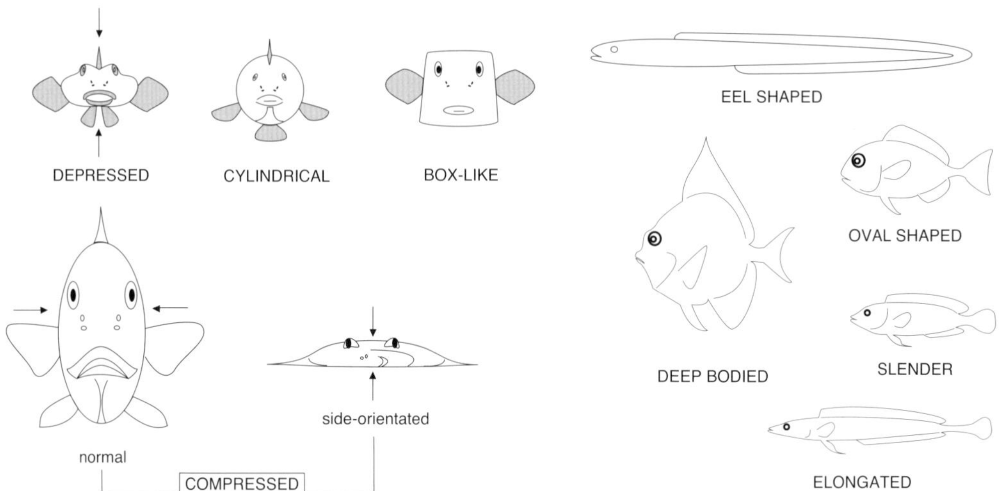

Shapes of fishes

Most people are familiar with fishes caught on a line and know the shape of an eel. The seahorse is not often recognised as a fish and represents one of the more unusually shaped types. Fish fill every niche of the aquatic habitat, like birds on the land, that require colour, size and shape to suit. Reef or sand dwellers, the pelagics, hunters and graziers have different needs and have adapted accordingly, and are readily noticed by shape. Fast fishes need to be streamlined, those living on the bottom and don't need to move can be shaped like a rock or a stick. Most fishes we see swimming around the reef, the groupers, damsels, fusiliers snappers etc, are perch-like in shape and fin features, however each group varies in varies ways. Some are short, others long, thick or thin, as shown above with the appropriate terms that are generally used. Some fishes have adapted to living in a different way to most, like the flatfishes that lay on their sides, or seahorses, ghostpipefishes and shrimpfishes that have a vertical composure. Consequently, flatfishes are compressed and not depressed, and those fishes swimming vertical are slender and not deep bodied.

Families & Species Accounts

CARTILAGINOUS FISHES

NURSE SHARKS
GINGLYMOSTOMATIDAE

Photo: Udo Kefrig, Mulaku Atoll

Tawny Nurse Shark
Nebrius ferrugineus

Maldivian name *Nidhan miyaru.* Max length: 3.2 m Total Length (TL). Viviparous (aplacental). Litter size one or two, although reported 20 to 30. Length at birth around 40 cm TL. IUCN status: Vulnerable.

Large adults are brownish-grey dorsally, paler ventrally, with a relatively long tail and two large similar-sized dorsal fins set well back on a cylindrical body. It has a broadly rounded, flattened head with relatively small, subterminal mouth situated well in front of small eyes. A pair of long, slender barbels is usually easily visible in front of the nostrils. These sharks have 5 gill slits, with no caudal keels or ridges on the body. Inhabits shallow lagoons and may venture to depths of about 70 m. Mostly nocturnal and hunts primarily for cephalopods (squid and octopus), but also takes crustaceans and other fishes. Has been observed in some locations at night foraging in large numbers. During the day, often seen in small resting aggregations inside sheltered crevices and caves, or under ledges. Known locally as the sleeping shark, *N. ferrugineus* is somewhat more reef-associated than *Stegostoma fasciatum* and is more often seen by divers. A moderate swimmer, not as fast as Blacktip or Grey Reef Sharks and generally considered harmless, however unprovoked bites have been reported, which may be accidental or food related. Tropical Indo-Pacific.

Photo: Guy Stevens, Felidhe Atoll.

ZEBRA SHARKS
STEGOSTOMATIDAE

Zebra Shark
Stegostoma fasciatum

Maldivian name *Hitha miyaru.* Max length: 2.35 m TL but reports of 3.5 m TL. Oviparous (retained oviparity). Up to 5 large egg cases per brood. Length at birth between 20 and 26 cm TL. IUCN status: Vulnerable.

Also known as the Leopard Shark, it has five longitudinal ridges on a cylindrical body, nasal grooves and a very long, low, blade-like caudal fin that measures almost as long as the rest of the body. Has a subterminal mouth, four main gill openings (gill slits 4 and 5 overlap) and two closely spaced spineless dorsal fins. Although typically seen alone, aggregates seasonally at certain times. A non-aggressive shark, often found resting on sandy substrate in channels during the day and more active at night. Frequently return to their favourite resting site. Egg-cases are anchored to the bottom with hair-like, adhesive fibres. Over a breeding season spanning several months, females may lay over 50 egg-cases in total. Diet consists mostly of gastropods and bivalves, but also crustaceans and occasionally bony fishes. A single species family related to wobbegongs and other catsharks. Widespread in the tropical Indo-Pacific

The young coloration is also the origin of the common name "Zebra Shark" and is thought to act as an anti-predator function, making individuals in a group harder to target. Photo: Ed Roberts, Aquarium.

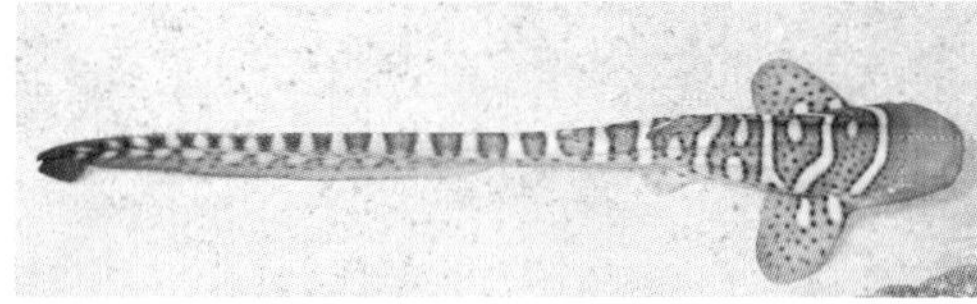

A juvenile Zebra Shark with a colour pattern intermediate between that of young and adults. As young juveniles grow to 50–90 cm long, the dark areas begin to break up, changing to a more spotted leopard pattern. Photo: Ed Roberts, Aquarium.

Photo: Guy Stevens, North Huvadhoo Atoll.

WHALE SHARKS
RHINCODONTIDAE

Whale Shark 'recharging' in South Ari Atoll. Photo: Melody Sky.

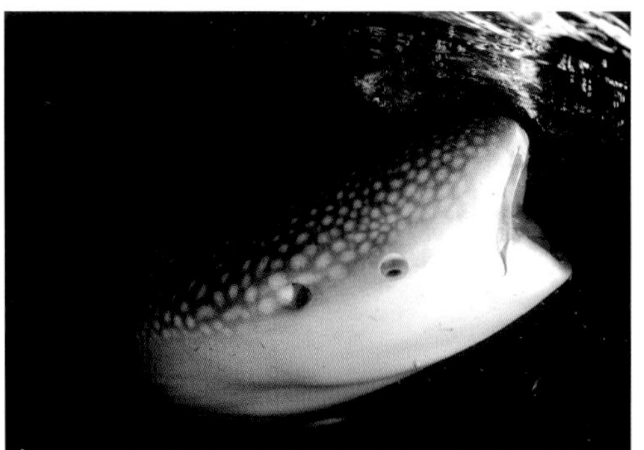

Whale Shark gulping. Photo: Guy Stevens, Kolhumadulu Atoll.

Whale Shark
Rhincodon typus

Maldivian name *Fehurihi.* Largest Measured to date 12.65 m TL; however reported at up to 18 m. Viviparous (aplacental). Largest litter recorded was about 300 pups. Up to 60 cm TL at birth. IUCN status: Vulnerable.

The largest of all fishes, the Whale Shark has an enormous, transverse mouth situated in front of the eyes near the snout tip, longitudinal body ridges, caudal keel, large first and small second dorsal fins and a semi-lunate caudal fin. It is primarily a planktivore, feeding on dense aggregations of euphausiid, copepods and fish eggs and occasionally targeting more mobile prey such as baitfishes. A filter feeder, but does not only rely on forward motion for filtration, but can suction feed by opening its large mouth and letting water rush in before being forced out through the gills. Prey is sieved out as water passes through curtains of gill-rakers. Suction feeding often results in the shark assuming a head-up, tail-down posture when feeding. Readily identified by its immense size, broad head, wide terminally positioned mouth and distinctive colour pattern of white stripes and spots set against a dark background dorsally and light ventrally. The pattern is formed of spots that sometimes coalesce to form short stripes. Worldwide in tropical seas.

Identification of whale sharks. The yellow square shows the region that should be targeted by photographers. The 3 reference points need to be visible in order to use photo-identification software. They include 1) top of fifth gill slit, 2) the point at which the most posterior edge of the pectoral fin intersects with the border of the dark dorsal surface and light ventral surface on the flank of the shark; and 3) the bottom of the fifth gill slit. At least 14 spots are required within the yellow shaded area to mark the whale sharks pattern. Photo: Neal Collins. Maldives Whale Shark Research Programme.

Whale sharks of South Ari Atoll

Richard Rees (www.mwsrp.org)

The southern tip of South Ari Atoll is a 12km stretch of reef that hosts whale sharks year round – unlike most other Whale Shark hotspots around the world, which are seasonal and usually coincide with feeding opportunities such as a coral or fish spawning events. It was declared a Marine Protected Area in 2009 and attracts a large and growing number of visitors. The Maldives Whale Shark Research Programme (MWSRP) is a long-term monitoring program that began in 2006 and has since had over 1000 separate Whale Shark encounters. Using a technique called photo-identification, which uses images of the shark's unique spot patterns as 'fingerprints', over 170 different individual sharks have been identified. The number of 'known' versus 'new' sharks has enabled researchers to estimate how many whale sharks are in these waters at any one time – surprisingly few with less than 200 estimated to be in South Ari waters at any one time.

The average length is just under 6 m, and since whale sharks are thought to mature at approximately 9 m in length, all are considered juveniles. Surprisingly, almost all are males with only 5% of the individuals found in South Ari being female.

Telemetry tagging work carried out in 2008 and 2009 showed whale sharks are highly mobile animals; constantly moving around the Maldivian archipelago and occasionally travelling thousands of miles south to the Chagos Bank and north to the Laccadives. Whale sharks are feeding less than 10% of the time at South Ari and tagging shows they dive incredibly deep, exploring layers in the water column as deep as 1600 m. At these depths water is not only cold (3°C) but also low in oxygen. The Whale Shark is a huge cold-blooded animal that requires ambient warmth and highly oxygenated water to keep functioning. South Ari, with its long, wide and shallow reef shelf, which drops off into very deep water, makes it the perfect haven to return and recharge after deep diving. Consequently, South Ari is a vitally important habitat for whale sharks, which also makes their predicted time at the surface especially attractive to the thousands of visitors who watch them every year.

Currently the main threats posed to the whale sharks in the Maldives are collision with vessels and disturbance of their natural behaviour by unregulated tourism. Careful management and continued research should ensure whale sharks of South Ari can be enjoyed for generations to come.

THRESHER SHARKS
ALOPIIDAE

Photo: Guy Stevens, Foammulah Atoll.

Pelagic Thresher Shark
Alopias pelagicus

Maldivian name *Kandi miyaru.* Max length: 3.9 m TL. Viviparous (with oophagy). Litter size of 2 very large pups. Length at birth 130 to 160 cm TL. Males mature at 7 – 8 years and females 8 – 9 years. IUCN status: Vulnerable.

A highly migratory species, found from the surface to depths of at least 152 m. Other members of the genus include the Common Thresher shark (*A. vulpinus*), and Bigeye Thresher Shark (*A. superciliosus*). All are characterised by a long, scythe-like, upper caudal fin lobe that is almost as long as the body, relatively stout but fusiform body, a conical snout, 5 relatively short gill slits, very small second dorsal and anal fins and long narrow pectoral fins. Eyes have no nictitating membranes. Distinguished from the other two species by nearly straight and broad-tipped pectoral fins and the white ventral colouration not extending over the pectoral and pelvic-fin bases. Eyes are moderately large, not extending onto the dorsal head surface (like the Bigeye Thresher Shark). Food preference is primarily squid and small bony fishes, which it stuns with its tail before capture. A shy species difficult to approach underwater, however is occasionally observed by divers, particularly around seamounts. Occasionally seen leaping out of the water. Oceanic and wide-ranging in the Indo-Pacific.

WHALER SHARKS
CARCHARHINIDAE

The whalers (or requiem sharks) are one of the largest family of sharks with 48 species in 12 genera worldwide, however relatively few species are in the Maldives. Most diagnostic features for the identification of carcharhinids (e.g the presence or absence of an interdorsal ridge, and tooth shape and numbers) are not practical for identification underwater, so careful observation of body shape and size, fin colouration and dorsal fin position should be noted. Whalers have ventrally placed mouths extending well past the eyes, 5 pairs of gill slits, circular eyes with nictitating membranes and 2 spineless dorsal fins; the first much larger than the second (except Whitetip Reef Shark and Sicklefin Lemon Shark). Except for the Tiger Shark, which is aplacental, all whalers are typically viviparous, with yolk-sac placenta.

Silvertip Shark

Carcharhinus albimarginatus

Photo: Guy Stevens, Mexico.

Maldivian name *Kattafuihi miyaru.* Max length: 3 m TL. Viviparous (placental). Litter up to 11, usually 5 or 6 pups. Gestation about 1 year. Length at birth 55 to 80 cm TL. IUCN status: Near Threatened.

Readily identified by first dorsal, pectoral, caudal and sometimes pelvic fins, with distinct white tips and margin posteriorly. First dorsal fin origin over or just anterior to pectoral fin rear tips. Most common around isolated islands, coral banks, reef drop-offs and along reef walls. Juveniles often observed in coastal shallows and outer-reef lagoons, while adults occur in deeper waters 30 m or greater adjacent to the atolls. Generally seen alone or in pairs. Regarded as potentially dangerous to humans, as they are known to approach divers quite closely. Widespread tropical Indo-Pacific. Mainly oceanic locations.

Grey Reef Shark

Carcharhinus amblyrhynchos

Maldivian name *Thila miyaru.* Max length: 2.25 m TL, usually about 1.8 m TL. Viviparous (placental). Litter 3 to 6 pups. Gestation about 1 year. Length at birth 50 to 60 cm TL. IUCN status: Near Threatened.

One of the most common species seen on tropical reefs. Its association with submerged reefs (thila), particularly in channels, gives this species its Dhivehi name. Often abundant at moderate depths of 30 to 50+ m and near coral reef drop-offs, however frequently seen in shallower waters. Also congregates near the mouths of channels running into atolls on the exposed side of the prevailing monsoonal currents. Mature females seen at shark-watching dive sites are known to disappear for a few weeks every year between March and May, probably for breeding. A stocky species, mostly uniform grey in colour with a white margin posteriorly on the first dorsal fin, and a distinct wide black margin along entire posterior margin on the caudal fin. Is known to show curiosity to divers and may circle in large groups at close range. In general not aggressive, but should not be challenged or provoked. Feeding such sharks may also lead to bites. When startled by divers, it may perform a threat display by wagging its head and tail in lateral sweeps, arching its back, raising its head and depressing its pectoral fins. Widespread tropical Indo-Pacific.

Photo: Marc Zaalberg, Noonu Atoll.

Photo: Guy Stevens, North Malé Atoll.

Silky Shark
Carcharhinus falciformis

Maldivian name *Ainumathi miyaru.* Max length: 2.6 m TL. Viviparous (placental). Litter typically 6 to 12 pups. Gestation 12 months. Length at birth 70 to 87 cm TL. IUCN status: Near Threatened.

A largely pelagic and abundant offshore species, adults are generally seen in open ocean, near drop-offs adjacent to deep water and on seamounts to depths of 50 m. Adults associate with free-swimming tuna and are a common bycatch of tuna purse seine and longline fisheries. Young individuals sometimes form large aggregations, possibly for defence, and often congregate with other fish under floating objects that drift with the prevailing currents. They have a slender, streamlined body with a relatively long, rounded snout. Skin is fine textured compared to other sharks. Distinguished from other members of the carcharhinids by a comparatively small first dorsal fin, which is more rounded and set further back on the body, with its origin distinctly behind the trailing edge of the pectoral fins. The tiny second dorsal fin has a long free rear tip, usually longer than fin height. Pectoral fins are long, narrow and sickle-shaped. The anal fin has a deep notch in the posterior margin and the caudal fin is relatively high with a well-developed lower lobe. Colour is dark grey to golden-brown dorsally, and white on the belly with a lighter stripe on the flank. The underside of the pectoral and pelvic fins may be dark. Prey is mostly bony fishes and squid. Silky sharks can be inquisitive and may also perform a threat display, where it arches its back, elevates its head and drops its tail and pectoral fins. Circumtropical, oceanic and coastal.

A young Oceanic Whitetip Shark showing distinctive white mottled fin-tips with some dark colouration retained from the juvenile stage. Photo: Naoko Taki. Huvadhoo Atoll.

Oceanic Whitetip Shark
Carcharhinus longimanus

Maldivian name *Feekanfaiy miyaru.* Max Length: 3.96 m TL, usually attains 3.5 m TL. Viviparous (placental). Litter 1 to 15 pups. Gestation 1 year. Length at birth 60 to 65 cm TL. IUCN status: Vulnerable.

Inhabits offshore oceanic waters but also quite common in the Maldives; in particular, juveniles are frequently seen inside the atolls. Most fins have white tips although juveniles may lack these and have black marks, including a saddle-like marking between the first and second dorsal fins. Adults often retain black pigment areas in the anal fin and caudal fin region. A large stocky grey or brownish shark, pale underside and readily distinguished from other sharks by broadly rounded first dorsal and pectoral fins. Often found in association with schools of tunas and mackerels. Their mottled white fin tips may resemble schools of baitfish, and attract an easy feed of tuna and mackerel. A large bycatch of tuna longline fisheries, the large fins are retained for their high value. Often regarded as dangerous and responsible for attacks on humans. Worldwide temperate and tropical seas.

Blacktip Reef Shark
Carcharhinus melanopterus

Juvenile in a lagoon. Photo: Marc Zaalberg.

Maldivian name *Falhu miyaru.* Max length: 1.8 m TL. Viviparous (placental). Litter 2 to 5 pups. Gestation 8 to 9 months. Length at birth 33 to 52 cm TL. IUCN status: Near Threatened.

Large adults often solitary, occasionally venturing into deep water but prefers shallow water and often seen swimming over sandbars and shallow reefs with the dorsal and upper caudal fin exposed. Juveniles are especially common in lagoons and often form small schools hunting small fishes in subtidal zones. One of the most noted species by snorkellers; also common in mangrove habitats. Brown to grey in colour dorsally, with pale white colour ventrally. Easily recognized by the a dark stripe on each flank extending from above the pectoral fin to the pelvic area and distinctive black fin-tips, especially on the first dorsal fin and lower lobe of the caudal fin. A fast, small shark, not considered dangerous, however it has been reported to bite people wading in shallow water. Widespread Indo-Pacific.

Photo: Rudie Kuiter, Java, Indonesia.

Spot-tail Shark
Carcharhinus sorrah

Maldivian name *Thilaa kolhu dhon miyaru.* Max length: 1.6 m TL. Viviparous (placental). Litter 1 to 8 pups. Gestation 10 months. Length at birth 45 to 60 cm TL. IUCN status: Near Threatened.

Rarely seen in the Maldives; although a widespread shallow water coastal species. A small, slender shark with long rounded snout and large circular eyes. Grey to bronze brown above and white below and conspicuous white band on flank. Characterised by a distinct black spot on the lower caudal fin and dark tips on second dorsal and pectoral fins. Second dorsal fin elongate and very low; interdorsal ridge present. Feeds mainly on fishes and cephalopods. Colour ranges from bronze to grey dorsally, shading to white ventrally. Widespread Indo-Pacific.

Photo: Guy Stevens, Goidhoo Atoll.

Photo: Rudie Kuiter, West Australia.

Tiger Shark
Galeocerdo cuvier

Maldivian name *Itfemunu.* Max length: 7.4 m TL. Viviparous (aplacental). Litter from 10 to 80 pups. Gestation 12 to 16 months. Length at birth 50 to 80 cm TL. IUCN status: Near Threatened.

A very large whaler shark that occurs in both shallow coastal and deep offshore waters. They have enormous livers that contain substantial quantities of oil. A scavenger that feeds on all kinds of large creatures including sea turtles, birds and mammals as well as fishes, crustaceans, and cephalopods. Although active mainly at night, large individuals may venture into lagoons or swim through gutters on reef flats during the day. One of the most dangerous sharks. Identified by a large, broad and bluntly rounded snout, lateral keels on caudal peduncle and a tapering caudal fin lobe with thin and pointed tip. Colour is grey on dorsal surface and white ventrally, with distinct vertically barred pattern on body flanks in juveniles, and faint or absent in adults. The Tiger Shark is the only aplacental viviparous member of the family. Found in all tropical seas, ranging into subtropical waters.

Sicklefin Lemon Shark
Negaprion acutidens

Maldivian name *Faihu femunu.* Max length: 3.1 m TL. Viviparous (placental). Litter 1 to 14. Gestation 10 months. Length at birth 45 to 80 cm TL. IUCN status: Vulnerable.

Prefers shallow inshore areas around sandy lagoons and mangrove estuaries, often resting on sandy flats but also in deeper waters on outer reef faces to about 90 m. Juveniles move onto tidal flats at high tide to feed. A slow-moving predator, they usually swim close to the substrate. Seldom travels long

Photo: Guy Stevens, French Polynesia.

distances and individuals can be found year-round returning to the same location. A stout-bodied shark with a short broad head and rounded snout with small eyes. Small nostrils bear triangular flaps of skin in front. The two dorsal fins are of approximately equal size, and the long pectoral fins originate below the third and fourth gill slits. Colouration is a uniformly plain yellowish-brown colour above and lighter below. Fins are hooked or sickle-shaped. Prey includes bony fishes, crustaceans, octopuses and stingrays. Adults generally shy and difficult to approach but should never be harassed or provoked; juveniles generally more inquisitive. Widespread but uncommon in the Maldives. Widespread in the tropical Indo-West Pacific.

Whitetip Reef Shark
Triaenodon obesus

A large pregnant female, with the end of her caudal fin bitten off. Photo Guy Stevens, Mulaku Atoll.

Maldivian name *Faana miyaru.* Max length: 1.6 m TL. Viviparous (placental). Litters of 1 to 5 pups. Gestation a little over 1 year. Length at birth 50 to 60 cm TL. IUCN status: Near Threatened.

Associated almost exclusively with coral reef habitats and mostly encountered near the bottom around coral heads and ledges and over sandy flats, in lagoons and near drop-offs adjacent to deeper water. Recognised by its slim, slender body and short, broad head, as well as by tubular skin flaps beside the nostrils, oval eyes and conspicuous white tips on the dorsal and upper caudal fins. Doral surface is greyish brown, usually with some scattered dark spots, and ventral surface pale. The second dorsal fin is almost as large as the first. A nocturnal hunter, usually seen during the day resting motionless on sand patches or inside caves. Sometimes forms loose aggregations. Generally shy but where accustomed to divers, can be approached at close range. A harmless species, adapted to feeding in small crevices and caves on small fish and cephalopods. One of the few species in which mating has been observed in the wild; they mate with their bodies angled upwards and their heads on the bottom. Widespread in the tropical Indo-Pacific.

Photo: Rudie Kuiter, Java, Indonesia.

HAMMERHEAD SHARKS
SPHYRNIDAE

Photo: Marco Carnovale, Rasdhoo Atoll.

Photo: Patrick Van Moer, Rasdhoo Atoll.

Scalloped Hammerhead Shark
Sphyrna lewini

Maldivian name *Kaaligandu miyaru.* Max length: 4.2 m TL. Viviparous (placental). Litter 15 to 31 pups. Gestation 9 to 10 months. Length at birth 42 to 55 cm TL. IUCN status: Endangered.

Adults mostly pelagic, ranging from the surface to depths of at least 300 m, but can also occur in inshore waters. Sometimes seen in large schools near coral reef drop-offs during the day. A large, more-or-less permanent aggregation occurs off the small island of Madivaru, in Rasdhoo Atoll. Occasionally makes close passes to inspect divers, but is neither aggressive nor dangerous. The hammer-shaped head is unique and thought to enhance their sensory capabilities, with eyes located at the tips of laterally expanded blades. The wing-shaped head also increases manoeuvrability, aiding in the capture of fast prey. The head has a central indentation at the front, and the side extensions are angled slightly backwards. The first dorsal fin is considerably larger than the second. Colour is olive or brownish grey dorsally and pale ventrally. Pectoral fin tips have a dusky ventral surface in adults. Pectoral, lower caudal and second dorsal-fin tips dark in juveniles. Feeds predominantly on fish, but also squid, rays and other animals, including sharks, moving into deep water at night to feed. Widespread, but patchily distributed in the Maldives. Circumglobal in tropical and warm-temperate seas.

Photo: Patrick Van Moer, Rasdhoo Atoll.

Great Hammerhead Shark
Sphyrna mokarran

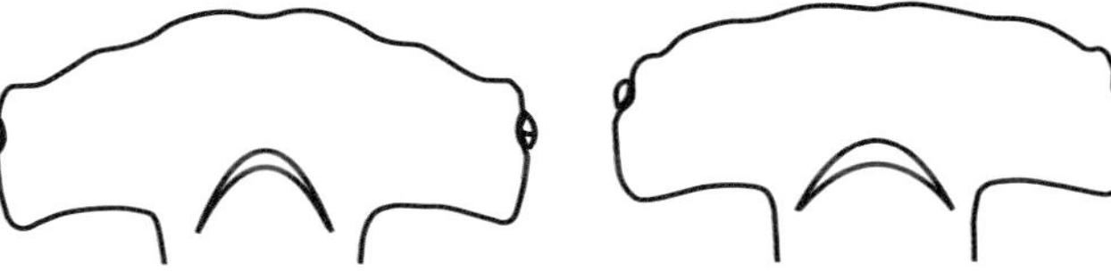

Left: Scalloped Hammerhead, head with nearly arched anterior margin, prominent median and lateral indents. Right: Great Hammerhead, head with nearly straight anterior margin, prominent median and lateral indents.

Maldivian name *Kaaligandu miyaru.* Max length: 6.1 m TL. Viviparous (placental). Litter 6 to 42. Gestation 11 months. Length at birth 50 to 70 cm TL. IUCN status: Endangered.

A widely distributed species that inhabits both coastal and offshore waters. A solitary, nomadic predator not often seen near other reef sharks. Uses its laterally expanded head to increase manoeuvrability and assist in the detection and capture of prey. In the Maldives, they have been observed chasing eagle rays across the sandy floor inside atolls and elsewhere, using their head to pin eagle rays on the bottom. Feeds on fishes, including sharks and rays, crustaceans and cephalopods. Light grey to brown dorsally and white ventrally. Fins are unmarked. Distinguished by nearly straight anterior margin on the head of adults, very tall pointed sail-like first dorsal fin and deeply notched pelvic and anal fins. Hammer-shaped head has a notch at the centre. World-wide temperate and tropical seas.

GUITARFISHES
RHINOBATIDAE

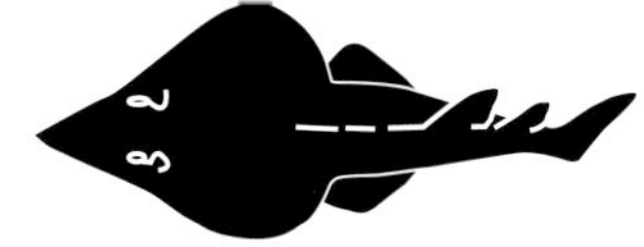

Bow-mouth Guitarfish or Shark Ray
Rhina ancylostoma

Maldivian name *Madi miyaru.* Max length: 2.7 m TL. Viviparous (aplacental). Litter 4. IUCN status: Vulnerable.

Photo: Lisa Allison, South Miladhunmadulu Atoll.

As the name implies, a ray with shark-like appearance; fishermen in the Maldives refer to them as sharks. Inhabits inshore areas and occurs on sandy substrate on the inner atoll floors, occasionally venturing into shallow lagoons. Identified by a broad rounded snout (more rounded than Giant Guitarfish, next page) with large pectoral fins, and a prominent ridge over the eyes and along the back and shoulders bearing large thorns. Bluish-grey or brownish above, with large white spots on fins, partial eye spots (ocelli) on pectoral fins; white below and black bars between the eyes. Feeds mainly on bottom crustaceans and molluscs. Widespread Indo-West Pacific.

Photo: Guy Stevens, South Maalhosmadulu Atoll.

Giant Guitarfish
Rhynchobatus djiddensis

Maldivian name *Madimiyaru.* Max length: 3.1 m TL. Viviparous (aplacental). Litter up to 10. IUCN status: Vulnerable.

Also known as the White-spotted Guitarfish. The head is triangular with a pointed snout, back with small thorns, and two large dorsal fins creating a shark-like appearance. Usually seen on sandy substrate on the inner atoll floors, occasionally venturing into shallow lagoons to feed on various invertebrates, including crabs, lobsters and clams, as well as bony fishes. Often bury themselves in sand so all that is seen are fins sticking out of the sand. Base of pectoral fins often with eye-spots (ocelli). Colour varies from almost entirely black to grey, or tan but most are olive green, with rows of small white spots on the upper body in longitudinal rows; light below. Generally shy harmless fishes that are difficult to approach when diving or snorkelling. They have been targeted and heavily overfished in the past in the Maldives. Widespread Indo-West Pacific, but may comprise a complex of several similar species.

Photo: Shaahina Ali, South Maalhosmadulu Atoll.

TORPEDO RAYS
TORPEDINIDAE

Electric Ray
Torpedo fuscomaculata

Photo: Azim Musthag, Malé Atoll.

Maldivian name *Assi Madi.* Max length: 65 cm TL. Viviparous (aplacental). IUCN status: Data deficient.

Usually seen near reefs on sandy or rubble substrates. A distinctive species, identified by its large disc relative to short tail, dorsal fins close together, large caudal fin with well-developed upper and lower lobes and rather small eyes. Electric rays have a set of powerful electric organs to stun prey and can give divers a nasty shock when handled or accidently resting on one that maybe hidden in the sand. They feed mostly on bony fishes including eels and a large expandable stomach accommodates some prey, which may be very large. Widespread Indian Ocean but comprises several localised forms in different areas. Due to their cryptic nature, this species is infrequently observed. Western Indian Ocean.

Photo: Marc Zaalberg, South Ari Atoll.

STINGRAYS
DASYATIDAE

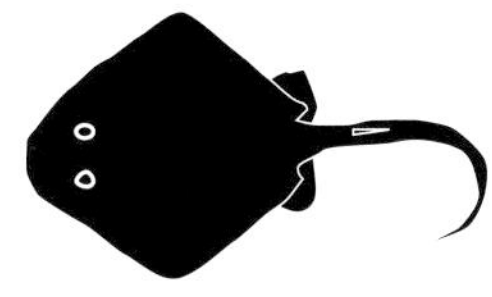

Smalleye Stingray
Dasyatis microps

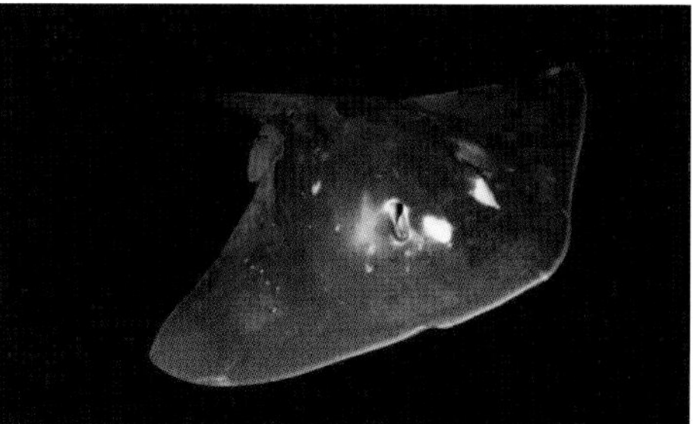

Photo: Adam Broadbent, Rasdhoo Atoll.

Maldivian name *Naru nagoo* madi. Max width: 2.2 m. Viviparous (aplacental). Litter 1 pup. Gestation 12 months. Width at birth about 33 cm. IUCN status: Data deficient.

A very large species that mainly occurs in deeper water. Disc is wide, apices are extremely angular and tail with a broad base before a large sting, but whip-like after. Has small eyes, large spiracles and is covered in numerous, small denticles. Pelvic fins are relatively large. Colour is pale brownish on dorsal surface, more pale ventrally. Not frequently observed but reliable sightings have been recorded of swimming in mid-water (off the reef) and happily hovering over deep water off Rasdhoo in Ari Atoll. Behaviour is reported more like that of mantas with rays swimming around divers at depths of 15 m to 30 m. Widespread Indo-West Pacific.

Pink Whipray
Pateobatis fai

Maldivian name *Naru nagoo madi.* Max width: 1.8 m. Viviparous (aplacental). Litter 2 to 6. Gestation 12 months. Width at birth about 55 to 60 cm. IUCN status: Least concern.

Not commonly seen when diving but often aggregates in small groups over shallow sandy substrates near sand cays and at resorts during stingray feeds. It has small eyes, small pelvic fins and a long whip-like tail with a large venomous spine at the base of tail, which is extremely sharp and can measure up to 16 cm in larger specimens. Colour is uniformly pink to brownish. Frequently misidentified for Jenkins' Whipray. Feeds on bottom-dwelling invertebrates. Widespread Indo-Pacific.

Photo: Jason Isley, North Huvadhoo Atoll.

Photo: Guy Stevens. Mulaku Atoll.

Mangrove or White-spotted Whipray
Urogymnus granulatus

Maldivian name *Naru nagoo madi.* Max width: 1.4 m. Viviparous (aplacental). Litter 2 to 6. Gestation 12 months. Width at birth about 55 to 60 cm. IUCN status: Vulnerable.

Occurs moderately common around reefs, entering shallow lagoons and waters with poor visibility, including mangrove habitats where they feed on small crustaceans. A large dark grey to black ray dorsally usually dusted with white spots and a broad-based tail with one or more venomous spines (or scar when dislodged) and white whip-like tail after spine. Ventral surface is white. Disc is almost circular to oval, with prominent denticles on head and along midline of tail. Small pelvic fins. Non-aggressive, but should be left alone. Feeds primarily on a variety of small fish, molluscs and crustaceans. Widespread Indo-Pacific.

Jenkins' Whipray
Pateobatis jenkinsi

Photo: Marc Zaalberg, South Ari Atoll.

Maldivian name *Naru nagoo madi.* Max width: 1.5 m. Viviparous (aplacental). Litter 2 to 6. Gestation 12 months. Width at birth about 23 cm. IUCN status: Least concern.

Occurs in large lagoons. A uniformly coloured yellow-brown stingray with long, whip-like tail black beyond the sting. Dorsally rough, with denticles on the centre of disc very closely spaced, with additional rows of enlarged thorn-like denticles present along the midline of the disc and tail before the stinging spine; unlike *H. fai* which has denticles widely spaced and no enlarged thorn-like denticles. Disc is rhomboidal and pelvic fins small. Non-aggressive, but it has up to 3 venomous spines on the tail and is a species that should be left alone. Feeds primarily on a variety of sand-dwelling molluscs and crustaceans. Widespread Indo-Pacific (if a single species), with patchy distribution in the northern Indian Ocean, east coast of South Africa and northern Australia.

Cowtail Stingray
Pastinachus sephen

Photo: Marc Zaalberg, South Ari Atoll.

Maldivian name *Naru nagoo madi.* Max width: 1.8 m. Length to 3 m. Viviparous (aplacental). Litter 2 to 6. Gestation 12 months. Width at birth 18 cm. IUCN status: Data deficient.

Also commonly known as Feathertail Stingray. Moderately common on sand flats, including intertidal zone, may enter freshwater, and often seen in large shallow lagoons. Active during the day and blows in sand to expose prey, which comprises most sand-dwelling invertebrates. Usually very shy and will flee from approaching divers when disturbed. A sandy coloured species with broadly rounded snout and small, widely spaced eyes. Tail has a broad base and a single venomous spine located well back dorsally of a large, feather-like ventral tail fold. Widespread Indo-Pacific.

Photo: Rudie Kuiter, Malé Atoll.

Photo: Randy Schafer, Ari Atoll.

Blotched Fantail Ray

Taeniurops meyeni

Maldivian name *Naru nagoo madi.* Max width: 1.8 m. Viviparous (aplacental). Litter 2 to 6. Gestation 12 months. Width at birth 30 to 35 cm. IUCN status: Vulnerable.

One of the largest rays with an almost circular disc commonly found around reefs in shallow depths and may enter deeper lagoons to feed. Largely nocturnal, feeding on a great variety of sand dwelling invertebrates as well as bony fishes. It has a single venomous spine on the tail, rarely two, and a prominent ventral skin fold to the tip of tail after the spine. Disc is dorsally variable in colour from grey to brownish with dark botches and small pelvic fins. A non-aggressive species, but often seen with raised spine pointed forward when threatened and like with any wild creature, it should not be interfered with. Widespread Indo-West Pacific.

Photo: Marc Zaalberg, Laamu Atoll.

Photo: Guy Stevens, Ari Atoll.

Porcupine Ray

Urogymnus asperrimus

Maldivian name *Naru nagoo madi.* Max width: 1.5 m. Viviparous (aplacental). Litter 2 to 6. Gestation 12 months. IUCN status: Vulnerable.

Not common and occasionally seen in large lagoons. A sandy coloured species with disc covered in sharp thorns located in rows parallel to its margins. Disc more oval shaped compared to other similar sized rays. Tail is relatively short and uniquely within its family, lacks a venomous stinging spine. Feeds mainly at night on crustaceans and sleeping fishes. Widespread Indo-Pacific and tropical waters of the eastern Atlantic.

EAGLE RAYS
MYLIOBATIDAE

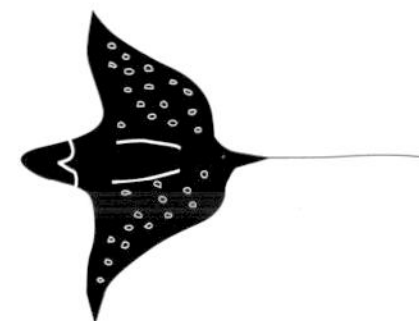

White-spotted Eagle Ray
Aetobatus oscellatus

Photo: Alike Schroeder, South Miladhunmadulu Atoll

Maldivian name *Vaifiya madi.* Max width: 3 m, commonly to 1.5 m. Tail up to 5 m long. Viviparous (aplacental). Litter 2 to 6. Gestation 12 months. Width at birth 17 to 36 cm. IUCN status: Not assessed.

A graceful, fast swimmer, often forming large schools well above the bottom or near the surface, and sometimes seen jumping high into the air. Prefers open water and descends to the bottom to feed, mainly over extensive sand-flats between shore and reefs in the afternoon. Has an angular disc, a small dorsal fin near the base of an extremely long, whip-like tail 2.5 to 3.0 times disc width (when undamaged), and one or more venomous spines located just behind the dorsal fin. Feeds by digging its duck-like snout in the sand to locate prey which it crushes with strong plate-like teeth. Prey includes clams, whelks, oysters, worms, and shrimps. Common throughout the tropical Indo-Pacific.

Ornate Eagle Ray
Aetomylaeus vespertilio

Photo: Guy Stevens, Felidhe Atoll.

Maldivian name *Vaifiya madi.* Max width: 3 m. Tail up to 2.5 m long. Viviparous (aplacental). Litter 2 to 6. IUCN status: Endangered.

A seemingly rare species reported from few localities scattered throughout the Indo-Pacific and occasionally photographed in the Maldives. Colour is dark to light brown on dorsal surface, white below. Easily identified when seen from above by its network of dark lines on the upper front half of disc and spotted pattern on back half of disc. Has a long whip-like tail, and no stinging spine. Sporadic Indo-West Pacific.

DEVIL RAYS
MOBULIDAE

The spot pattern on the white ventral side is clustered around the lower abdominal region. Photo: Guy Stevens, Foammulah Atoll.

Oceanic (Giant) Manta Ray
Manta birostris

Maldivian name *En madi.* Max width: 6.8 m, weight up to 2 tonnes. Viviparous (aplacental). Litter 1 pup on average. Width at birth 1.5 to 2.0 m with a weight of 35 kg. IUCN status: Vulnerable.

Often found in association with offshore oceanic islands along the outer atoll reefs adjacent to deep drop-offs. Infrequently encountered in the Maldives; usually solitary travellers occasionally stopping to visit 'cleaning stations'. The largest of all rays and easily recognised by the large frontal lobes, known as cephalic fins, situated just in front of the eyes on either side of their head. When feeding, these fins unfurl to form paddle-like appendages to funnel planktonic prey into the large cavernous mouths. The prey is then filtered from the water by sieve-like plates in the gills, called rakers. Mouth is terminal

The Oceanic Manta Ray is predominantly black above and has distinct white shoulder markings, forming a letter "T" in black across the top of the head, except in all-black individuals. Photo: Guy Stevens, South Maalhosmadulu Atoll.

(faces forward) in the *Manta*, unlike the *Mobula*, where mouth is ventral (underside). Tail is shorter than disc width and lacks a stinging spine. A small dorsal fin is located near the tail base. Distinguished by a knob-like bulge at the base of their tail, which is absent on the majority of reef manta rays. Distinct dorsal markings across the top of the head and ventral spot patterns is the best way to identify between the two manta species. Circumtropical and pelagic, mainly in tropical seas but occasionally migrates to temperate waters.

Reef (Alfred) Manta Ray

Manta alfredi

Maldivian name *En madi.* Max width: 5 m. Viviparous (aplacental). Litter 1 pup on average. Width at birth 1.5 to 2.0 m. IUCN status: Vulnerable.

The Maldives is home to the world's largest known population of this species and, unlike Oceanic Manta Rays, they are mainly resident to an atoll and unlikely to leave the Maldives. They follow the seasonal fluctuations in productivity of their planktonic food and individuals are commonly encountered by divers and snorkellers at well-known cleaning stations. The Reef Manta Ray is smaller than its oceanic cousin, but all mantas start off small so size is not necessarily a good identification feature. Easily identified by the dorsal markings and ventral black spot pattern. Tropical Indian and Pacific Oceans in association with coral reefs.

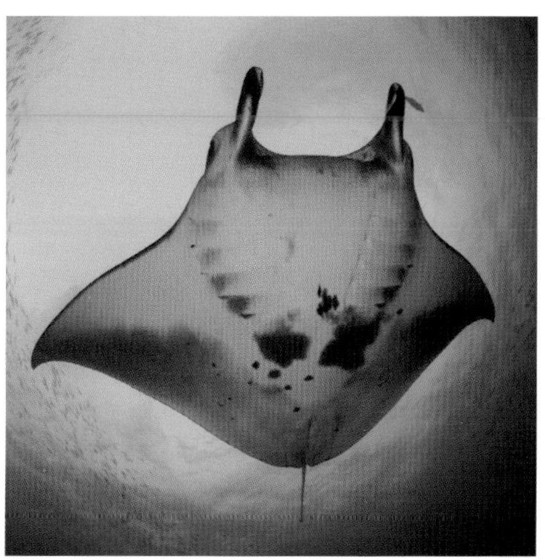

Ventral black spot pattern is often between the branchial gill slits and spread across the trailing edge of pectoral fins. Photo: Guy Stevens, Malé Atoll.

On the Reef Manta Ray, the transition between the white and black shoulder markings is blurred along the colour boundary forming more of a 'Y' shaped pattern across the head and down the centre of its back. Photo: Guy Stevens, South Maalhosmadulu Atoll.

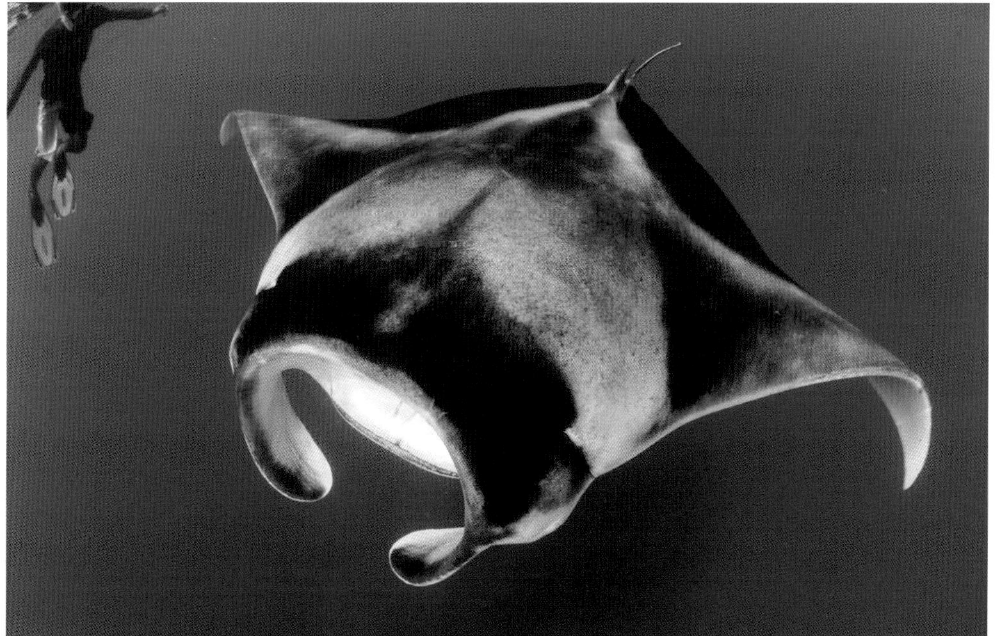

Photo: Guy Stevens, Malé Atoll.

Short-fin Pygmy Devil Ray
Mobula kuhlii

Maldivian name *En madi.* Max width: 1.20 m. Viviparous (aplacental). IUCN status: Data deficient.

The Short-fin Pygmy Devil Ray is by far the most commonly encountered by divers and snorkellers and is often mistaken for baby manta rays. When fully grown they are still much smaller than a new born baby manta. The shape of the cephalic fins when rolled up, look like horns projecting off their head, hence the name "devil rays". Mobula rays have a lower jaw that rests much further back than the upper, unlike the manta ray which has evenly aligned jaws and a large mouth at the front of the head. Generally found in schools of 3 to 20 individuals cruising along the outer atoll reef crests and slope, although super schools of over 100 individuals are sometimes encountered when the rays come together during the mating season, often leaping out of the water during courtship rituals. Colouration is dark brown above and white below. Tail is shorter than disc width and there is no tail spine. Dorsal fin is often white-tipped and the pectoral fins have slightly curved tips. This species is found throughout the Indo-West Pacific.

Spine-tail Devil Ray
Mobula japanica

Maldivian name *En madi.* Max width: 3.10 m, usually no more than 1.5 m. Viviparous (aplacental). Litter 1 pup on average. Width at birth 85 to 92 cm. IUCN status: Near Threatened.

An oceanic species by nature, occurs singly or in small groups occasionally close to shore. Blue-mauve and purple dorsal surface and bright white belly below. The top of head has a thick dark band, which stretches from eye–eye, which is thought to act as a brain warming device. The inner surface of cephalic fins are silver grey with black tips. It has a long, whip-like tail longer than disc width and a spine at the base of the tail. The dorsal fin is always white-tipped. Pelagic and circumtropical.

Photo: Guy Stevens, South Ari Atoll.

Manta Rays of the Maldives

Anne-MarieKitchen-Wheeler(www.mantaresearch.com)

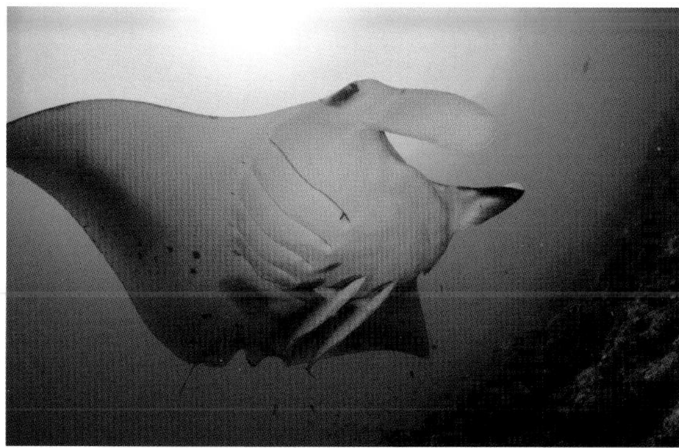

"Brenda", the oldest manta ray recorded in the Maldives. Photo: Guy Stevens, Malé Atoll.

The Maldives archipelago contains an estimated 10,000 individual manta rays – the world's largest known population of manta rays. This population primarily consists of the smaller Reef Manta Ray (*Manta alfredi*), but the larger Oceanic Manta Ray (*Manta birostris*) is occasionally seen, which accounts for less than 1% of mantas reported. Pre-2009, all mantas were designated under the species *Manta birostris*, but research into the Maldives population by The Manta Ecology Project, which commenced in 2001, has contributed to the current scientific opinion that there are at least two species of *Manta*.

The majority of mantas appear to remain resident of an atoll, moving from east to west and back with the changes of prevailing monsoons each year, and will be most likely reported at sites on the leeside to the prevailing winds. For example, mantas are commonly reported at Lankan reef site on the east side of North Malé Atoll from April to November. The same mantas have also been reported around Boduhithi, on the west side of the atoll, from December to March.

It is unknown how long mantas live, but based on photo-identification of a well-known North Male Atoll manta known as "Brenda" since the mid-1980's, it is known she is at least 36 years old, and likely to be significantly older. Mantas in aquaria may have one pup per year from a pregnancy. However, in the Maldives adult female mantas become pregnant much less frequently than this (every 3-5 years may be more typical) but the reason is unknown. Generally, female mantas are larger than male mantas although male mantas may grow as large as females.

There appears to be two mating seasons in the Maldives consisting of four-week periods around October/November and March. These periods occur just before the changes in the prevailing monsoon and are probably connected to increased plankton productivity, which appears to occur at these times. During these periods it is common to observe chains of males chasing females in their attempts to impress the female with their swimming prowess.

It appears that mantas do not establish long-term relationships and form groups, but they aggregate when feeding and behave co-operatively. Some examples of social learning have been described yet new-born mantas are left to fend for themselves as there is no maternal care of offspring.

Although mantas are pelagic and spend most of their time in the epipelagic and pelagic zones, large numbers of mantas are commonly reported in-shore during these times at either cleaning or feeding areas where they are easily observed by divers and snorkellers. However, mantas remain around the Maldives archipelago throughout the year, with individuals regularly travelling between atolls. Some mantas appear to perform long-distance migrations, traversing the entire length Maldives. One manta ray first observed in Ari atoll, in the centre of the Maldives, was subsequently observed in the northernmost atoll of Haa Alifu; the sites are 270 km apart.

Although our knowledge on *Manta* species has significantly increased in the past 10 years, there is still much that is unknown.

Identify Your Manta

Guy Stevens (www.mantatrust.org)

Manta Feeding Photo: Guy Stevens, Ari Atoll.

With the world's largest known population of manta rays, the Maldives is the most reliable place to study these amazing animals. Since the Maldivian Manta Ray Project (MMRP) began in 2005, over 3,000 different individual manta rays from more than 25,000 sightings have been recorded. It is possible to identify every individual because each has its own unique pattern of black spots on their predominantly white ventral (belly) surface. Just like a fingerprint, these patterns do not change throughout the lives of the mantas, enabling each individual to be tracked as it is sighted over the decades. Every new manta, or a re-sighted individual, helps to better understand the population size, composition, migratory routes, reproductive output, native ranges, and areas of critical habitats — all of which are important in developing effective management and conservation strategies.

The Manta Trust has research and conservation projects in 16 different countries around the world and by submitting images and sighting encounters – whether in the Maldives or elsewhere – through the online submission form, anyone with a camera can contribute directly to the global research and conservation of manta rays. Images, with details including where and when the manta was seen, can be emailed directly to IDtheManta@mantatrust.org. If a manta, which has never been seen before is spotted, then the Manta Trust will ask the photographer to give it a name.

The area between the branchial gill slits and the abdominal region is used for the identification of mantas. Photo: Guy Stevens, South Maalhosmadulu Atoll.

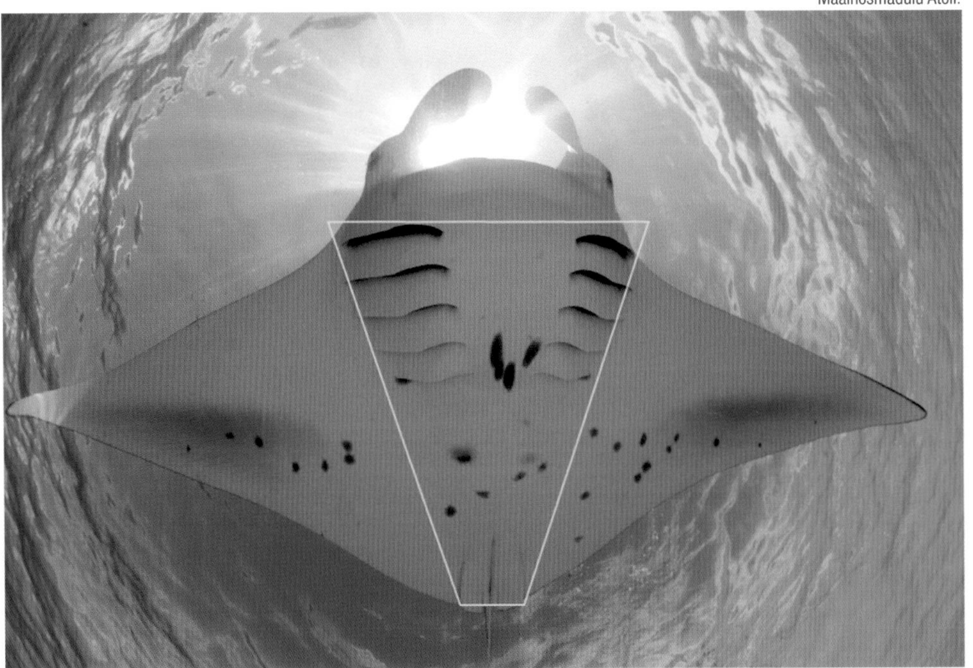

Families & Species Accounts

BONY FISHES

MORAY EELS
MURAENIDAE

A large family of eels with at least 10 genera and an estimated 170 species worldwide, or over 200 species according to some authors. About 40 species have been recorded from the Maldives but the majority are very secretive and rarely seen by divers, as they live inside the reef or in holes in sand. Only a few species are common on reefs, and these are usually seen during the day with just their heads visible from holes. Some species emerge at night to openly hunt over reefs and sand bottoms. Morays are carnivores and eat a mixture of invertebrates whole such as shrimps, octopus and fishes, including smaller eels. Their body is nearly all muscle and they are extremely strong with powerful jaws. They can attack larger creatures or engage in mauling activities with other morays, using their twisting body to rip away pieces of flesh. Some species are capable of knotting their body for leverage. Normally eels are shy but may get used to divers. Large individuals can be several metres long and have the potential to injure humans. Feeding these creatures has resulted in divers being hospitalised and therefore should not be encouraged.

Black Cheek Moray
Gymnothorax breedeni

Common on reef walls and steep slopes with holes to depths up to 20 m, however, usually only the head is visible. A territorial species, that can be aggressive towards divers and will bite if provoked. Easily identified by the distinctive black patch mark below the eye. Widespread throughout the Indian Ocean, ranging to some oceanic locations in the Pacific. Length to 65 cm.

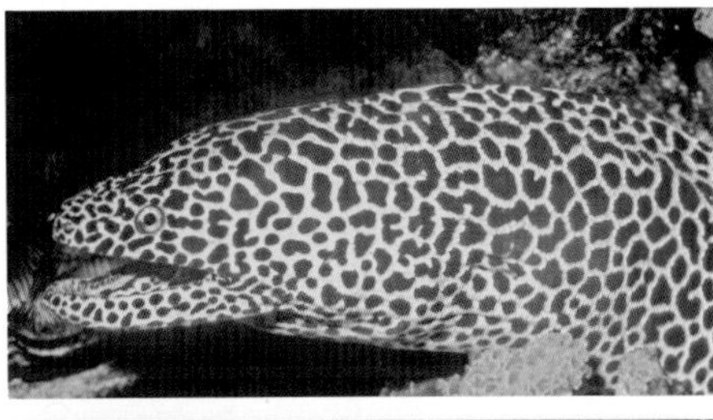

Honeycomb Moray
Gymnothorax favagineus

A basically white species with black blotches and white interspaces that form a honeycomb pattern. The size of the blotches varies between individuals, according to their overall size and habitat. Individuals living on clear coral reefs usually have proportionally less black than those in turbid waters. Has been observed in depths of 45 m, but also as shallow as six metres. Widespread Indo-Pacific. One of the largest morays, to about 2 m in length.

White-mouth Moray
Gymnothorax meleagris

A common species that prefers very shallow depths and juveniles are often in tidal zones. Occurs in corals, rubble on reef flats and in harbours. Identified by the white inside of its mouth, in contrast to a dark outer skin with small white spots. Widespread Indo-Pacific. Length to 60 cm.

Yellow-mouth Moray
Gymnothorax nudivomer

Occurs on inner and outer reef slopes, usually in depths over 30 m in the Maldives. White-spotted, sometimes in reticulated patterns. Best identified from similar species by the bright yellow inside the mouth. Widespread Indo-Pacific. Length reported up to 1 m.

Giant Moray
Gymnothorax javanicus

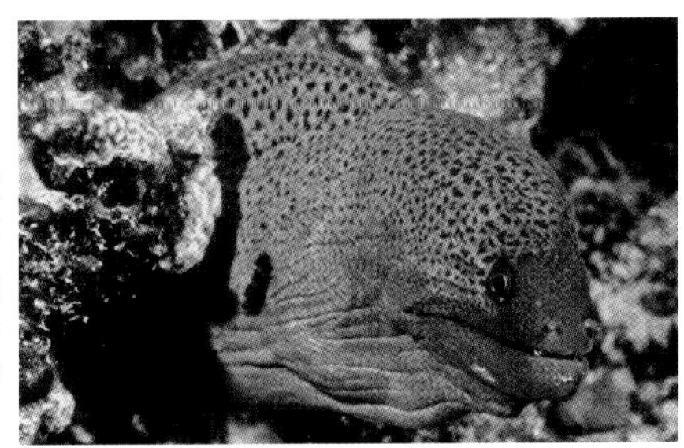

Lives in various reef habitats, from intertidal to about 50 m depth. The largest known Indo-Pacific moray and best distinguished by the numerous small dark spots on top of the head and back. A widespread species and often common. Reported to a length of 2.4 m and a weight of just over 30 kg.

Yellow-margin Moray
Gymnothorax flavimarginatus

Occurs in various reef habitats but prefers clear coastal reefs. Similar to the Giant Moray, but has a mottle pattern and a purplish-grey snout in large individuals. Small juveniles are sometimes yellow with brown mottling. Not common in the Maldives. Widespread Indo-Pacific. Length is to 1.2 m.

Little Moray
Gymnothorax richardsoni

A small species that lives in shallow rubble lagoons and coastal reef flats and often seen under large, loose, dead coral pieces to depths of about 10 m. Identified by a dense, starry pattern that extends along most of the body in an indistinctive dark banding. Widespread Indo-Pacific. Length to 30 cm.

Bar-tail Moray
Gymnothorax zonipectis

Occurs in various habitats from clear lagoon reef formations, shallow reefs with dense coral growth to deep coral reefs and sometimes in deep caves along drop-offs. Secretive amongst corals or in reef during the day, but sometimes detected at night in the open. Widespread Indo-Pacific. Length reported to 45 cm, usually to about 30 cm.

Spot-face Moray
Gymnothorax fimbriatus

Prefers protected inshore waters among dead corals, common in harbours and in small caves on slopes to about 45 m depth. A pale species with small black spots on the face when adult however, spots are proportionately much larger in young. Length reported to 80 cm, largest recorded in Malé harbour in photograph is about 65 cm.

Photo, juvenile with shrimp: Bali, Indonesia.

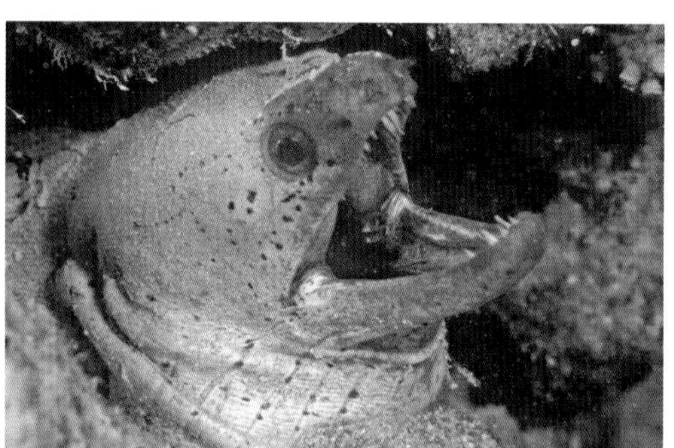

Undulate Moray
Gymnothorax undulatus

Occurs in the Maldives on protected reefs and in lagoons to about 20 m depth. A common species usually only seen at night when it hunts fishes that sleep in reef crevices. Can be aggressive towards divers. The snout is often yellow. Widespread Indo-Pacific. Length to at least 1 m.

Y-patterned Moray
Gymnothorax berndti

Photo: aquarium, Japan.

Prefers rock and sponge habitats, usually over 30 m depth. A rare but very distinctive species with a pale grey colour and y-patterns along its entire body. Originally described from Japan, the species is also known from Taiwan and Hawaii. Length to 1 m.

Zebra Moray
Gymnomuraena zebra

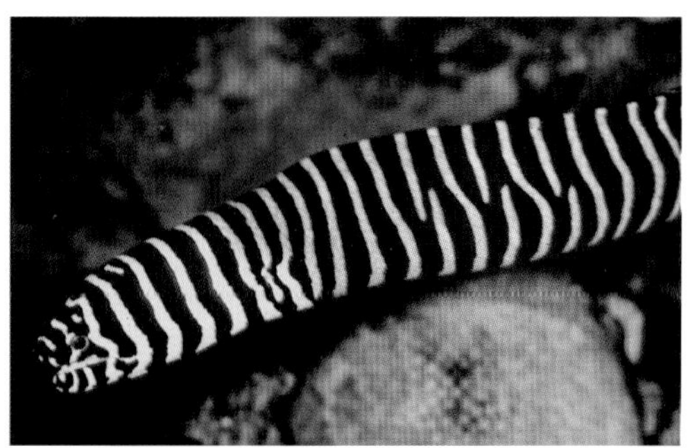

Occurs on shallow reef flats and slopes to 50 m depth, occasionally in pairs. Very secretive and shy and even at night is quick to retreat out of sight. Easily recognised by its close-set narrow dark bands. Widespread Indo-Pacific. Length to 1 m.

Barred Moray
Echidna polyzona

Occupies various shallow reef habitats, usually coastal and siltier zones, but is secretive during the day and not often seen. Mainly out at night, when in search of crabs and shrimps. Has a distinctive banded pattern as a juvenile that gradually breaks up into a blotched pattern. Widespread Indo-Pacific. Length to 60 cm.

Clouded Moray
Echidna nebulosa

A common shallow water species in protected areas such as harbours, usually amongst dead coral rubble pieces and mostly in depths less than 10 m. Sometimes hunts for crabs during the day in seagrass and rubble-mixed habitats. Has a distinctive starry pattern along the body, forming a series of dark blotches with some yellow spots. Widespread Indo-Pacific. Length to 60 cm.

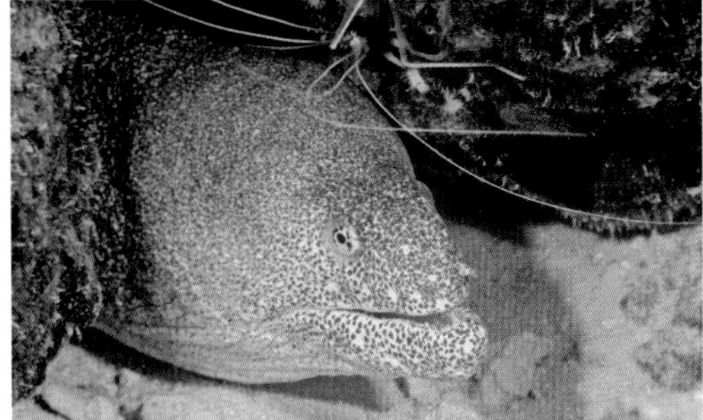

Peppered Moray
Gymnothorax pictus

Often occurs just below the intertidal zone in dead reefs, holes or where rubble pieces are piled up below jetties. They feed primarily on crabs and have been seen leaping at them just above the water line. Recognised by the pale grey to white colour and fine dark spotting. A common eel that prefers silty reefs. Widespread Indo-Pacific. Length to 1 m.

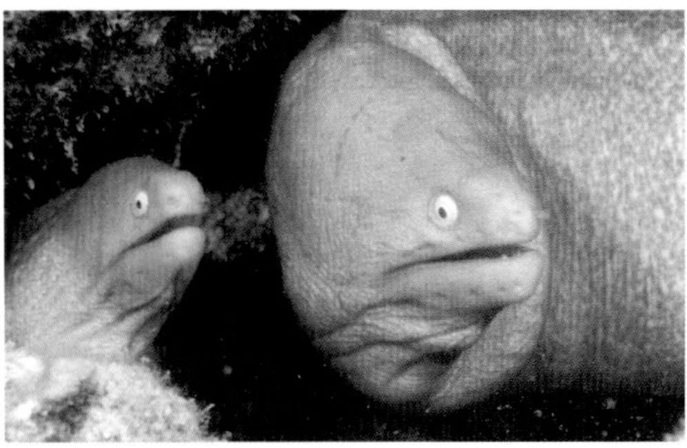

White-eyed Moray
Gymnothorax thyrsoideus

A common Maldives species, especially in silty harbours, but also seen deep and often on shipwrecks in coastal waters to depths of about 35 m. Sometimes several are living together or mixed with other species. Easily recognised by the bright white colour in the eyes. Widespread Indo-Pacific. Length to 65 cm.

Ribbon Eel
Rhinomuraena quaesita

Occurs on reef crests and slopes, from 3 m to at least 40 m depth. Lives in mixed sand and reef habitats and usually seen with just the head exposed. Waving a finger in front of the head, at a safe distance, may draw the eel out further. It seems to have poor eyesight and relies on smell and its ability to sense pressure changes to catch prey, usually small fishes such as damsels. Readily identified by its unusual shape and colour. Uncommon in most of the Maldives, and only known to dive-guides in a few localities. Length to 1.2 m.

Photos from top left: Female, showing signs of black colour fading, and several months later when changed to blue phase. Ripe females are thought to turn all yellow but are rarely seen.

Photos below left: Female swimming on sand slope during the day. Occasionally they swim from one burrow to another.
Below right: Blue male, usually larger and more commonly observed than the female.

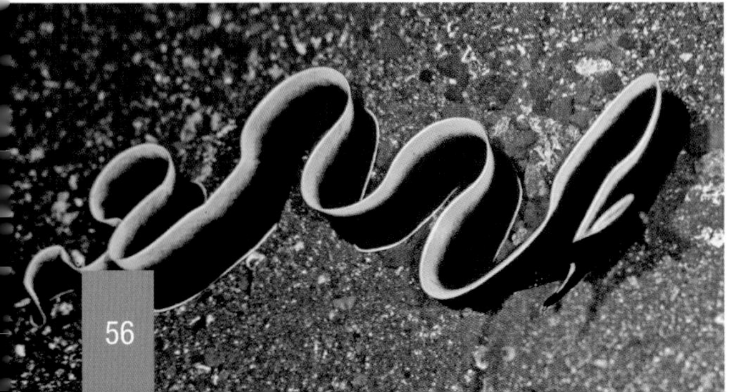

SNAKE & WORM EELS
OPHICHTHIDAE

A very large and diverse family, dividable into several sub-families with some 50 genera and more than 250 species worldwide; however comparatively few are seen by divers. Most species live completely buried in sand or mud, and only a few just show their head. About 15 species are known from the Maldives but no doubt many more will be discovered in time. Several of the photographs included here are new records for the Maldives. In these eels, the eyes are placed about centrally above the mouth. They are typically very long and often have a bony tail end that enables them to quickly bury backwards into the bottom. Some species are small and look more like worms than fish, while others are snake-like. Some actually mimic banded sea snakes and move about openly during the day in lagoons and over shallow reef flats. Their diet comprises fishes and invertebrates, such as octopuses and shrimps. In Australia, a snake-eel has been observed eating a snapping shrimp.

Napoleon Eel
Ophichthus bonaparti

Occurs in various sand and rubble habitats from shallow lagoons to deep sand flats. A very distinctive species identified by the colour pattern on the head and body, however the body is rarely seen unless a specimen is caught. Body is broadly banded, in contrast to the unusual blotches on its head. Typically seen as shown in the photograph. Widespread Indo-Pacific. Length to 75 cm.

Crocodile Eel
Brachysomophis crocodilinus

The eyes on this species are placed far forward over its very long jaws, near the tip of its snout, which gives it an unusual look. With only the head exposed from the sand, the species is easily overlooked as its colour matches its surroundings. Not commonly observed and only known from a few sightings throughout the Indo-Pacific. Length to 1 m.

Black-pitted Sand-Eel
Pisodonophis cancrivorus

The pores on the head are black and usually stand out when the eel is brown. Colour varies according to the habitat it lives in and in the Maldives, specimens are normally a very pale colour, like the sand. Usually seen with just its snout and eyes above the bottom, while the rest of the body is vertical below the sand. Widespread Indo-Pacific. Length to 75 cm.

Photo below: Mabul, Malaysia.

Marbled Snake-Eel
Callechelys marmorata

A variable species, from a plain sandy colour to dense black mottling on the head, which is usually the only part visible. Like most sand eels, little is known about their behaviour. Seen on sand flats from 5 m to 30 m. Widespread Indo-Pacific and ranges into warm-temperate zones. Length to 60 cm.

Banded Snake-Eel
Myrichthys colubrinus

Occurs in shallow protected bays and lagoons. The only sand eel generally observed by snorkelers, this species is often mistaken for a sea snake. As a mimic of a highly venomous creature, it shows little fear and hunts during the daytime for small fishes in holes and crevices. In Japan, this eel species has been seen being eaten by the sea snake it copies. Widespread Indo-Pacific, with some geographical variations in the depth of the bands encircling the body. Length to almost 1 m.

Photo: Flores, Indonesia, large individual hunting on a shallow reef flat during the day.

Spotted Snake-Eel
Myrichthys maculosus

A nocturnal species that hunts mainly on shallow reef flats, but ranges to depths of about 30 m. Often seen in silty coastal habitats. White to yellowish with rounded black blotches with some spot size variation between light and dark habitats. Widespread Indo-Pacific. Length to almost 1 m.

Photos: Bali, Indonesia. Large individual hunting on a rubble slope at night.

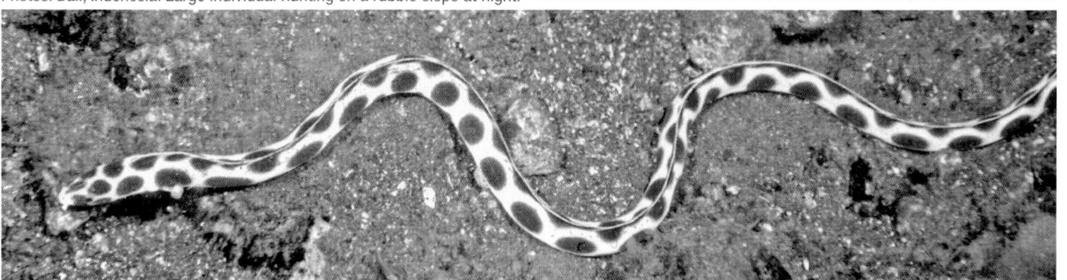

GARDEN EELS
CONGRIDAE

Best known in this family are the garden eels, placed in the sub-family HETEROCONGRINAE. The other subfamily group: congers, the deep-water members, are not included here. As suggested by their common name, garden eels often form large colonies on sand flats. They rise vertically out of the sand, to about half of their body length, to feed on plankton. The exact number of species is unknown and several species were only recently discovered. At least three species occur in the Maldives.

Spaghetti Eel
Gorgasia maculata

Congregates in great numbers on sand flats or gentle slopes in depths of 30+ m, especially in current-prone places. It extends itself a long way out of the sand, without leaving the ocean bottom, to grab plankton drifting past in currents. Common in the Maldives. Probably restricted to Indian Ocean, although several similar species are elsewhere. Length to 70 cm, body depth about 6 mm.

Spotted Garden Eel
Heteroconger hassi

Found in most sand habitats, from shallow to deep-water flats or gentle slopes. Especially prevalent in current-prone areas and often occurs in large colonies. Easily recognised by the two large black spots on its sides. A common species. Widespread Indo-Pacific. Length to 40 cm.

Splendid Garden Eel
Gorgasia preclara

Occurs singly or in small, scattered colonies in current areas. Rarely seen by divers and usually occurs in deep water of 30+ m depth. Identified by its orange colour, which may appear grey at depth and its large pale spots. Seems to be widespread Indo-Pacific. Length to 40 cm.

HERRINGS
CLUPEIDAE

This very large family of mostly small fishes includes about 65 genera and 180 species globally. The largest species live in temperate seas and are commercially fished, however tropical species are considered baitfish. They feed on zooplankton. The small species are almost impossible to identify in the wild. Only one species occurs in great numbers in the Maldives and is included here.

Gold-spot Herring
Herklotsichthys quadrimaculatus

Large, dense schools are often evident from the surface and appear as a single, dark mass suspended just away from the water's edge along the beach. In the Maldives, there is usually a Heron patrolling the beach nearby for an easy feed. Widespread Indo-Pacific. Length to 15 cm.

HARDYHEADS
ATHERINIDAE

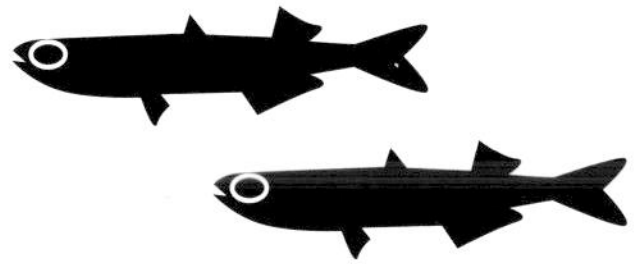

A large family of small silvery fishes that has about 29 genera and 150+ species. They are mainly coastal species, often found in estuaries with some entering freshwater. Only three species are recorded from the Maldives, two of which are commonly seen along beaches. They are planktivores and hunted by semi-pelagic species, such as immature trevallies or jacks, and often targeted by sea birds.

Robust Hardyhead
Atherinomorus lacunosus

Commonly swims along beaches with Gold-spot Herrings, often mixing in the schools. They are less reflective than other species and scales over its back are outlined by dark edges. Widespread Indo-Pacific. Length to 13 cm.

Silver Hardyhead
Hypoatherina barnesi

Swims with herring but form their own dense schools, swimming just outside the herring schools but usually closer to the surface. A silvery, reflective species. Widespread Indo-Pacific. Length to 10 cm.

HALFBEAKS
HEMIRAMPHIDAE

A family of surface fishes with about 12 genera and 80 species worldwide, five of which have been reported from the Maldives. Elsewhere, they are also known as garfish. They are primarily tropical marine species that school in coastal waters and estuaries, but some have adapted to freshwater. The lower jaw is greatly extended and their diet comprises algae, plankton and insects that are taken on or near the surface. Two species are commonly seen in the Maldives and are included here.

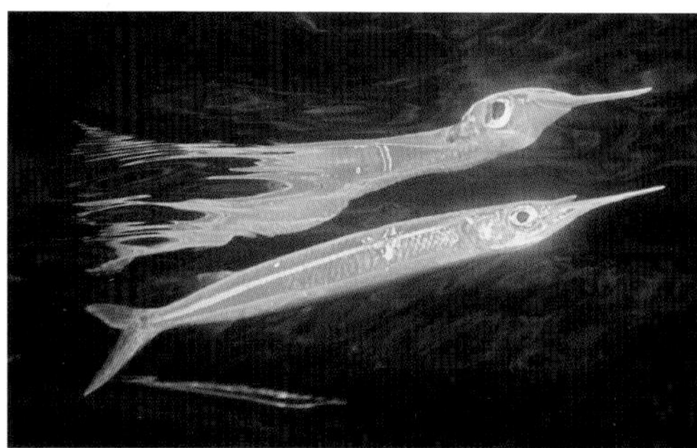

Dussumier's Halfbeak
Hyporhamphus dussumieri

Forms schools over seagrass beds in clear water lagoons. Spawns above the seagrass and its sticky eggs sink amongst the plant. A silvery species, with a greenish or bluish tinge and a rather large tail fin. Widespread Indo-Pacific. Length to 25 cm.

Reef Halfbeak
Hyporhamphus affinis

Forms schools over sand flats, behind reefs, or along beaches. A bluish silvery species, rather slender and not a particularly large tail fin. Widespread Indo-Pacific, mainly oceanic islands. Length to 25 cm.

NEEDLEFISHES
BELONIDAE

A family of surface fishes sometimes called longtoms or seagars, with about 10 genera and 30 species worldwide of which five species in four genera are reported from the Maldives. They are silvery, reflective, elongated fishes with greatly extended jaws and numerous slender teeth. Jaws are proportionally shorter in small, young fish compared to semi-adults. Longtoms swim just below the surface and hunt small surface fish, which in turn, are hunted by large pelagic fishes, like tuna. They leap and leap into the air to escape, often skipping along on their tail and seemingly running on the water's surface. The larger species often hunt solitary while some small species form schools. The three species most commonly seen in the Maldives are included here.

Schooling Needlefish
Platybelone argalus

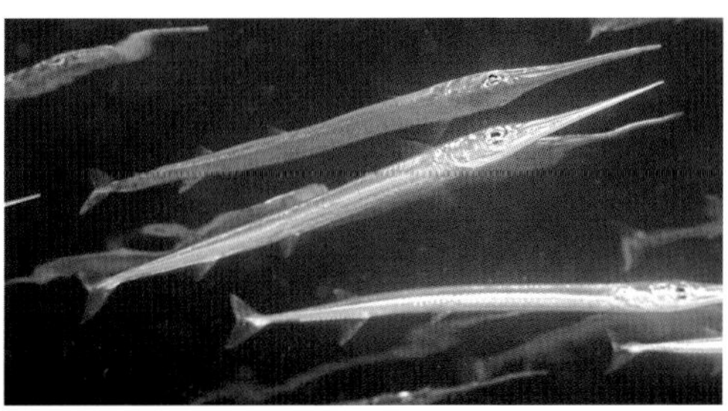

Often congregate in large schools, just below the water's surface in sheltered parts of reefs adjacent to deep current channels. Widespread Indo-Pacific. Sub-species in the Red Sea and Atlantic. Length to 45 cm.

Slender Needlefish
Strongylura leiura

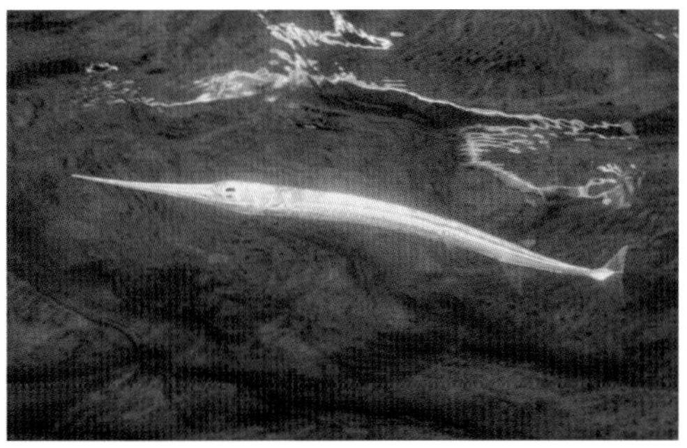

Patrol along beaches where small herring and hardyheads congregate. Usually seen singly, but they have some cunning hunting tactics and a few can group together, swimming apart but within each other's vision. A common slender species with very long jaws. Widespread Indo-Pacific. Length to 70 cm, including the long elongated jaws.

Crocodile Needlefish
Tylosurus crocodilus

Large individuals are usually seen swimming solitary, adjacent to shores over sand or reef. Adults are easily recognised by their large size and proportionally short snout, but the length of the snout varies with growth and can be relatively long in half-grown individuals. This species is wide ranging in all tropical seas and comprises a number of sub-species. Length to 1.3 m.

EELTAIL CATFISHES
PLOTOSIDAE

Eeltail Catfishes belong to a very large group of mainly freshwater fishes, which comprise about 25 families globally. The family PLOTOSIDAE comprises eight genera but divers in tropical Indo-Pacific waters including the Maldives commonly see only one species. Catfishes have venomous spines in their fins that can inflict painful wounds and repeated stings can be fatal. This family has an eel-like tail, compared to the forked tail of most other catfish families.

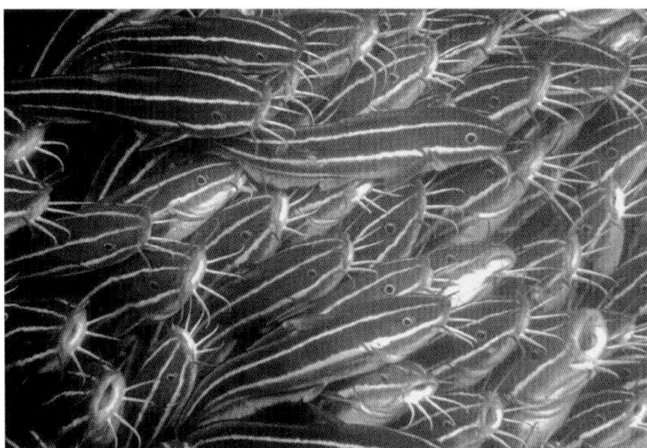

Striped Catfish
Plotosus lineatus

Prefers coastal silty conditions and rarely seen on coral reefs. In the Maldives, it occurs in silty enclosed harbours. Adults are more solitary and found mainly in ledges during the day, while scavenging for food at night. Seasonally, juveniles swim in dense formations, appearing as a single dark body changing shape. Juveniles feed on detritus from the bottom surface. Length is to 25 cm.

LINGS
OPHIDIIDAE

A very large highly diverse family with about 50 genera and over 150 species globally. Most are found in deep and temperate seas. Divers in the Maldives regularly see only one species.

Bearded Rockling
Brotula multibarbata

Occurs on coastal coral reef slopes, usually in 10+ m depth. This multi-barbell species is usually mistaken for a catfish. It hunts at night for sleeping fishes and various mobile invertebrates and retreats quickly into crevices in the reef when caught in light. It can swim as fast backwards as forwards. Length to 60 cm, although usually seen to about 40 cm.

ANGLERFISHES
ANTENNARIIDAE

A large family of specialised fishes in 12 genera and 41 known species worldwide. Most are found in continental waters and six species are reported from the Maldives. They are not only cryptic but also masters of camouflage looking like a sponge or some other part of the reef. Juveniles of some species on the other hand can be brightly coloured, apparently mimicking bad tasting slugs (nudibranchs) or flatworms. Anglerfishes attract their prey with a bait, or luring apparatus, that is dangled in various ways above their large mouth. Once in reach, the victim is sucked up with lightning speed. The luring apparatus is a highly evolved part of the dorsal fin and varies greatly between different species. It comprises two parts: a thin rod that is situated on the snout, and the bait at the end of the rod. The length of the rod varies, depending on the species, and the shape at the bait unfolds to mimic a small fish, invertebrate or worm. In addition, the mimic-bait is moved just as the real prey would swim, making it very convincing. Whilst some species eat almost anything that moves, others specialise in particular prey species. Tropical species are known to produce pelagic eggs, while those living in sub-tropical zones lay eggs in reef crevices that are guarded by the female. Anglerfishes are also known as anglers in South Africa, and called frogfishes in America.

Giant Anglerfish
Antennarius commerson

Usually live in large open caves and often found on jetty pylons. Small juveniles hide in reefs and are sometimes found under large rubble pieces. Adults mimic sponges, matching their colour perfectly. With large individuals, the whole fish looks like a separate sponge. Large individuals are mainly orange in the Maldives, but also black, although they are very difficult to find. Widespread Indo-Pacific. Length to 35 cm.

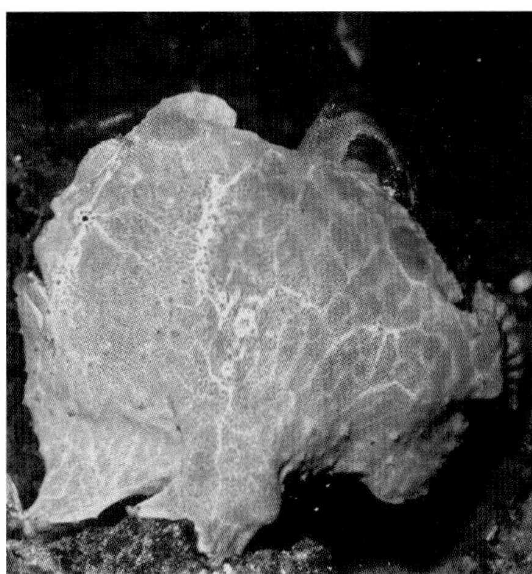

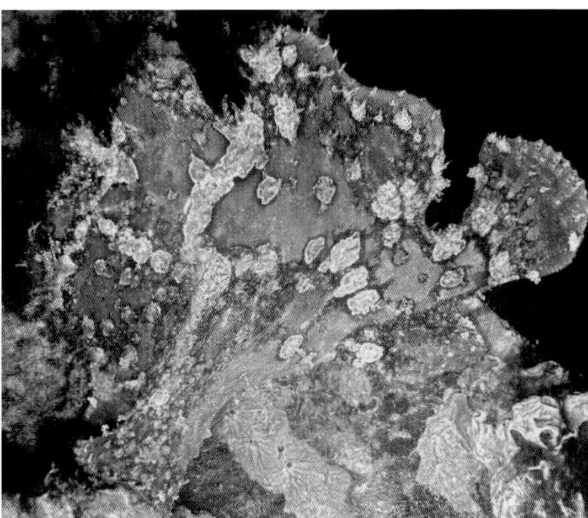

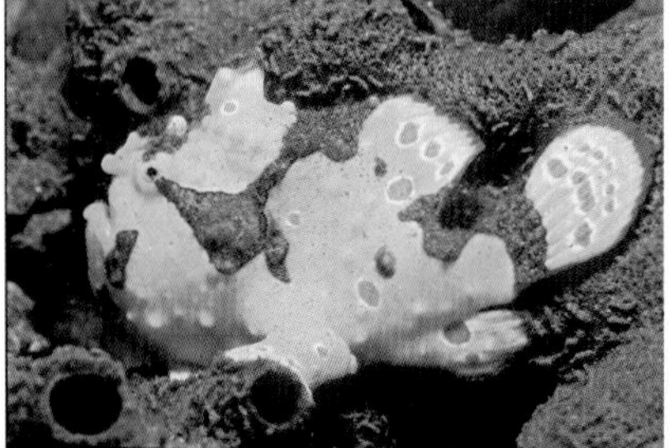

Clown Anglerfish
Antennarius maculatus

Adults found in sponge areas, often in silty inshore habitats. Usually yellow with saddle-like reddish patches and wart-like swelling over body and fins. Small juveniles are bright yellow or white and are often found sitting on dark backgrounds mimicking a nudibranch. The bait represents a small fish. Widespread tropical Indo-Pacific. Length to 10 cm.

Painted Anglerfish
Antennarius pictus

Occurs on sheltered reefs between 3 and 50 m depth. One of the most variable coloured species at all stages. Adults mimic sponges and corals and range from white to black and from yellow to red. Sometimes with different coloured patches or ocelli all over the body. Small juveniles are often found on sand and rubble and mimic nudibranchs and flatworms, and later sponges for camouflage. The tips of pectoral fins are nearly always white. Widespread Indo-Pacific. Length to 16 cm.

Photos: left, camouflaged adult; right, juvenile, about 40 mm long, showings flatworm colouration.

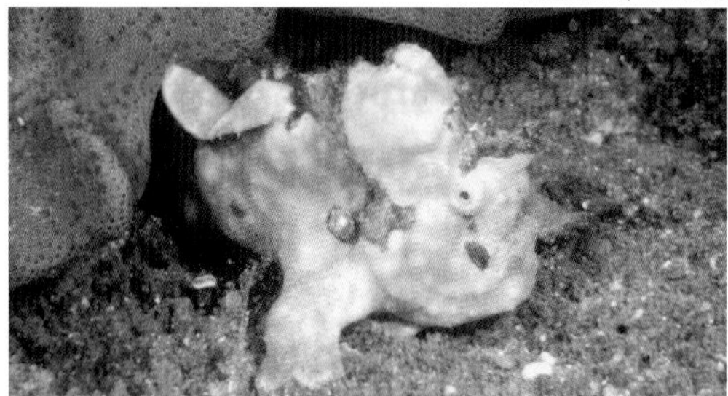

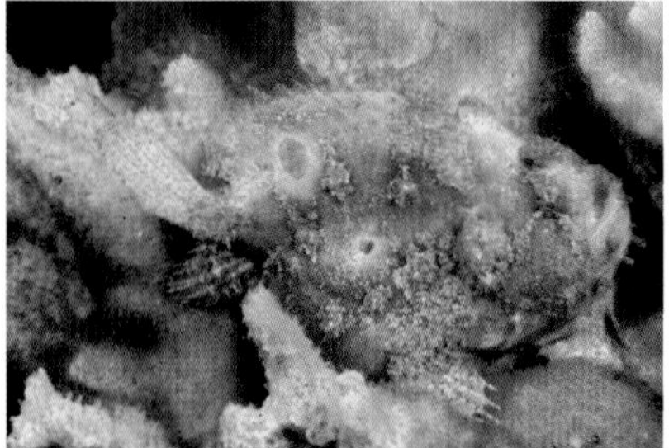

Spotfin Anglerfish
Antennatus nummifer

Prefers clear outer reef conditions. Usually found in small crevices on steep walls or in sponges and matches colour of sponges in the area. A dark spot, slightly larger than its eye, is usually obvious at the base of the dorsal fin. It has a shrimp-like bait and feeds on small fishes. Widespread tropical Indo-Pacific. Length to 10 cm.

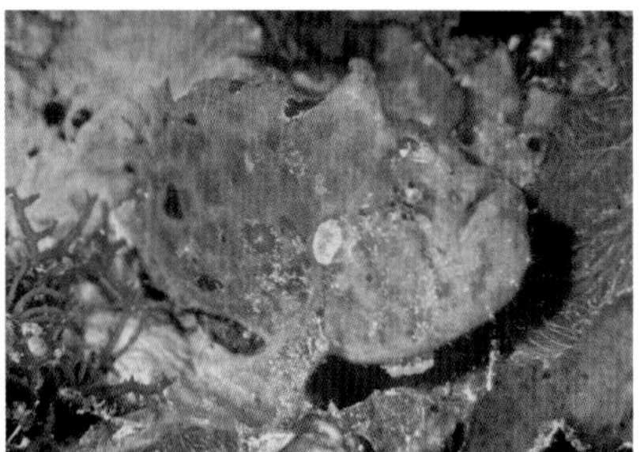

Freckled Anglerfish
Antennatus coccineus

Often found on sponges or algae reef. It changes colour quickly when moving about and is typically highly camouflaged. Varies in colour from grey, brown to yellow and sometimes reddish brown, to match its habitat. Reported to 75 m depth, but is mostly found in less than 10 m. Widespread Indo-Pacific, ranges into subtropical waters.

Sargassum Anglerfish
Histrio histrio

Lives in floating sargassum weeds, especially when large amounts accumulate during the wet seasons and drift into areas by chance. Divers rarely see it unless purposely looking amongst the weeds. It produces eggs in a mucus raft amongst the weeds. Widespread Indo-Pacific. Length to 15 cm.

LIZARDFISHES
SYNODONTIDAE

A small, tropical global family with five genera and about 50 species, of which three genera and at least nine species occur in the Maldives. The genus *Harpadon*, known as Bombay Ducks, is only found in very deep water, while *Bathysaurus*, the deep-sea lizardfishes, live in depths over 1000 m. Lizardfishes mainly hunt fishes and swimming invertebrates and are capable of swallowing surprisingly large prey whole. These efficient predators lay in ambush to strike at prey with a burst of speed. Some bury themselves in the sand with just their eyes exposed. Sometimes they target specific prey species, often blennies such as the sabretooth blennies and the false cleanerfish, but most take a variety of reef fishes. The jaws have one or more series of needle-like teeth along the entire length. Some species are very similar and identification can be difficult in the wild or from photographs.

Blotched Saury
Saurida nebulosa

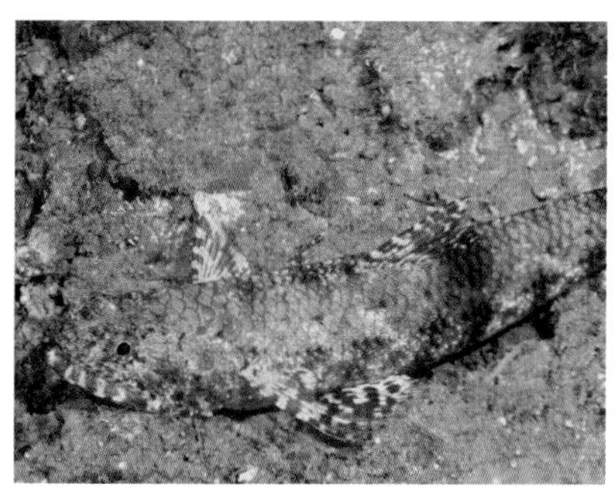

Usually found partly buried in the sand, close to reef edges or on open rubble patches on reef crests. Prefers shallow coastal, often silty habitats, and enters estuaries. Usually has a series of small dark blotches in a line along the middle of its sides and two dark blotches over its back. The dark blotches are narrow when the fish is on light sand and broad when on dark sand. Widespread Indo-Pacific. Length to 16 cm.

Reef Saury
Saurida gracilis

Occurs in shallow coastal reefs to deep offshore and is reported to 100+ m depth. Often found resting in the open on reef rubble patches. Rather stocky compared to other species and usually has large, dark blotches and strongly marked fins. Widespread Indo-Pacific. Length to 20 cm.

Indian Lizardfish
Synodus indicus

The Maldives habitat includes steep sand slopes whipped-up by tidal currents, from 3 to 20 m depth. Common on the lower part of slopes and seen partly buried. This species reported throughout the Indo-Pacific to depths of 100 m, but not often observed by divers. Length to 33 cm, largest seen in the Maldives was about 15 cm. The photographs of this species represented a new record for the Maldives.

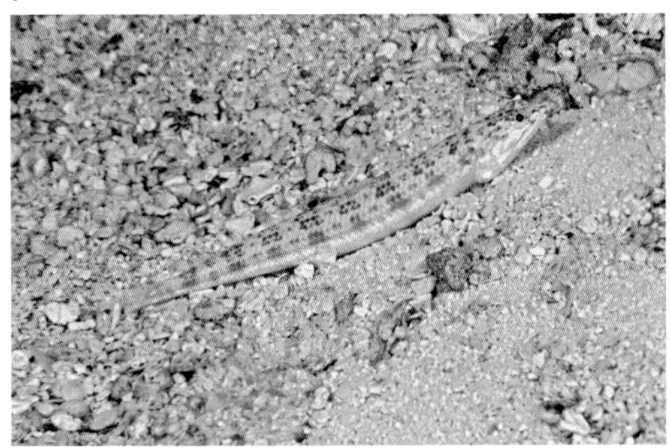

Grey-streak Lizardfish
Synodus dermatogenys

Mainly found buried in sand near reefs or in lagoons near remote bommies surrounded by sand, but also on the reef. Mostly seen in less than 20 m, but reported deep offshore as well. Colour is highly variable and ranges from a sandy colour to contrasting blotches on reefs. Fins are often yellowish and a bluish grey streak along the upper side is usually evident. Common in the Maldives. Widespread Indo-Pacific. Length to 22 cm.

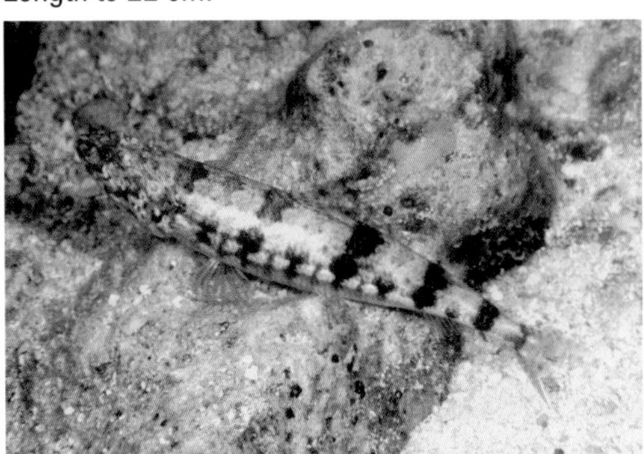

Variegated Lizardfish
Synodus variegatus

Occurs on inshore reef crests and slopes to 25 m depth. Primarily found on rubble reef and not usually buried in sand. The mid-side line comprises more elongated blotches compared to similar species, sometimes almost forming a stripe, which is usually a reddish colour. Widespread Indo-Pacific. Length to 25 cm.

Nose-spots Lizardfish
Synodus binotatus

Occurs on inshore reefs to about 15 m depth. A reef species that is less common and easily overlooked because of its similarity with other species. It has two small, black spots on the tip of its snout, usually very distinct, but these can be present in several other species. Best identified by body colour. The part in front of the dorsal fin is often lighter than the rest, as shown in the photograph. Widespread Indo-Pacific. Length to 20 cm.

Tail-blotch Lizardfish
Synodus jaculum

Habitat ranges from shallow protected rubble-reef flats to sand flats over 30 m depth. Sometimes swims high above the bottom, an unusual behaviour for shallow water members in this family. Easily recognised by the dark blotch on the tail fin base and it often has a shiny, green back. Pale on sand and darker on reefs. Uncommon in the Maldives and probably only occurs in deep waters. Widespread Indo-Pacific. Length to 20 cm.

Red-marbled Lizardfish
Synodus rubromarmoratus

Usually found on rubble slopes at the base of drop-offs or near remote bommies on sand in the deepest lagoons. Prefers depths of 30+ m and is rarely seen in shallower depths. Photographs were taken in 42 m depth. Have strongly defined, broad saddles that are often bright red in colour. Widespread Indo-Pacific. Length to 15 cm.

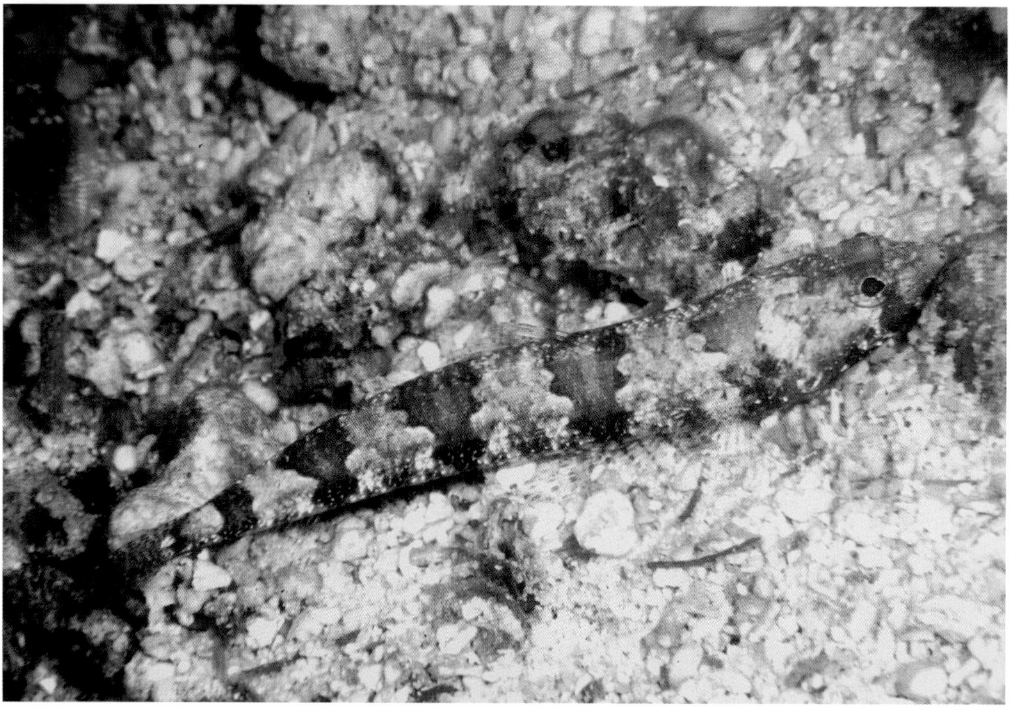

Painted Lizardfish
Trachinocephalus myops

Found in a large depth range, from very shallow sand flats and slopes to depths of about 200 m. It typically buries itself in sand with just the eyes exposed. Usually discovered by divers when about to put a hand or knee on it, before it dashes off to bury itself elsewhere. Not often seen in the Maldives and this photograph is the first record of this species for the region. Widespread Indo-Pacific. Length to 25 cm.

BONEFISHES
ALBULIDAE

This is a very small family of 3 genera with at least 5 species worldwide in the genus *Albula*. The body of bonefishes is elongate and only slightly compressed. Their most distinctive external feature is the overhanging snout and ventral mouth. The fins are all soft-rayed and the caudal fin is deeply forked. Bonefishes get their name from the numerous fine bones in the flesh. These fishes are renown world-wide as hard fighting game fishes.

Sharpjaw Bonefish
Albula neoguinaica

A marine and estuarine species typically found inside lagoons. They forage in sand to feed on small clams, various worms and crustaceans. Body is slender with a protruding snout. A fighting fish popular with fly fishermen. Indo-Pacific. Length to 1 m.

FLASHLIGHT FISHES
ANOMALOPIDAE

A small family with six genera and five species. Only the genus *Photoblepharon* has two species, one of which occurs in the Maldives. These fishes possess a prominent light organ below the eye that is used to detect prey at night. A black membrane can block the light out, enabling the fish to dart away and avoid predators. Bacteria living symbiotically on a special patch of skin produce the light. During the day, these fishes live in dark caves or tunnels deep in the reefs. They come out when dark and often rise from deep water to the shallows on moonless nights.

Red Sea Flashlight Fish
Photoblepharon steinitzi

Only seen at night in loose groups along deep drop-offs where they feed on zooplankton. Usually occurs in depths over 25 m, but they may rise to shallower depths on dark nights in pursuit of food. They have been reported occurring in shallow depths in the Red Sea area. Only known from the West Indian Ocean and Red Sea to the Maldives, however a very similar species occurs in the west Pacific Ocean. Length to 11 cm.

SQUIRRELFISHES and SOLDIERFISHES HOLOCENTRIDAE

This large family comprises two sub-families: HOLOCENTRINAE, the squirrelfishes and MYRIPRISTINAE, the soldierfishes. The groups are presented here separately.

SQUIRRELFISHES HOLOCENTRIDAE-1

Squirrelfishes are distinguished from soldierfishes by the much larger spine on their gill cover - which is venomous in some species - and their pointier head. Of the three genera and over 30 species, two genera and at least 14 species occur in the Maldives. Some species form groups in caves during the day but their activities are mainly nocturnal. Many other species are secretive during the day and are rarely seen, except at night, when they hunt near the bottom for shrimps or other swimming crustaceans as well as small fishes. Some species are numerous in coral rich lagoons that provide good shelter during the day, but others are rarely seen because of their preference for deep water along outer reef walls.

Three-spot Squirrelfish
Sargocentron melanospilos

Only recently found in the Maldives. An aggregation of about 20 individuals was found underneath the shipwreck of the 'Maldives Victory' at 35 m depth and several more individuals were photographed elsewhere in the Maldives. The colouration is slightly different from Pacific fish and matches *S. marisrubri*, which was recently described from the Red Sea. However, scale and fin counts match the Pacific population. Widespread Indo-Pacific. Length to 25 cm.

Photo, aggregation above sand: shipwreck 'Maldives Victory'.

Fine-lined Squirrelfish
Sargocentron microstoma

Occurs either singly or in small groups on shallow protected reefs. Often seen amongst coral during the day but rarely observed out in the open. Recognised by the fine red lines over each scale row and the thickened white interspace that often forms a streak below the back of the dorsal fin. Moderately common in the Maldives between 1 and 10 m depth. Widespread Indo-Pacific. Length to 20 cm.

Crown Squirrelfish
Sargocentron diadema

Habitat ranges from shallow reef crests to deep along walls to at least 30 m depth. Often forms aggregations near large caves and swim openly about, but remain close to the bottom. The dorsal fin on the back has diagnostic colouration but looks almost black in the natural light of deep water. The most common Maldives species in the genus. Widespread Indo-Pacific. Length to 17 cm.

Blue-lined Squirrelfish
Sargocentron tiere

Occurs on semi-exposed reef flats to 20 m depth. Shy during the day and usually stays in the back of long caves. Its red face markings and the several reflective white lines along lower sides can identify it. In natural light, the lines reflect blue. Widespread Indo-Pacific. Length to 30 cm.

Pink Squirrelfish
Sargocentron tiereoides

Usually seen only at night along steep slopes and walls with crevices and caves. Common at particular sites in the Maldives but readily dives for cover in holes when exposed. It has evenly spaced lines over body and a distinctive pinkish look. Widespread Indo-Pacific. Length to 16 cm.

Speckled Squirrelfish
Sargocentron punctatissimum

Mainly occurs on shallow exposed reef slopes. Occasionally seen at night on protected inner reefs that have steep slopes and walls with crevices and caves. The red band along the top of its first dorsal fin identifies it. This photograph shows the species in night colour. It is paler during the day with fine dark spots. Widespread Indo-Pacific. Length to 20 cm.

Red-face Squirrelfish
Sargocentron violaceum

Occurs in protected clear water habitat between 5 and 30 m. A solitary and secretive species, but occasionally seen during the day in front of narrow crevices or holes in reefs. Easily recognised by its distinctive colouration. Widespread Indo-Pacific. Length to 25 cm.

White-tail Squirrelfish
Sargocentron caudimaculatum

Habitat ranges from shallow waters to about 30 m depth. Forms groups in caves during the day, mostly along steep slopes and walls. Tail is whitish during the day, but the entire fish becomes bright red at night. Widespread Indo-Pacific. Length to 25 cm.

Sabre Squirrelfish
Sargocentron spiniferum

Occurs in deep lagoons to outer reefs, often with large coral heads, sheltering below overhangs to at least 30 m depth. In the Maldives, it often occurs in small groups although elsewhere usually seen solitary. Also called the Giant Squirrelfish because it is the largest squirrelfish species. Widespread Indo-Pacific. Length to 45 cm.

Spotfin Squirrelfish
Neoniphon sammara

Usually occurs in shallow reef crests and lagoons amongst tall corals, often in groups to depths of about 15 m. Best recognised by black in the dorsal fin combined with thin lines along the body. In general, the most common species in the genus. Widespread Indo-Pacific. Length to 24 cm.

Mouthfin Squirrelfish
Neoniphon opercularis

Usually seen deep along outer reef walls, secretive in crevices during the day, generally to 20+ m depth. Sometimes in small groups or mixed with other squirrelfishes. Erects its white-tipped, black dorsal fin when alarmed, which resembles a large mouth with a series of shark-like teeth. The largest species of the genus. Widespread Indo-Pacific. Length to 35 cm.

Silver Squirrelfish
Neoniphon argenteus

Mostly a lagoon species and in the Maldives is common around large, isolated coral heads in less than 10 m depth. Usually observed in small groups scattered through the corals. Recognised by the lack of lines or black in the dorsal fin. Widespread Indo-Pacific. Length to 25 cm.

Yellow-striped Squirrelfish
Neoniphon aurolineatus

Occurs in outer reef waters of the Maldives. A rarely observed species, that prefers depths of 40+ m throughout its Indo-Pacific range. Has distinctive thin yellow lines along its body. Length to 22 cm.

SOLDIERFISHES
HOLOCENTRIDAE-2

A large group with about 70 species worldwide, eight of which are known from the Maldives. Soldierfishes have extremely large eyes and a blunt snout. They are nocturnal and feed mainly in open water away from reefs or walls on large zooplankton such as shrimp and crab larvae. During the day, some species congregate in large open caves or below overhangs of reef. Some species swim against the ceilings in an inverted position with their belly towards the ceiling or the sides, while other individuals within the same group may swim in the normal way. Some species and most juveniles are extremely secretive and are only seen at night, swimming above corals or near the bottom. Most species are found in depths less than 30 m, but some venture deeper. Although some species were formerly known as squirrelfishes, this name is now reserved for the previous group.

Immaculate Soldierfish
Myripristis vittata

Also known as the White-tipped Soldierfish. Forms schools in caves, mostly along walls to at least 30 m depth. Often swims inverted on ceilings. First dorsal fin has distinctive white tips at the end of each spine. Probably the most common soldierfish throughout its range, including in the Maldives. Widespread Indo-Pacific. Length to 20 cm.

Big-eyed Soldierfish
Myripristis pralinia

Inhabits shallow protected inner reefs, usually from shallow to 15 m depth. Secretive during the day and usually only seen at night swimming above corals, but it is quick to dive for cover when exposed to light. Distinguished by dark bar that ends abruptly on rear edge of gill cover. Widespread Indo-Pacific. Length to 20 cm.

Crimson Soldierfish
Myripristis murdjan

Often seen solitary on shallow coastal reefs, but also enters deep water and is commonly found inside shipwrecks. Several very similar species have white edges on their fins. This species has large scales and a red first dorsal fin. Probably not as common as suggested in literature, as its name is often applied to other species. Widespread Indo-Pacific. Length to 25 cm.

Yellow-fin Soldierfish
Myripristis berndti

Mostly found in clear water lagoons and protected reefs, sheltering below reef overhangs in small groups during the day to depths of about 25 m. Almost identical to the Crimson Soldierfish, but distinguished from similar species by red spines on the fins and yellow membranes. Widespread Indo-Pacific. Length to 30 cm.

Epaulette Soldierfish
Myripristis kuntee

Usually form groups that swim in front of large caves. A pale looking soldierfish that is common on shallow reef slopes that range to moderate depths along outer reef walls. Widespread Indo-Pacific. Length to 20 cm.

Violet Soldierfish
Myripristis violacea

Occurs in clear water protected reef habitats ranging from deep lagoons to outer reefs, usually in depths over 20 m. Depending on its mood, it may be pink or pale with dark outlines on each scale. Moderately common in the Maldives. Widespread Indo-Pacific. Length to 25 cm.

Splendid Soldierfish
Myripristis melanosticta

Usually found in depths over 20 m, swimming openly around large shelving coral heads. In natural light, they look almost white with black fins, as the blue water filters out the colour red. Uncommon in the Maldives but occurs in groups where found. The recent use of *M. botche* for this species was incorrect. Widespread Indo-Pacific. Length to 25 cm.

Photo below-left, pair: Flores, Indonesia. Photo below, in natural light.

Shadowfin Soldierfish
Myripristis adusta

In the Maldives, this species usually occurs near large reef overhangs singly or in pairs in depths from 10 to at least 40 m. It has a dark spot behind its head, as opposed to the bar of similar species. The largest species and often noticed by divers. Widespread Indo-Pacific. Length to 35 cm.

SEAMOTHS
PEGASIDAE

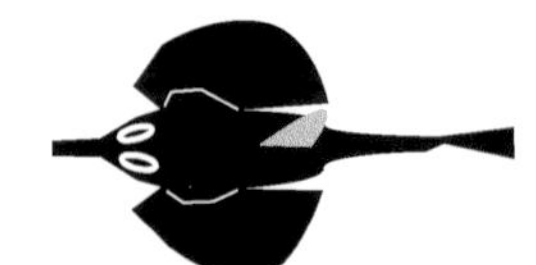

A small Indo-Pacific family with two genera and five species, one of which is reported from the Maldives. They are peculiar little fishes with a bony body and pronounced snout, which has a protractible mouth underneath. The body plates are like those in pipefishes, but the body is highly depressed. The paired ventral fins below the body are reduced to slender but strong structures that in combination with their large side fins are used to walk with. The large pectoral fins gave them the common name of seamoth. Diet comprises tiny bottom-dwelling creatures.

Little Dragonfish
Eurypegasus draconis

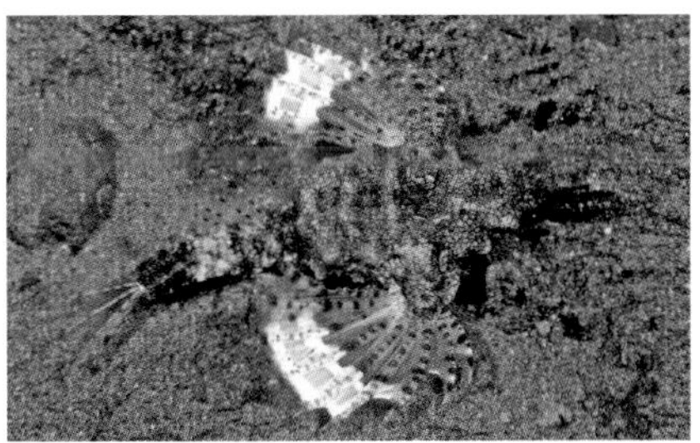

Occurs in sheltered bays to depths of about 15 m. An easily overlooked species, that usually matches the sandy colour on which it lives. Juveniles often mimic bits of shell in the area. Adults usually bury themselves during the day and divers usually only discover them by accident. Only during the spawning period are they easily seen, when the female is gravid and at dusk when males are courting and change colours for the occasion. Length to 8 cm. The Slender Seamoth, *Pegasis volitans*, is also likely to be found in the Maldives, as it has a long pelagic stage and could drift in from other regions.

TRUMPETFISHES
AULOSTOMIDAE

A family with a single genus and two species divided between the Pacific and the Atlantic oceans. A cunning predator that feeds primarily on small fishes.

Trumpetfish
Aulostomus chinensis

Inhabits coastal to outer reefs, often along the upper edge of slopes. Often rest in deep water along walls in large black corals. They match the colour of larger bottom-feeding fishes and swim very close, to get near unsuspecting prey. Colour is variable from brown or grey with various markings, and juveniles often banded or lined. A bright yellow form commonly occurs in the Maldives. Widespread Indo-Pacific. Length reported to 90 cm, but rarely exceeds 60 cm.

FLUTEMOUTHS
FISTULARIIDAE

A single genus family with four species worldwide of which one species is commonly seen in shallow depths on tropical reefs of the Indo-Pacific. Flutemouths inhabit shallow coastal reefs as well as deep water. They are sometimes seen in small schools swimming near the bottom on reef crests. At night they are usually near the bottom over sand flats. Their diet comprises primarily other fish species.

Smooth Flutemouth
Fistularia commersonii

Usually found in protected areas, swimming during the day near the bottom above sand, or on rubble areas near the reef. It occupies various habitats from silty lagoons to outer reefs. Reported to depths in excess of 100 m. Large individuals are usually deep and may come up shallow at night to feed. Widespread Indo-Pacific. Length to 1.5 m.

GHOST PIPEFISHES
SOLENOSTOMIDAE

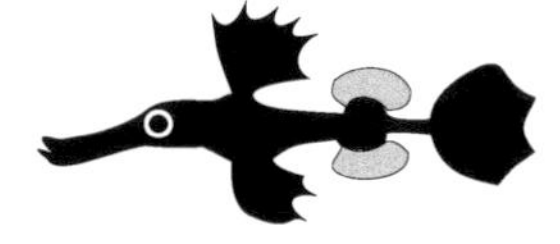

A small tropical Indo-Pacific family that comprises a single genus and at least five species, three of which are known from the Maldives. The family is closely related and superficially very similar to the true pipefishes, but have larger fins. Additionally, the female incubates the eggs in a pouch, rather than the male, as in the pipefishes. Preliminary studies suggest that males may become females. Pelagic larvae reach a large size before settling on the bottom. Post-larvae are about half the adult size and almost transparent, colouring up and growing quickly after settling. Most species swim near vertically with the head down, searching for small invertebrates near the bottom. Often seen along reef margins near feather stars or weeds, depending on the species. Occurrence in the Maldives is probably intermittent as these fishes appear to live annually and could be expatriates from continental waters.

Ornate Ghost Pipefish
Solenostomus paradoxus

Occasionally seen in the Maldives, usually close to gorgonian or soft corals. Colour is highly variable from pale with pinkish spots to near black with some red markings. Identified by the normally elaborate colour patterns or the narrow, regularly placed skin flaps on the snout. A common species elsewhere in the Indo-Pacific, found from a few metres to about 25 m depth. Sometimes in pairs or small groups. Length to 10 cm.

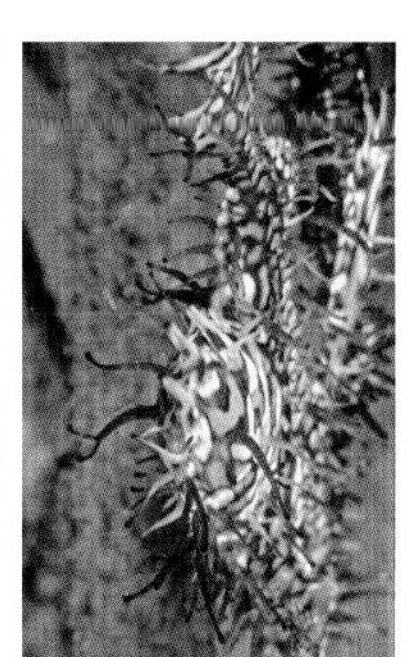

Coralline Ghost Pipefish
Solenostomus halimeda

Mimics the coralline algae *Halimeda macroloba* and is easily overlooked. The algae grow on sandy and rubble substrate and in the Maldives are often found on the bottom of caves along slopes and drop-offs. Also known from Malaysia and Indonesia and appears to be widespread Indo-Pacific. Found to depths of 15 m. A small species, the adult is about 65 mm, which is smaller than the post-larval stage of other similar species, which it has been confused with.

Robust Ghost Pipefish
Solenostomus cyanopterus

Mimics seagrass and varies in colour from green to dark brown. Commonly forms pairs and is normally found on the edge of seagrass beds, floating with separate small patches of seagrass. Also seen on reefs with rich algae growth to 15 m depth. Widespread Indo-Pacific. Largest species grows to 15 cm in some areas, but more commonly to 12 cm.

PIPEFISHES
SYNGNATHIDAE

A large family with over 50 genera and about 220 species worldwide, of which eight genera and 14 species have been recorded from the Maldives. More can be expected. This highly diverse family is unique in its reproductive methods, in which the female takes the eggs to the sperm. She then deposits them into a pouch or onto the underside of the male's body, where they become embedded into the skin, and in the process, are fertilised. The male becomes pregnant and incubates the eggs for almost one month, giving birth to young that are either pelagic or ready to settle on the bottom. Much of the reproductive activities are related to big tides that phase with the moon cycle. Diet comprises small, crawling or swimming invertebrates, such as mysids and larval shrimps.

Reef-top Pipefish
Corythoichthys haematopterus

A common shallow water species on rubble and sand patches or along reef edges, usually in depths of a few metres. Often found in pairs and brooding males are usually obvious by the swollen pouch, which sits about halfway along the body. Males also have a series of dark blotches along the pouch. Widespread Indo-Pacific. Length to 17 cm.

Photo below, a common shallow water species: *Corythoichthys haematopterus.*

Schultz's Pipefish
Corythoichthys schultzi

Occurs in various habitats from protected shallow sand-rubble flats, to rubble patches on reefs and in deeper lagoons to about 20 m depth. Often in areas with sparse algae or soft coral growth. Snout is long and usually has several small white spots and body has a longitudinal-lined pattern. Widespread Indo-Pacific. Length to 16 cm.

Yellow-banded Pipefish
Corythoichthys flavofasciatus

Commonly occurs on coarse rubble with dead coral pieces or in harbours where coral is piled. Usually found in pairs to depths of a few metres. Snout is short compared to other similar species and body has a diffused dark-banded pattern with yellow, scribbled lines in between. Widespread Indo-Pacific, but with some variations. Length to 15 cm.

Cheeked Pipefish
Corythoichthys insularis

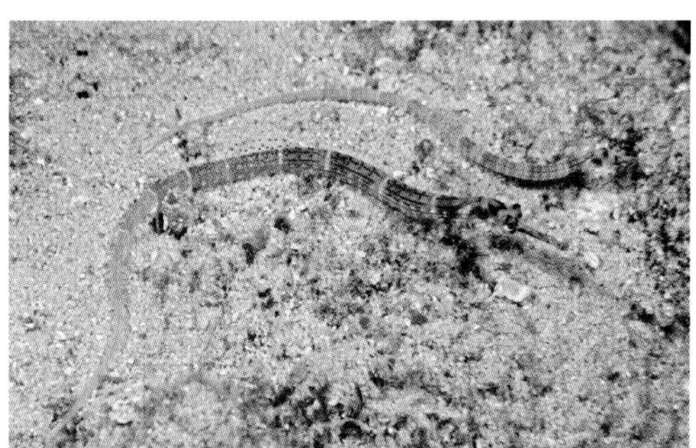

Moderately common in the Maldives, usually occurs in pairs on rubble along the outer reef walls at the bottom of caves or ledges. Mainly known from depths between 15 and 40 m. Snout is long and the head has large dark spots. The body has evenly-spaced pale, thin vertical bands. Western Indian Ocean only. Length to 12 cm.

Long-snout Stick Pipefish
Trachyrhamphus bicoarctatus

Prefers current channels, but also found in still lagoons or in slight current zones with mixed algae, sand or rubble. Easily overlooked, looking like a stick lying on the sand and coloured like similar items on the bottom nearby. Black to brown or yellow in colour with series of evenly spaced light bands or finely spotted. The head is at a slight angle to the body and the front part of body is raised above the sand. Widespread Indo-Pacific. Length to 40 cm.

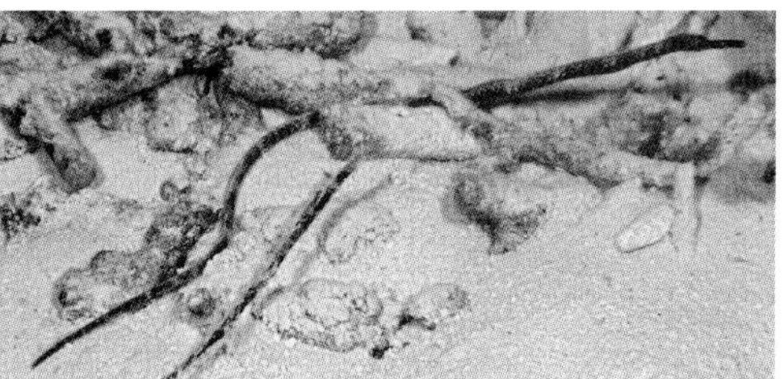

Short-bodied Pipefish
Choeroichthys brachysoma

Occurs in shallow water to about 20 m depth. A secretive species usually found in sheltered seagrass beds under dead coral pieces or with dark objects. Identified by shape and colour, this species is deep-bodied, dark brown and has a few white spots. Widespread Indo-Pacific. Length to 65 mm.

Many-bands Pipefish
Dunckerocampus multiannulatus

Common in the Maldives from shallow lagoons to deep out reef walls to about 35 m depth. A free-swimming species found below overhangs or in the back of caves where it swims upside down against the ceiling. Adults usually occur in pairs. The male carries eggs externally, which are partly embedded into the skin underneath the body. Engages in cleaning small fishes. Indian Ocean, ranging to Andaman Sea. Length to 17 cm.

Blue-stripe Pipefish
Doryrhamphus excisus

Secretive in coral-heads in shallow lagoons, including seagrass beds. Adults, usually in pairs and seen swimming upside-down against the ceilings of caves or overhangs. Colour is yellow to bright orange and a bright blue mid-lateral stripe. Widespread tropical Indo-Pacific. Length to 65 mm.

Double-chin Pipefish
Doryrhamphus bicarinatus

Secretive but common in the back of caves or narrow passages of lagoon coral bombies. Often seen in cleaning stations with shrimps picking parasitic crustaceans off other fishes for food. Adults occur in pairs and often together with the Many-bands Pipefish. Males of this species have two bony knobs under the snout. First record for the Maldives, previously only known from the east African coast. Length to 80 mm.

Common Seahorse
Hippocampus kuda

Seahorses are rare in the Maldives and appear to be expatriates from mainland waters. This species often attaches itself to floating weeds and could be expected to enter Maldivian waters during the wet season. Recognised by smooth body and low crown on the head. Length to 20 cm.

Spiny Seahorse
Hippocampus jayakari

Spiny species usually occurs at moderate depth in algae and sponge-dominated habitats. This species has been reported as *Hippocampus hystrix* from the Indian Ocean, but *H. hystrix* occurs in the Western Pacific only. The spiny species found in the Maldives is most likely identical to those found in the Red Sea and the Arabian Seas. Its pelagic juvenile stage could expatriate to the Maldives Islands.

FLYING GURNARDS
DACTYLOPTERIDAE

A small family with two genera and seven species worldwide with one species reported from the Maldives. They feature very large wing-like fins that are used for display. In small juveniles, they often possess a large eye-like mark on the wings that are suddenly displayed when approached. In addition, part of the fins has thickened free rays near the head that are used for walking and probing the bottom to disturb prey. The fins throw a large shade and may also assist to catch prey.

Flying Gurnard
Dactylopterus orientalis

Very rare in the Maldives and possibly an expatriate from continental waters from pelagic larvae. Enters shallow sandy bays and feeds on bottom fish. Spreads out large fins when approached but may suddenly withdraw them to swim away. Widespread Indo-Pacific. Length to 30 cm.

LIONFISHES AND SCORPIONFISHES
SCORPAENIDAE

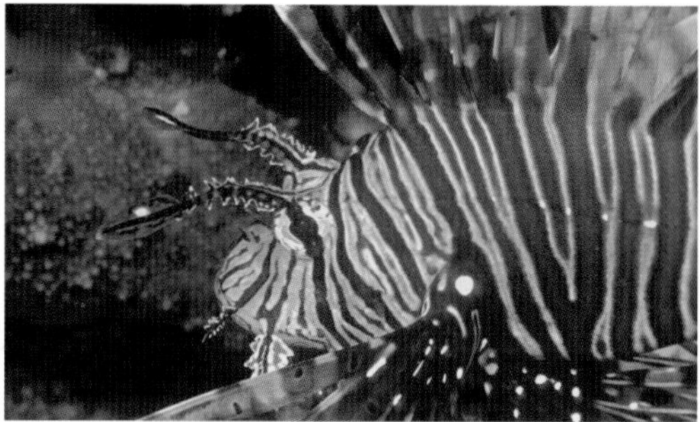

Photos: left juvenile, right adult. Tentacles above eyes are usually long in juveniles and leaf-like in adults.

A large and complicated family, divided into at least 10 sub-families with an estimated 70 genera and 350 species globally. Several groups are not well known. About 25 species have been recorded from the Maldives but more can be expected. This family includes many venomous and potentially dangerous species, such as stonefish and lionfish, but all scorpionfishes are capable of giving nasty stings with their dorsal fin spines. When alarmed, the fin is raised and it may charge if cornered. Stings are usually caused when handling the fish or when accidentally touched. The venom is neutralised by heat. Apart from lionfishes, most species have excellent camouflage and hide in reefs. Some are rarely seen and live very deep or secretively inside reefs and are only known from specimens trawled and collected with chemicals. Diet comprises fishes and mobile invertebrates. Only those likely to be seen by divers have been included here.

LIONFISHES
SCORPAENIDAE-1

Common Lionfish
Pterois volitans

Lives in various habitats, from remote coral bommies in lagoons to caves along deep drop-offs. Hunts small fishes and uses its large fins to corner them. The best-known lionfish, easily recognised by long feathery fins. Some variation between continental and oceanic populations. The continental form, often referred to as *P. miles*, not in the Maldives. Widespread Indo-Pacific. Length to 35 cm.

Spotfin Lionfish
Pterois antennata

Commonly occurs on coral reefs, usually at coral bases in well-protected surroundings or in holes, with its tail towards the front of the crevice. Has tall feathery dorsal fin and long white filamentous rays on pectoral fin. Most common where there is some algae growth, in depths between 6 and 30 m. Widespread Indo-Pacific. Length to 20 cm.

White-lined Lionfish
Pterois radiata

Prefers habitat with little or no hard coral growth, mainly in dead coral areas with algae or other non-stinging types of growth, and caves along steep slopes to about 25 m depth. Dark overall colour and thin white lines identify this species. Widespread Indo-Pacific, but rare in many areas. Length to 20 cm.

Zebra Lionfish
Dendrochirus zebra

In the Maldives, mainly found in silty still lagoons and harbours, often with remote debris or rubble piles on the sand. Also inhabits shallow to deep sand flats with large coral heads, probably in excess of 45 m. Has large pectoral fins but lacks elongate pectoral rays. Reported to 80 m in other areas. Widespread Indo-Pacific. Length to 20 cm.

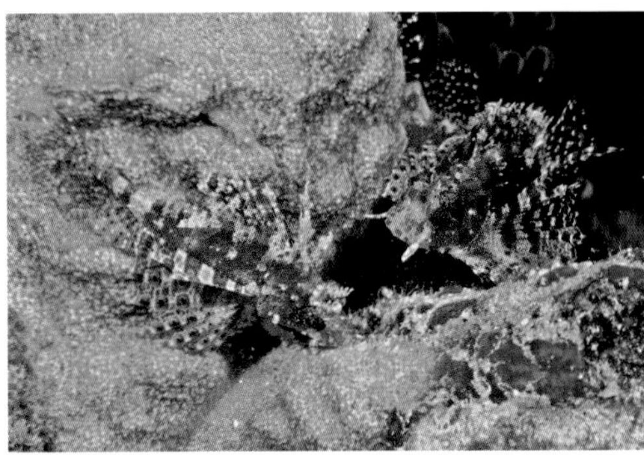

Dwarf Lionfish
Dendrochirus brachypterus

Occurs in various habitats with sponges and algae and is common under jetties on pylon crossings or on deep remote reef outcrops on sand. Lacks elongate pectoral rays. Variable in colour from brown to red with light or dark bands, rarely bright yellow. Widespread Indo-Pacific. Length to 15 cm.

Two-eyed Lionfish
Dendrochirus biocellatus

This is the least observed lionfish. Mainly nocturnal and lives in sponges and caves in sheltered reefs. At night, they come out in the open on shallow reef flats where they hunt for shrimp. Identified by pair of dark spots on back dorsal fin. They are rare in the Maldives. Widespread Indo-Pacific, but generally not common. Length to 13 cm.

SCORPIONFISHES
SCORPAENIDAE-2

Common Scorpionfish
Scorpaenodes guamensis

A small secretive species usually found when turning over dead coral pieces in shallow lagoons or well-protected reef flats. Several very similar species, best recognised by a large dark blotch on the gills. Widespread and locally common in various areas of the Indo-Pacific. Length to 12 cm.

Shortfin Scorpionfish
Scorpaenodes parvipinnis

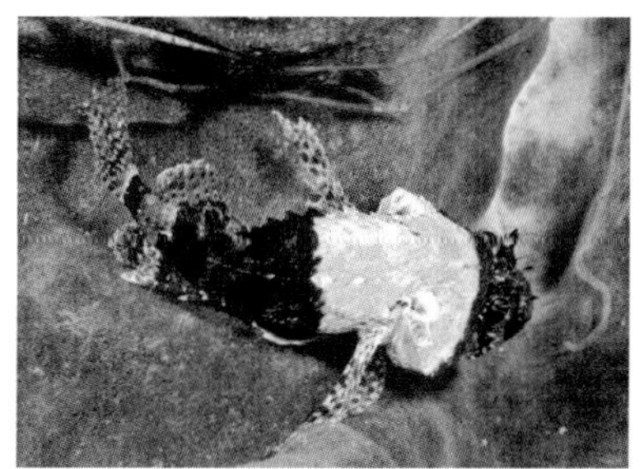

A small species usually seen at night along inshore reef walls dominated by algae growth, or on sponges. Recognised by the large pale body area behind its head. Depth ranges from 10 to 50 m. Widespread Indo-Pacific. Length to 85 mm.

Blotchfin Scorpionfish
Scorpaenodes varipinnis

A well camouflaged species on coastal reefs to 20 m depth, sometimes on jetty pylons with good sponge growth. A dark-looking fish with red markings on the head and the fin bases. Widespread Indo-Pacific. Length to 12 cm.

False Stonefish
Scorpaenopsis diabolus

Well camouflaged among coral rubble in shallow protected reef flats and harbours. A distinctive species identified by the large and unusually shaped head, which resembles a piece of dead coral. Often mistaken for a stonefish. Widespread Indo-Pacific. Length to 18 cm.

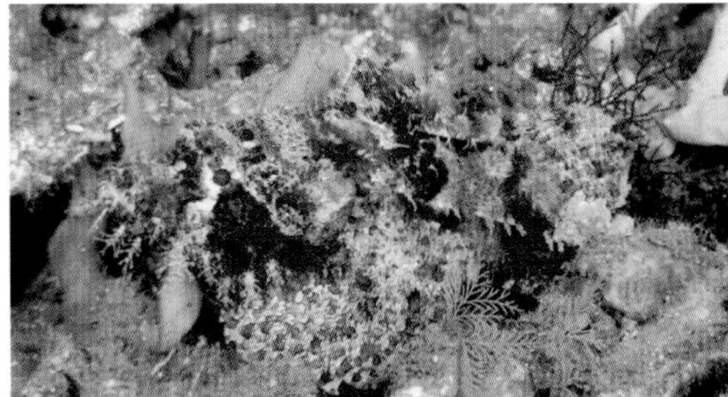

Smallscale Scorpionfish
Scorpaenopsis oxycephala

The largest scorpionfish in the Maldives where common on sheltered reefs from a few metres depth to about 20 m. Often seen at night when it tends to be out in the open, possibly because the artificial light shows the fishes colour better. Widespread Indo-Pacific. Length to 35 cm.

Coral Scorpionfish
Sebastapistes cyanostigma

Usually inhabits shallow surge zones along the top of drop-offs with rich coral growth. A small colourful species that lives between branches of fire corals or in the protection of other stinging corals. Body is pink with yellow spots all over, although at night spots are white. Widespread Indo-Pacific. Length to 10 cm.

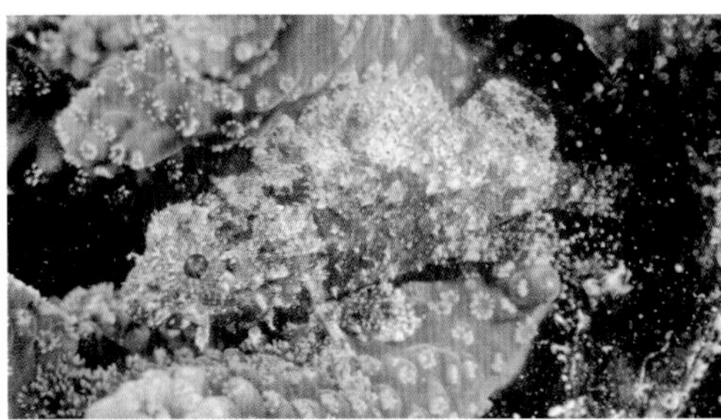

Barchin Scorpionfish
Sebastapistes strongia

Occurs in sheltered coastal reefs and harbours, in depths of a few metres. A small, well-camouflaged species found under coral rubble or amongst the bases of coral branches. It has a mottled colour pattern and often large tentacles above eyes. Widespread Indo-Pacific. Length to 6 cm.

Reef Stonefish
Synanceia verrucosa

Mainly occurs in still places on the reef crest with mixed coral and algae cover, and in harbours partly buried amongst large pieces of coral rubble. The most dangerous stinger and venom injected by the spines on its back causes excruciating pain that can be fatal, several deaths have been reported. Widespread Indo-Pacific. Length to 38 cm.

Photo left: Harbour colour (Malé harbour). Photo right: Reef colour.

Paper Scorpionfish
Taenianotus triacanthus

Inhabits clear coastal to outer reef habitat from shallow depths to a reported depth of 135 m. Highly variable in colour to suit surroundings, from white, dark purplish brown to bright yellow and pink. Recognised by the flat body with sail-like fin over back, but easily overlooked. Often observed next to sponges or on top of corals. Widespread Indo-Pacific. Length to 10 cm.

Photos: showing colour variations.

WASPFISHES
TETRAROGIDAE

A moderately sized family of small and often little known species with an estimated 15 genera and 40 species. Only two species are known from the Maldives. They are similar to scorpionfishes but the fin over top is well forward on the head, starting in front of the eyes. Most species live on soft bottom, mixed rubble, algae or weeds and sponges. Diet comprises mainly small invertebrates.

Spiny Leaf-Fish
Ablabys macracanthus

Occurs in protected still habitats, adults on moderately deep soft-bottom slopes to about 50 m depth and juveniles sometimes shallow in sparse seagrass beds. Variable in colour from grey and yellowish brown, to dark brown and almost black. Known from scattered Indo-Pacific localities, including Indonesia, Malaysia and Philippines. Length to 18 cm.

Photo below left, adults: Flores, Indonesia. photo below, juvenile: Mabul, Malaysia.

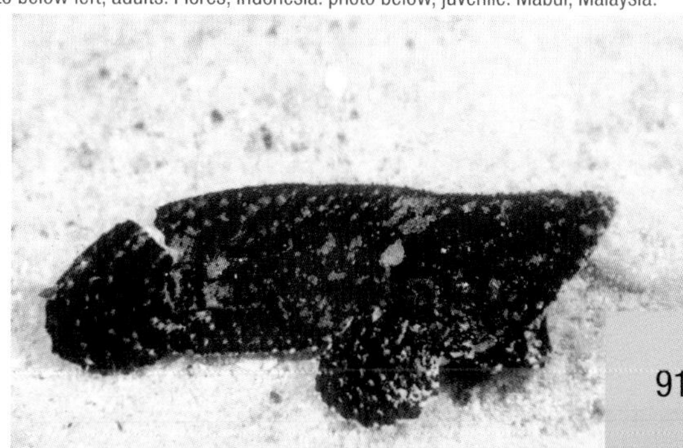

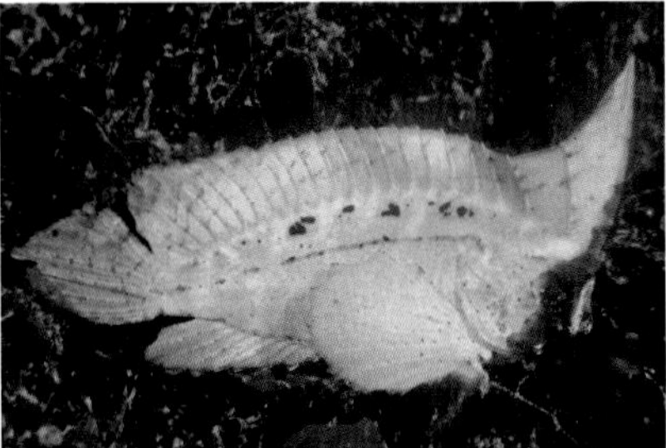

Indian Leaf-Fish
Ablabys binotatus

Occurs in soft-bottom habitats with sponge, coralline algae growth and weeds. Inhabits sub-tidal areas to 25 m depth. Well camouflaged and mainly active at dusk, sometimes moving to more open areas. Very similar to the Spiny Leaf-fish, but has a taller dorsal fin pointed high above its head, and fewer rays in the anal fin. West Indian Ocean only. Length to 15 cm.

FLATHEADS
PLATYCEPHALIDAE

A large family, primarily Indo-Pacific with an estimated 18 genera and 60 species. Most species are restricted to mainland waters and divers encounter only a few in the Maldives. Two common species are included here. Most tropical species are small and reach about 30 cm. They remain buried in the sand with just their eyes exposed, particularly during the day. At night they are more active and occasionally sit on top of the sand. They feed on fishes and swimming invertebrates, such as squid. They have large, flattened, bony heads that are often armed with spiny ridges.

Fringe-lip Flathead
Sunagocia otaitensis

Inhabits shallow sand and mud flats and only comes out at night. Usually found in small, spread-out groups in sheltered bays. There are several similar species, but this one has strongly marked ventral and pectoral fins, which range from spotted in colour to almost all black. Widespread Indo-Pacific. Length to 25 cm.

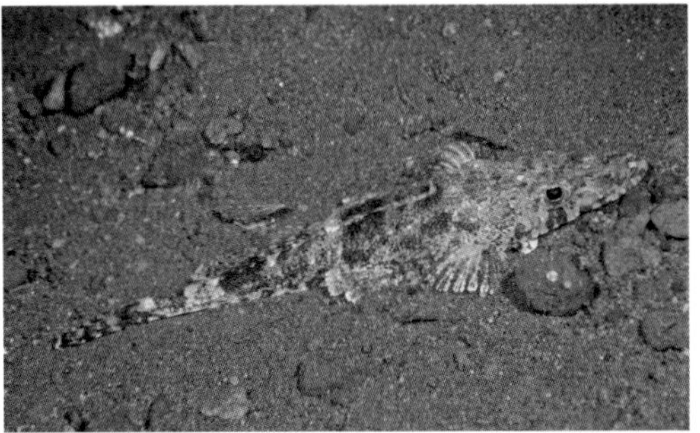

Long-snout Flathead
Thysanophrys chiltonae

Inhabits coarse sand and mud slopes, usually between 6 and 25 m depth. Mainly observed at night. Best identified by the double dusky bar below the eye and white-marked ventral and pectoral fins. Widespread Indo-Pacific. Length to 25 cm.

SOAPFISHES, ROCK CODS, GROUPERS & BASSLETS
SERRANIDAE

A large and complicated family of many distinctly different groups and future studies will probably separate these into families in their own right. Including all the various groups there are about 50 genera, and well over 400 species. For simplification, the various groups are presented here separately as part of the family Serranidae.

SOAPFISHES
SERRANIDAE-1

A small group of fishes that has a toxin in the skin that is released when under stress to deter predators. The toxin can kill other fishes if they are all collected and kept together in the same small container and can also cause irritation to sensitive areas of human skin. The Yellow Soapfish has bright colours and swims openly about, while its juveniles often mimic venomous blennies to avoid predation. Other species are more shy and stay under reef cover or very close to crevices. Prey consists primarily of fishes and shrimps. Reef basslets are closely related and included in this group. These small, active hunters live in the back of large caves.

Snowflake Soapfish
Pogonoperca ocellata

Occurs on sparse reef or around small coral bommies along the bases of reefs. A rare fish in general, it appears to prefer moderate depths in the Maldives from about 30 m down. Distinguished by a skin flap on the chin, numerous white spots and black saddles on the back. This photograph, taken at Maalhoss in 42 m, represents the first record for the Maldives. West Indian Ocean only, replaced by sibling *P. punctata* in the Pacific, and Christmas Islands in the East Indian Ocean. Length to 33 cm.

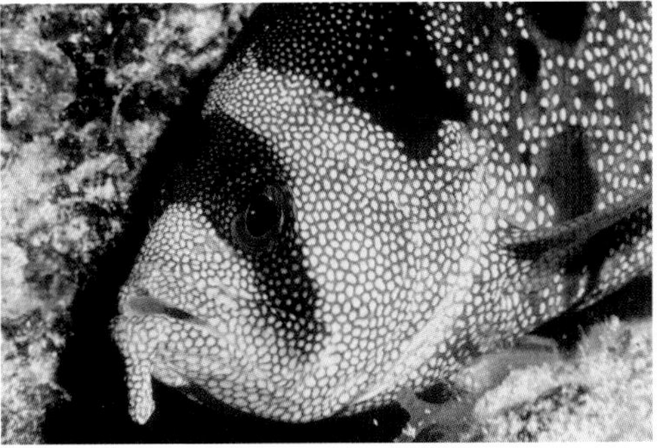

Lined Soapfish
Grammistes sexlineatus

Juveniles are commonly found in shallow protected reef flats and slopes among large coral rubble pieces, until about 15 cm long. Adults appear to move to very deep water and are rarely seen. Reported to over 150 m depth. Large adults have a series of elongated spots that replace lines from their earlier stages. Widespread Indo-Pacific. Length to 27 cm.

Yellow Soapfish
Diploprion bifasciatum

Also known as Yellow Emperor. Prefers silty reefs and harbour conditions. Patchy occurrence in the Maldives. Distinguished by a broad black bar on the body and narrow black bar through the eye. Adults often in small groups below jetties with large rock or boulder formations. Has a large mouth and feeds primarily on other fishes. Widespread Indo-Pacific. Length to 25 cm.

Arrow-headed Soapfish
Belonoperca chabanaudi

Typically lives in small, dark caves and tends to stay in the shade when at the entrance. Has a yellow blotch on its tail base, which is usually noticed by divers whilst the rest is absorbed in the background. Mainly occurs along outer reef walls in about 20 m depth. Widespread Indo-Pacific, where found in various depths. Length to 15 cm.

African Reef Basslet
Liopropoma africanum

Common in the Maldives but lives in the network of tunnels and crevices typically found in the back of large overhanging reefs, or in caves along the outer reef slopes and wall. Usually discovered using a torch, but quickly disappear, however they are curious and turning off the light may bring them back. West Indian Ocean only, occurring in depths to 50 m. Length to 85 mm.

Pinstriped Reef Basslet
Liopropoma susumi

Lives in the back of large caves along outer reef walls, secretively moving through narrow crevices or tunnels, usually solitary. Its thin, longitudinal lines identify it. Moderately common in the Maldives, in depths to at least 30 m and sometimes in shallow lagoons. Widespread Indo-Pacific. Length to 92 mm.

GROUPERS
SERRANIDAE-2

The largest group includes the groupers, sometimes called cods or rock cods, usually in relation to a particular genus. Most species reach a moderate size for a reef fish and the largest, the Giant or Queensland Grouper is reported up to 3 m. The smallest species are about 20 cm long, but most grow well over 30 cm in length. Nearly all of the Maldives species live on reefs where adults swim openly about, but when approached, they quickly retreat to cover, if not accustomed to divers. A few species can be found on open sand substrate but these are usually in close vicinity of some solid objects with places to hide. Juveniles are secretive and stay in the protection of reefs. Diet comprises a variety of mobile invertebrates and fishes, and some species are cunning predators. For example, some juveniles mimic small-mouthed wrasses to get close to unsuspecting prey. Most adult groupers are active at dusk and take advantage of the confusion or arguments between other fishes when many are looking for sleeping places in reefs. This is the best time for them to snare potential prey. Habitats range from shallow lagoons to deep outer reefs, depending on the species.

Indian Coral Grouper
Plectropomus pessuliferus

Occasionally sighted along outer reef slopes in the Maldives and recorded from depths between 20 and 145 m. Generally a rare species known mainly from the Indian Ocean, but also from localities such as Fiji in the Pacific Ocean. The Red Sea population is differently coloured and is regarded as a sub-species. Length to 60 cm, although reported to 90 cm.

Squaretail Coral Grouper
Plectropomus areolatus

A common Maldives fish, often numerous in large and deep lagoons, although generally a rather flighty fish. Found in depths ranging from shallow reef channels to about 30 m, but occasionally on deeper slopes. Best recognised by the straight vertical edge of the caudal fin. Widespread Indo-Pacific. Length to 75 cm, rarely over 60 cm.

Black-saddle Coral Grouper
Plectropomus laevis

Occurs inshore to outer reef habitats. Juveniles found in various depths and adults venture well beyond diving depths. The juvenile and semi-adult have bright yellow fins and prominent black bars on a white body in 'footballer' colours, which are readily recognised. Small juveniles mimic the poisonous Saddled Pufferfish. A moderately common fish throughout the Indo-Pacific. Widespread Indo-Pacific. Length to at least 1 m.

Vermilion Rock Cod
Cephalopholis miniata

Also called Coral Rock cod. Adults sometimes in small groups, usually to depths of about 20 m but sometimes deeper. One of the most common shallow water reef species throughout the Indo-Pacific, including the Maldives. Adults distinguished by many blue spots on an orange-red background while small juveniles are without spots and appear more like basslets, but stay close to the corals. Widespread Indo-Pacific. Length to 40 cm.

Six-spot Rock Cod

Cephalopholis sexmaculata

Usually found in large caves and below overhangs of reef along deep walls from 6 to at least 50 m depth. Often swims vertically or upside down, orientating the belly to the nearest part of the reef. Distinguished by dark bars on the side that are darkest on the upper back. Widespread and common Indo-Pacific species, including the Maldives. Length to 45 cm.

Peacock Rock Cod

Cephalopholis argus

Found in various coral habitats but in the Maldives mainly on reef crests in 6 to 10 m, although it ventures into deep water at times. Often seen resting in the shade of overhanging corals. Identified by colouration, often by a white blotch in front of the pectoral fin base. Widespread Indo-Pacific. Length to 45 cm.

Dusky-banded Rock Cod

Cephalopholis boenak

Prefers silty coastal and protected inner reefs. Uncommon in the Maldives, but common in continental waters where it lives in shallow reefs to about 20 m depth. The dusky broad bands over its body and a large black spot at the rear of the gill cover can identify it. Widespread Indo-Pacific. Length to 30 cm.

Tomato Rock Cod

Cephalopholis sonnerati

A common widespread Indo-Pacific continental species, ranging in depth to over 100 m. In the Maldives, it appears to be restricted to deep water and is found on isolated coral bommies on sand slopes in 30+ m depth. It changes drastically in colour from juvenile to adult and adults can display a blotched pattern at times. Length to 50 cm.

Orange Rock Cod
Cephalopholis spiloparaea

Mainly found on reef slopes and walls in depths over 20 m, especially slightly silty inner reef slopes. Moderately common in the Maldives and best identified from the following species, the Blackfin Rock Cod, by the pale pectoral fins on its sides and the white colour, usually present at the corners of the caudal fin. Length to 25 cm.

Blackfin Rock Cod
Cephalopholis nigripinnis

Moderately common in the Maldives on reef crests with rich coral growth. Easily confused with the Orange Rock Cod, but lacks the white colour in its tail and has dusky, rather than pale, pectoral fins as an adult. Widespread Indian Ocean and east to Java. In the Pacific, replaced by the Flagtail Rock Cod *C. urodeta*, which is readily recognised by white stripes in its tail. Length to 30 cm.

Leopard Rock Cod
Cephalopholis leopardus

Common on rich coral reefs from inshore to outer reef in three to 25 m depth. The smallest fish in the genus, most easily recognised by its tail pattern. Varies in colour from light brown to bright orange or red. Tail pattern is always diagnostic and includes a dark patch on upper edge of tail base. Widespread Indo-Pacific. Length to 20 cm.

Harlequin Rock Cod
Cephalopholis polleni

Usually found deep under overhangs, from 10 to 50+ metres. Easily recognised by ornamental colours. Juveniles are pinkish with yellow colour. Rare in the Maldives. Appears to be widespread Indo-Pacific. Common in Indonesia. Length to 35 cm.

White-square Grouper
Gracila albomarginata

Uncommon in the Maldives, but seen along deep water drop-offs to at least 70 m, but also swimming into shallow reef crest areas in less than 6 m depth. May follow divers when not aware of it, but quickly move off when approached. Identified by large white blotch on upper side and black spot on the tail base. Widespread Indo-Pacific. Length to 45 cm.

Red-flushed Grouper
Aethaloperca rogaa

Juveniles often found among rich coral growth on shallow reef crests. Adults on reef slopes with large caves and often on shipwrecks to at least 50 m depth. Recognised by plain, dark grey colour and deep body. Widespread Indo-Pacific. Length to 70 cm.

Lunar-tailed Grouper
Variola louti

Common on outer reefs, often in surge zones. Small juveniles are secretive in reefs but individuals between about 15 and 25 cm were seen swimming openly with *Paruneneus macronema*, the Long-barbell Goatfish, matching their colour perfectly in an obvious case of mimicry. Widespread Indo-Pacific. Lengths to 80 cm, but usually large adults move to deep water.

White-edged Lyretail
Variola albimarginata

Mainly seen along deep outer reef walls in the Maldives in depths of 30+ m. Distinguished from the previous species by a white edge, rather than yellow, on the end of its tail fin and the general colouration of the adult and juvenile forms. Widespread Indo-Pacific. Length to 65 cm.

Foursaddle Grouper
Epinephelus spilotoceps

Common in the Maldives on shallow reef crests and slopes with good coral growth to about 20 m depth. Appears to come out of hiding mainly at dusk. Spotting small on the head and black saddles usually distinctive in adults but are occasionally absent. Widespread Indo-Pacific. Length to 35 cm.

Black-spot Grouper
Epinephelus melanostigma

Rarely seen in the Maldives. Prefers inshore and often silty reef habitats with mixed algae and coral growth, usually in depths less than 10 m. The black saddle spot on back can identify it. Widespread Indo-Pacific. Length to 35 cm.

Greasy Grouper
Epinephelus tauvina

Occurs from shallow reef flats to about 50 m depth. Distinguished from other species by similar spot size on body and snout. In other species, spots are usually smaller on the snout. Widespread Indo-Pacific. Length to 70 cm.

Snubnose Grouper
Epinephelus macrospilos

Mainly seen on outer reef slopes in the Maldives and fairly common in surge zones between 6 and 10 m depth. A rather shy species that occurs in rich coral growth areas. Widespread Indo-Pacific. Indian Ocean populations have larger spots than those of the Pacific. Length to 50 cm.

Photo right, adult with cleaner-wrasse: Java, Indonesia.

Honeycomb Grouper
Epinephelus merra

The most common and one of the smallest species, often abundant in shallow reefs, from coastal silty habitats to outer reef areas. Occurs in deep lagoons to about 25 m depth. In adults, the dark blotches that run centrally along the fish's sides, often join and form short horizontal bands in the darker areas. Widespread Indo-Pacific. Length to 28 cm.

Small-spotted Grouper
Epinephelus coeruleopunctatus

Mainly found on inner reefs and sheltered lagoons. Prefers a shallow habitat, usually less than 20 m in the Maldives. Juveniles often observed in brackish water during the wet season. Variously spotted with small dark spots, often mixed with larger white, rounded blotches of mixed size, with some blotches eye-sized. Widespread Indo-Pacific. Length to 60 cm.

Photo right: juvenile Flores, Indonesia.

White-speckled Grouper
Epinephelus ongus

Usually seen solitary in caves with rich invertebrate growth along outer reef walls and slopes from 10 m down. Juveniles remain secretive in corals. Body is dark with pale spots that extend over fins, sometimes with large pale blotches over the body. Widespread Indo-Pacific, but uncommon in the Maldives. Length is to 35 cm.

Photo right: juvenile Flores, Indonesia.

Squaretail Grouper
Epinephelus areolatus

Prefers a silty bottom, open sand with small coral heads or solid debris with coverage. Usually found in depths over 10 m, at the base of slopes where the bottom becomes flat. Recognized by the thin, straight white edge at the end of the tail. Not commonly seen in the Maldives. Widespread Indo-Pacific. Length to 40 cm.

Long-spined Grouper
Epinephelus longispinis

Prefers silty reef conditions, such as sheltered, muddy areas with isolated coral pieces or debris on the open bottom. Juvenile found among weeds on rocks or dead coral pieces in depths between inter-tidal to over 30 m. Widespread Indian Ocean, ranging into the West Pacific to Flores, Indonesia. Length to 55 cm.

Snout-spots Grouper

Epinephelus polyphekadion

Usually found in crevices and small caves of protected reefs to about 20 m depth. Best identified by double black spots on the tip of snout, but this may be obscured in large individuals that can look very similar to the Flower Grouper (below). Moderately common throughout the Maldives. Widespread Indo-Pacific. Length to 75 cm.

Photos from top right: juvenile, intermediate and adult.

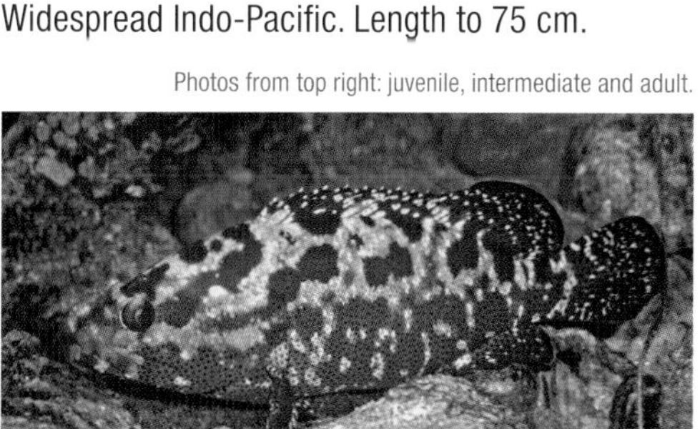

Wavy-lined Grouper

Epinephelus undulosus

Typically found on open silty-sand and muddy habitats. Usually a flighty species that dives into holes of remote bommies or under pieces of debris. Widespread Indo-Pacific, mainly mainland waters and rare in the Maldives. Length to 45 cm.

Flower Grouper

Epinephelus fuscoguttatus

Adults usually found in or near large caves, ranging from deep lagoons to outer reef slopes, but mostly in shallow depths to about 10 m. The most common large species in many areas of the Maldives. Outside the Maldives, juveniles are known to enter brackish water near freshwater habitats. Widespread Indo-Pacific. Length to 90 cm.

Photo left, juvenile: Flores, Indonesia.

Photo, plain colour juvenile

Giant Grouper
Epinephelus lanceolatus

Not uncommon in the Maldives, but usually seen as an adult along deep outer reef slopes or on current-prone channel reefs. Juveniles are secretive and rarely seen until they change to adult colours. The largest in the genus, well over 1 m long in adult form, and similar to Snout-spots Grouper (previous page) but brown blotches on sides are generally more diffuse. Also called Queensland Groper in Australia. Widespread Indo-Pacific. Length to 2 m, although reported much larger in some areas.

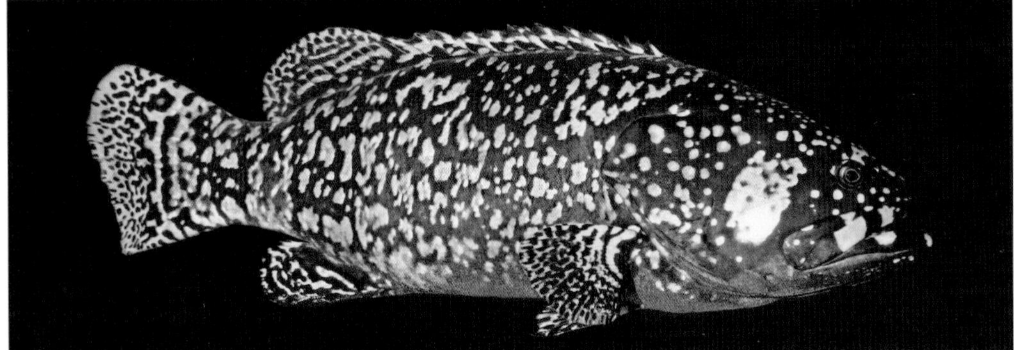

Blacktip Grouper
Epinephelus fasciatus

Also known as Red-barred Cod. Common in the Maldives on reef crests in about 6 m depth, but ranges to deep water as well. Distinguished by reddish bars, dark shading on head and black and white dorsal fin spine tips. Some forms show no banding at all. Widespread Indo-Pacific. Length to 35 cm.

Photo left, banded form.

Yellow-fin Grouper
Epinephelus flavocaeruleus

A common mainland species that occurs in shallow protected reefs and lagoons in the Maldives and sometimes under jetties at resorts. Replaced by sibling *E. cyanopodus* in the Pacific, which differs primarily by the lack of yellow fins when adult. Widespread Indian Ocean, ranging to Bali, Indonesia. Length to 90 cm, based on records.

Photo left, adult.

White-lined Grouper
Anyperodon leucogrammicus

Inhabits shallow reef crests, to moderately deep slopes with tall coral coverage, but rarely deeper than 25 m. Adults may occur in small, loose groups that swim in the protection of the corals. Small juveniles mimic small-mouthed striped wrasses or other non-fish predators to get close to prey, mainly small damselfishes. Widespread Indo-Pacific and common in the Maldives. Length to 50 cm.

Photos: Small juvenile right, intermediate below, adult above.

BASSLETS
SERRANIDAE-3

A group of small, colourful fishes that are all planktivores in the Maldives; elsewhere, relatives are bottom-feeders. Scuba divers and snorkellers commonly observe them. The eye-catching species form large schools when feeding in currents on zooplankton, often well above the reef. Basslets start their adult life as female and females then change sex to become male, replacing males that have died or left the group. The males are particularly colourful and display themselves with fins erect, to each other as well as to females, and often form schools of their own. In many areas, females outnumber males and each male will dominate a group of females in what is known as haremic behaviour. However, most of the Maldives species seem to be an equal sex ratio.

Threadfin Basslet
Nemanthias carberryi

Inhabits clear water reef crests and slopes to about 20 m in depth, often in large schools. A very common species in the Maldives that have several colour forms that may mimic other basslets or small fusiliers that share the same reef. Highly variable, from plain pinkish with tiny yellow spots all over, to partly bright yellow, sometimes with a mimic bright red dorsal fin. Males have two filamentous rays heading the dorsal fin. West Indian Ocean. Length to 12 cm.

Yellow-back Basslet
Pseudanthias bicolor

Mainly a deep-water species found along steep outer reef walls to at least 70 m depth, although in the Maldives, it has been photographed in relatively shallow waters at 25 m depth. Usually forms small groups near caves and often swims inverted inside the caves. The lower half of its body looks blue in natural light. Males have two filamentous rays heading the dorsal fin, which have thickened tips. Widespread Indo-Pacific. Length to 13 cm.

Photo, displaying male: Bali, Indonesia.

Two-spot Basslet

Pseudanthias bimaculatus

A deep-water species, that usually occurs in small groups in current prone areas. Males have a dark blotch between the fourth and sixth spine of the dorsal fin, and a second, less obvious blotch, on the lower lobe of the caudal fin. The body is ornamented with yellow, iridescent blue margins on the fins. Females are mainly deep pink with yellow over the back and vertical fins. Widespread Indian Ocean, ranging to Bali, Indonesia, with some variations in Indonesia that are possibly subspecies. Length to 14 cm.

Photos: male left, female right.

Yellow-eye Basslet

Pseudanthias lunulatus

A deep water species found along outer reefs in small groups. Occurs in the Western Indian Ocean and Red Sea, but is rarely seen in depths shallower than 50 m. Males feature a yellow triangular saddle below the spinous part of the dorsal fin. Females are a plain pinkish orange. Both sexes have a lunate shaped tail. Length about 10 cm.

Red Basslet

Pseudanthias cooperi

Prefers deep slopes and forms schools at remote coral bommies. In the Maldives, it occurs in small groups mainly in depths over 30 m. Both juveniles and females are dark red, while the male pales during display and shows a dark central bar on the body sides. Moderately common in the Maldives. Widespread Indo-Pacific. Length to 12 cm.

Photo: displaying male.

Yellow-tail Basslet
Pseudanthias evansi

Usually form schools along the upper edge of drop-offs, feeding well away from the reef. Found from near surface waters, when feeding, up to about 20 m depth. Schools are often mixed with similar sized, yellow backed fusiliers and are easily overlooked in open water. Brightly coloured with pink and yellow, but the pink appears blue in natural light. A common Maldives species. Indian Ocean only. Length to 12 cm.

Pink Basslet
Pseudanthias hypselosoma

In the Maldives, mainly deep in 30+ m with remote coral bommies, although elsewhere often very shallow. Forms small groups and in the Maldives, often mixed with Red Basslets. Males have a red blotch in the dorsal fin that appears black in natural light. Occurs in the West Pacific, ranging into the Indian Ocean, as far west as the Maldives. Length to 12 cm.

Flame Basslet
Pseudanthias ignitus

Usually swims in schools along the upper edge of drop-offs with tall coral growth to depths of about 15 m. Males often display with fins erected to intensify the colours. They have a bright red dorsal fin and red bands over the outer rays of the caudal fin and body turns yellow. Common in the Maldives. Distribution is restricted to oceanic regions, from the Maldives to the Andaman Sea. It replaces sibling *P. dispar* in the Pacific. Length to 9 cm.

Short-snout Basslet
Pseudanthias bimarginatus

A small and rarely observed deep water species. Identified by the pink lines on top of the head, from tip of snout to each eye, that meets at beginning of the dorsal fin. In the male, the lines continue and thicken over the back. Originally found in the Philippines at 60 m depth. Also known from the Solomon Islands at depths of 35 m. These two photographs, a pair, were photographed at 42 m at the base of a large coral head, away from the reef and surrounded by course rubble. Length to 65 mm.

Photos: upper male, lower female

Resplendent Basslet
Pseudanthias 'pulcherrimus'

Mostly found deep along current-prone slopes and drop-offs in depths of over 20 m. Often seen in large caves swimming inverted on the ceilings. A moderately common species in the Maldives and easily overlooked; being mistaken for the Orange Basslet, which is similar and often abundant in the same habitat. Restricted to the West Indian Ocean only but seems identical to *P. randalli* in the Pacific. No original description but published in Smith's Sea Fishes, Smith & Heemstra, 1986. Length to 65 mm.

Photos: left female, right male.

Orange Basslet
Pseudanthias squamipinnis

Occurs in most habitats, from shallow lagoons to deep outer reef walls to at least 40 m. Juveniles and females are bright orange. Males turn red with yellow sides and have an elongated third dorsal fin spine, also seen in very large females likely to change into males in the near future. Very common in the Maldives and often abundant on reef crests. A widespread Indo-Pacific species but has several geographical variations and no doubt several subspecies. Length in the Maldives to 10 cm.

Photo upper: Displaying male.

DOTTYBACKS
PSEUDOCHROMIDAE

A large family of small, often colourful, Indo-Pacific fishes with at least six genera and 70 species, four of which are reported from the Maldives. The family is dividable into sub-families: the PSEUDOPLESIOPINAE, sometimes called Rock Basslets, and the PSEUDOCHROMINAE, the dottybacks, two of which are included here. Many species are cryptic and have only recently been discovered, with at least two new species in the Maldives, and others expected. They are very territorial and aggressive, mostly moving about in the back of caves that provide shelter with narrow crevices. Their colours easily identify species, but some are variable and can differ between sexes. Diet comprises various small animals, including other fishes.

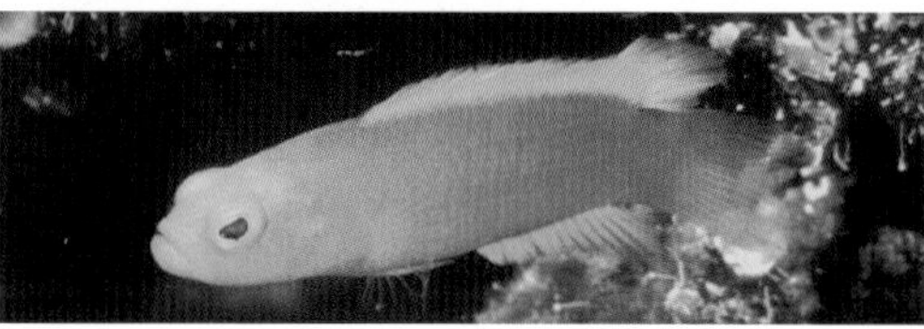

Yellow Dottyback
Chlidichthys inornatus

A common Maldives species, that lives in caves and ledges along steep slopes and drop-offs on inshore reefs. The brightly coloured males are easily noticed, but females are usually nearby. Found in shallow depths to about 20 m. Also known from Sri Lanka and Chagos. Length to 45 mm.

Pink-head Dottyback
Pseudoplesiops sp. 1

An undetermined species that appears to be new. Found in clear water drop-offs with rich invertebrate growth, swimming in a typical darting style in narrow crevices in depths over 20 m. Length about 40 mm.

LONGFINS
PLESIOPIDAE

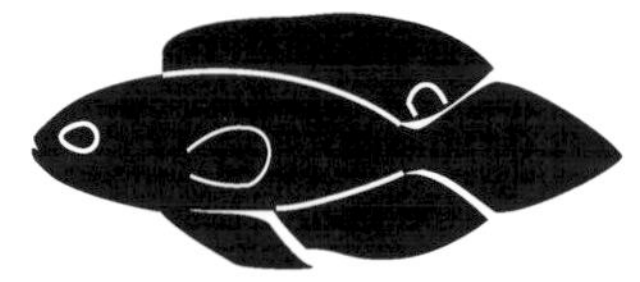

A small Indo-Pacific family with seven genera and about 20 species as presently defined. Some species, such as mouth-brooders, are doubtfully included. Only two species are known from the Maldives, but only one commonly seen by divers is included here.

Comet
Calloplesiops altivelis

Inhabits inshore to outer reefs, in depths from three to at least 50 m. Moderately common in the Maldives, but lives secretively in the back of caves or holes amongst boulders, and is usually only noticed by divers when inspecting dark places with a torch. Easily identified by shape and colour and a pale-edged black spot at the rear of dorsal fin. Widespread Indo-Pacific. Length to 16 cm, but usually smaller in the Maldives.

TRIPLE TAILS
LOBOTIDAE

This family comprises a single genus and species with a global distribution in tropical seas. Juveniles float below sargassum weed rafts and can be dispersed over great distances.

Triple Tail
Lobotes surinamensis

Divers rarely see the Triple Tail in the Maldives and juveniles usually appear during the wet season. Adults occur in silty habitats, mainly inshore. Juveniles are yellowish, mottled to brown and mimic leaves. They swim below weed rafts or under debris that originates from land. Adults are drab dark brown to black. Identified by humped forehead and large rounded posterior lobes of the dorsal and anal fins. Widespread in all tropical seas and occurrence in the Maldives probably fluctuates greatly between wet seasons. Length to 1 m.

Photo left, adult: Java, Indonesia; photo right, juvenile: Flores, Indonesia.

TRUMPETERS & GRUNTERS
TERAPONTIDAE

A moderately large family with 16 genera and about 40 species, of which only one is known from the Maldives. Trumpeters are usually striped and are primarily marine but commonly enter estuaries. The grunters are primarily freshwater and the 30 or so species are confined to the Australia - New Guinea region. Some species are caught on lines and typically make loud grunting noises that are produced with the swim bladder. Diet comprises various small animals, including insects, and some nibble on algae.

Crescent Perch
Terapon jarbua

An inshore species, usually seen in very shallow water. Adults swim in loose groups over sand or mud flats close to beaches or around jetties in harbours. Juveniles are intertidal and sometimes enter freshwater. Easily recognised by a banded pattern that is similar from juvenile to adult. Length to 25 cm.

FLAGTAILS
KUHLIIDAE

A small family of perch-like fishes, with a single genus presently recognized and about 6 species including one in the Atlantic and one in the Maldives. They are coastal fishes that congregate in surface waters around reef outcrops in surge zones during the day and feed in open water on zooplankton at night.

Flagtail
Kuhlia mugil

Flagtails school in surface waters in turbulent zones, usually around reef outcrops that break the surface. Juveniles are more intertidal. Not commonly observed by divers and usually only seen when entering or leaving the water while shore diving. Widespread Indo-Pacific, ranging to sub-tropical waters. Length to 20 cm in tropical waters, larger in cooler zones.

BIGEYES
PRIACANTHIDAE

A small family with four genera and about 17 species globally in tropical and sub-tropical waters, two of which are known from the Maldives. Easily recognised by their large eyes, shape and colour. They are nocturnal fishes that feed in open water at night, capturing relatively small creatures in the zooplankton with their large mouth.

Crescent-tail Bigeye
Priacanthus hamrur

Found during the day in sheltered parts of reefs or in deep lagoons, sometimes swimming more openly about when forming schools. Best identified by the crescent tail shape. Colour is variable from silvery-pink to red, sometimes with dusky bands that can be turned off at will. Occurs in depths between 10 and 100 m. Widespread and usually common Indo-Pacific. Length to 45 cm.

Glass-eye
Priacanthus blochii

Occurs on protected reefs and in lagoons. Known depth range is 3 to 30 m, but in the Maldives probably extends much deeper. Very similar to *P. hamrur* but readily identified by rounded caudal fin. Widespread Indo-Pacific. Length to 30 cm.

Blotched Bigeye
Heteropriacanthus cruentatus

Secretive in reefs during the day, usually moderately deep. Tail has rounded corners and body has a blotched pattern. It floats above reefs at night to catch zooplankton. Observed from 3 to 30 m depth. Widespread Indo-Pacific and also Atlantic, ranging into sub-tropical waters. Length to 32 cm.

CARDINALFISHES
APOGONIDAE

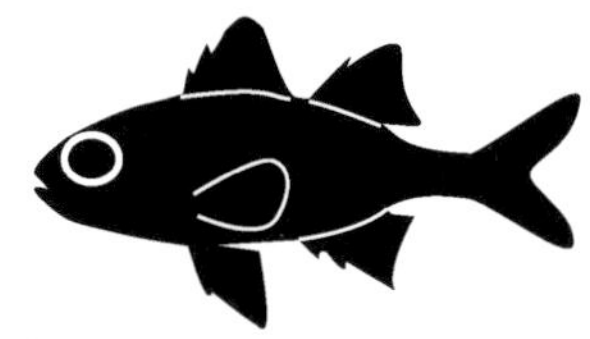

A very large family of mostly small fishes in tropical and subtropical seas with at least 26 genera and probably well over 250 species globally. Many species are still undescribed and with many similar species there is confusion about the application of names. At least 40 species occur in the Maldives and no doubt more will be found. Habitats range from estuaries (few enter freshwater) to deep off-shore. Cardinalfishes are nocturnal but may feed on plankton during the day, and some juveniles mainly feed during the day. Several species form schools during the day that shelter from current in the protection of reefs. At night they disperse away from reefs and feed in open water, with some drifting near the bottom while others feed high in the water column. Many species are extremely secretive and are only seen at night, and sometimes, even then, only in the back of dark caves. Females are usually more colourful than males and court the male during spawning. The male then takes the eggs into the mouth to incubate. Diet comprises various small animals, including other species of fish.

Tiger Cardinalfish
Cheilodipterus lineatus

Inhabits sheltered reef slopes and large coral heads in lagoons, usually sheltering below overhangs or in small caves. Occurs singly, in pairs or in small loose groups and shallow to about 30 m depth. Generally common throughout the Western Indian Ocean and in the Red Sea. Length to at least 22 cm, some Maldives fish appear particularly large compared to those elsewhere.

Arrow-tooth Cardinalfish
Cheilodipterus artus

In the Maldives this species is found mainly in the back of large caves along inner reef walls in 10 to 35 m depth, sometimes in small loose groups. Elsewhere it also occurs in shallow lagoons under jetties or in staghorn corals, often forming large dense schools. Distinguished from other species by 8 to 10 stripes and a black spot at the tail base. Widespread Indo-Pacific. Length to 12 cm.

Toothy Cardinalfish
Cheilodipterus isostigma

In the Maldives it is a common species, especially in deep lagoons among staghorn corals in 10 to 15 m depth. Juveniles occur solitary, while adults in pairs, usually several present and each pair protecting its territory during the day. Nearly identical to *C. quinquelineatus*, but body stripes are thinner and snout appears slightly longer. Appears to be widespread Indo-Pacific. Length to 11 cm.

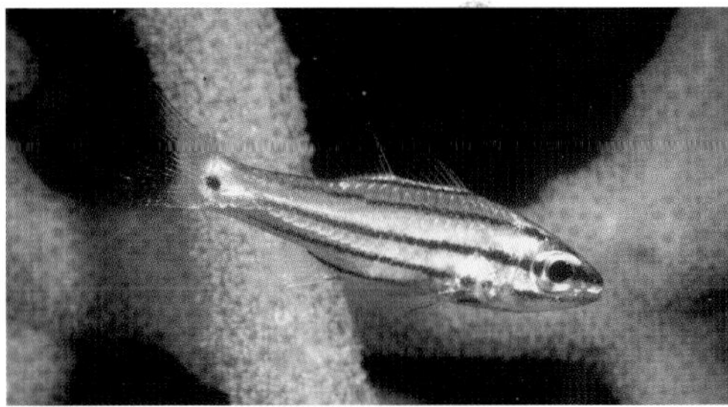

Five-line Cardinalfish
Cheilodipterus quinquelineatus

Forms small groups below overhangs over sand or in spaces between large coral heads. Usually to 15 m depth, but occasionally deeper on outer reefs. Identified by 5 stripes along body and a black spot at the tail base. Widespread and generally common throughout Indo-Pacific. Length to 10 cm.

Narrow-striped Cardinalfish
Apogon angustatus

A common shallow water species, mainly on reef crests in 6 to 15 m depth. Has a distinctive base spot on its tail fin that finishes its mid-body stripe. Widespread Indo-Pacific. Length to 11 cm.

Black-striped Cardinalfish
Apogon nigrofasciatus

A common species in caves, crevices, steep slopes and drop-offs. Occurs in depths from 6 to 40 m, either individually or in pairs. There are two forms, differentiated by yellow or white interspaces between the broad black stripes. Only the latter species is found in the Maldives. The former appears to be restricted to Indonesia while the latter is widespread Indo-Pacific. Length to 10 cm.

Copper-striped Cardinalfish
Apogon holotaenia

Photographed in the Maldives for the first time, in 35 m depth. A pair was found on an open sand and rubble bottom, sheltering with small coral outcrops on the sand. Known from the western Indian Ocean, usually reported occurring in coastal and shallow habitat. Reports from Pacific locations are probably based on similar species. Length to 8 cm.

Pearly-lined Cardinalfish
Apogon taeniophorus

Normally found intertidal on sheltered reef crest under large loose coral pieces, rarely deeper than 10 m. Originally named from the Maldives. Several similar species, best recognised by the partially thickened lower stripe. Widespread Indo-Pacific. Length to 10 cm.

Short-striped Cardinalfish
Apogon sp. 1

Only one pair found at Maalhoss in Baa Atoll in 42 m depth. For coverage, the pair used large rubble pieces, overgrown with coralline algae, at the base of a remote coral head. Very similar to *A. franssedai* from Indonesia that lives at comparable depths but in large caves. Length about 55 mm.

Plain Cardinalfish
Apogon apogonides

Commonly found around deep coral outcrops on sand flats, usually just away from the main reefs in depths of about 30 m, however juveniles may occur shallower. Forms small groups during the day. Plainly coloured, except on the head of adults, which show some colouration. Widespread Indo-Pacific. Length to 10 cm.

Maldives Cardinalfish
Apogon sp. 2

An undescribed species, known only from the Maldives. It is closely related to *A. properuptus* from Australia and Indonesia, and has been misidentified as *A. cyanosoma*. A common species in lagoons and harbours and often in groups consisting of pairs. Shallow to about 20 m depth. Length to 7 cm.

Spiny-head Cardinalfish
Apogon urostigma

Common in the Maldives, usually on sheltered spots near surge areas on outer and inner reefs. Forms small groups during the day. Highly variable in colour, juveniles usually with a thick black stripe and a large black spot on caudal fin base that is just above centre. The stripe and spot can completely disappear in large adults, but these can be distinguished by the yellow first dorsal-fin. Widespread Indo-Pacific. Length to 15 cm.

Spiny-eye Cardinalfish
Apogon melanorhynchus

Occupies various reef habitats and usually seen in depths between 6 and 25 m. Seen in small groups during the day and usually shelters below reef-overhangs over sand. Disperses at night, swimming low over open sand-flats. Identified by thick mid-lateral stripe, which tapers at the end and followed by a large spot at the same level on the tail base. Some variations occur when the stripe fades to barely a trace. Generally common and widespread Indo-Pacific. Length to 10 cm.

Tapered-line Cardinalfish
Apogon fraenatus

Very common in the Maldives in sandy lagoons, to about 10 m depth. Seems to prefer large corals of the species shown in the background of the photographs. Many pairs share such habitats, but they territorial and disputes are common when space is limited. Identified by pale colour and tapering mid-lateral stripe. With or without a caudal-fin base-spot and when present at a level just above the stripe. The spotless form is often referred to as *A. abrogramma* and now appears to be a junior synonym. The spot on *A. fraenatus* in the Maldives is normally present in the morning, but fades in the afternoon and absent at night, as shown in centre photograph. Widespread Indo-Pacific. Length to 12 cm.

Big-eye Dusky-cardinalfish
Apogon savayensis

Appears to be very common in the Maldives. Usually in large coral heads on the bottom of sandy lagoons at about 10 m. Not too secretive and easily seen during the day in narrow crevices. At night, it emerges to swim over the sand and rubble. Appears dusky-looking with indistinct barring on sides, has a black saddle on its caudal fin-base that quickly fades below the lateral line, and broad black leading margins on the dorsal fins. Widespread Indo-Pacific. A small species to 8 cm long.

Barred Dusky-cardinalfish
Apogon similis

Inhabits sheltered lagoons with rich coral growth and forms small groups during the day inside branching corals. One of the few dusky species seen during the daytime. Possibly widespread Indo-Pacific, but various forms may represent different species. Length to 65 mm.

Clear-finned Dusky-cardinalfish
Apogon guamensis

Inhabits mainly clear coastal drop-offs to outer reefs to depths of about 25 m. Very secretive in reefs, often found in narrow crevices in the back of caves and usually hiding from view. Emerges at night but swims close to the reef. Distinguished by plain fins. Widespread Indo-Pacific. Length to 10 cm.

Yellow-edged Cardinalfish
Apogon luxuria

Found on sheltered reefs with rich coral growth, hiding at the base of dense branching corals during the day. Moderately common in the Maldives but usually only seen at night when swimming above corals. Has yellow edges on the last three fins. Widespread Indo-Pacific. Length to 10 cm.

Grey-ring Cardinalfish
Apogon cf. *annularis*

Found on sheltered reefs in lagoon and rubble-reef slopes to 10 m depth in the day and above reefs at night. An undetermined species similar to A. annularis from the Red Sea. One of a group of about seven similar species typically dusky coloured with an angular line below the eye and a dark spot or bar on the base of the tail. Length to 10 cm.

Cave Cardinalfish
Apogon evermanni

Lives inverted on the ceiling of large caves. Found during the day but more often noticed at night in torchlight. Common in the Maldives between 6 and 35 m depth but reported to 70 m. Easily recognized by distinctive red colouration, dark stripe behind the eye and small white spot behind second dorsal fin. Widespread Indo-Pacific and also Atlantic Ocean. The most widespread cardinalfish. Length to 12 cm. Photo shown, as photographed.

Night Cardinalfish
Apogon doryssa

Commonly found on night dives along steep slopes and drop-offs, swimming in the shelter of caves and ledges. Some pearly spots located above the head distinguish this species from similar ones that could occur in the Maldives. Widespread Indo-Pacific. Length to 50 mm.

Long-spine Cardinalfish
Apogon leptacanthus

Occurs in schools amongst corals or in holes in rubble piles in lagoons and harbours during the day. Moves out separately over sand, feeding close to the sand on small shrimps. Adults identified by the tall first dorsal fin. Widespread Indo-Pacific. Length to 60 mm.

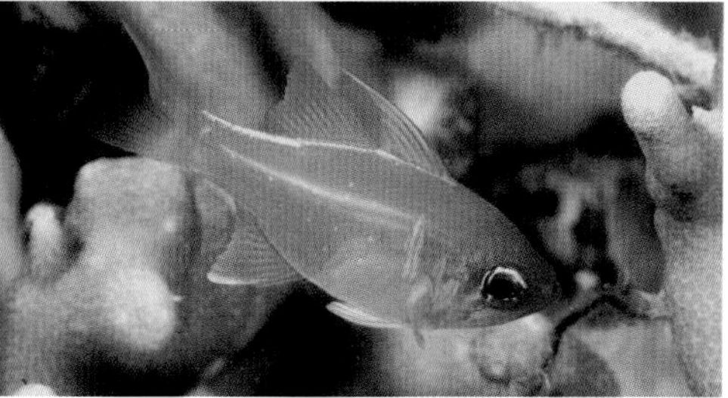

Fragile Cardinalfish
Apogon fragilis

Found in shallow lagoons and harbours, in staghorn coral or rubble walls in holes. Often mixes with other species and is best distinguished by the black spot near its tail and black tips on the tail fin. Previously only known from the West Pacific, this is the first record for the Maldives. Length to 45 mm.

Sangi Cardinalfish
Apogon thermalis

Found on sheltered sand slopes and harbours to about 20 m depth, usually with remote outcrops of dead coral on sand or with large anemones. Identified by dark stripe from tip of snout running through eye and a small, black spot at the base of each dorsal fin. Photographed in Male Harbour, this is the first record of this species for the Maldives. Widespread Indo-Pacific. Length to 8 cm.

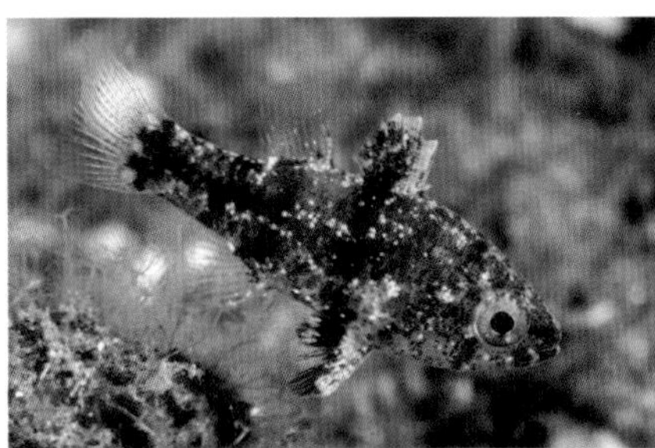

Harbour Cardinalfish
Foa fo

Inhabits sheltered habitat from coastal silty bays to deep off shore soft bottom to at least 50 m depth. Found with soft corals, weeds and sponges during the day and occasionally under the mantle of large anemones. Widespread Indo-Pacific, previously included with *F. brachygramma* a Hawaiian species. Length to 45 mm.

Elat Cardinalfish
Foa abocellata

A small, secretive species found on the bottom at night, hunting small prey on reefs or on sand nearby. Easily overlooked and probably mistaken for a juvenile of another species. Known from 6 to 25 m depth. Indian Ocean, ranging to Bali, and is replaced by *F. ahimsa* in the Pacific. This species was previously wrongly placed in *Fowleria* and is most similar to *Foa*. Length to 5 cm.

Variegated Cardinalfish
Fowleria variegata

Inhabits coastal shallow reefs and harbours in rubble or dead coral pieces. Rarely seen unless disturbing the bottom or diving in silty habitats at night. Colour varies from brown to near black with a mottled pattern. Distinguished by a spot on the gill. Widespread Indo-Pacific. Length to 8 cm.

Cross-eyed Cardinalfish

Fowleria isostigma

Inhabits coastal and inner reefs from intertidal zones to about 20 m depth, usually in dense reefs comprising mostly rubble with mixed algae and coral cover. Secretive, and usually seen in small passages or holes, even at night. Identified by an eye-sized spot on the gill and faint vertical barring on body. Widespread Indo-Pacific

Peppered Cardinalfish

Fowleria punctulata

Common in the Maldives but secretive and usually found in very shallow protected reef habitats from intertidal to about 10 m depth. Colour is pale to reddish brown with distinctive rows of horizontal black spots on the body, which distinguishes this species from similar ones. Widespread Indo-Pacific. Length to 9 cm.

Painted Cardinalfish

Archamia fucata

Inhabits various habitats in lagoons with rich coral growth or separate large coral patches isolated by sand. Forms schools during the day. Colour is highly variable, depending on the surroundings: ranging from plain, near white, to strongly lined with orange. Occurrence is patchy in the Maldives. Widespread Indo-Pacific. Length to 10 cm.

Nose-spot Cardinalfish

Rhabdamia cypselura

Usually found in sheltered parts of reefs or on the side of large, remote coral heads on deep sand flats to 50m. Forms large and dense schools during the day. Sometimes, small groups can be found in caves. Best recognised by the semi-translucent brown or yellow colour and dark spots on the snout. Widespread Indo-Pacific. Length to 55 mm.

Slender Cardinalfish
Rhabdamia gracilis

Forms small schools during the day, usually near coral bommies in depths over 10 m. At night, drifts individually above reefs or over sand to feed on zooplankton. Translucent white and silvery on the abdomen and has black tips on the tail fin. Widespread Indo-Pacific, usually common in the Maldives but not often seen. Length to 6 cm.

Black-tail Cardinalfish
Pseudamia hayashii

Even during the night, this nocturnal species is only seen in the back of far-reaching, large caves. Tail fin is usually darker than the body and in juveniles the tail fin is black. Known from scattered localities in the Indo-Pacific and this represents the first record for the Maldives. Photographed in a large cave at 25 m depth and was locally common. Length to about 65 mm, although reported up to 10 cm.

Tail-spot Cardinalfish
Pseudamia gelatinosa

Only seen at night, usually on open sand slopes with small reef outcrops, swimming just above the bottom. In torchlight, it sinks to the bottom, as shown in the photograph. Tail has about eye-size spots on the base and upper part of fin; this is usually more distinct in adults that have a lighter fin. Widespread Indo-Pacific. Length to 11 cm.

TILEFISHES
MALACANTHIDAE

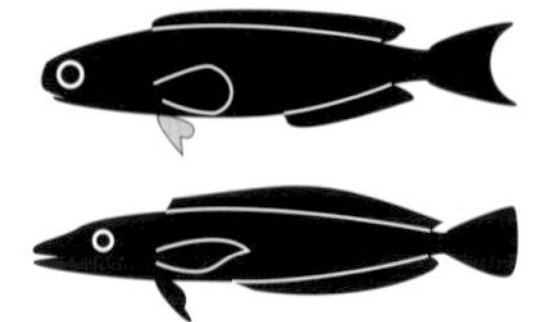

A small tropical fish family, with two genera and about 10 species. Only one species is known from Atlantic seas, and at least four species occur in the Maldives. Tilefishes live in relatively deep water and only two, commonly known as blanquillos, enter shallow depths. Adults often pair and many are nest builders, making large seamounts in deep water. They feed on various small bottom creatures.

Flagtail Blanquillo
Malacanthus brevirostris

Unusually fairly deep in the Maldives to 20+ m on open sand flats near low reefs or rubble patches. Digs holes under solid rubble pieces for shelter and nesting, and occurs both individually or in pairs. A pair of dark stripes on the tail identifies it. Post-larvae large, about 75 mm long. Widespread and often common in the Indo-Pacific. Length to 30 cm, usually about 20 cm.

Blue Blanquillo
Malacanthus latovittatus

Large adults swim above rubble flats of reefs or along reef bases and sand channels between reefs. Juveniles occur low on the bottom on small sand patches within reefs and have a colour pattern similar to some juvenile wrasses, which appears to work as a deterrent to predators. Distinguished by broad black stripe that extends onto the tail. Adults enter shallow reef flats but are more commonly seen in 20 or more metres depth. Widespread Indo-Pacific. Length to 35 cm.

Photo left, small juvenile.

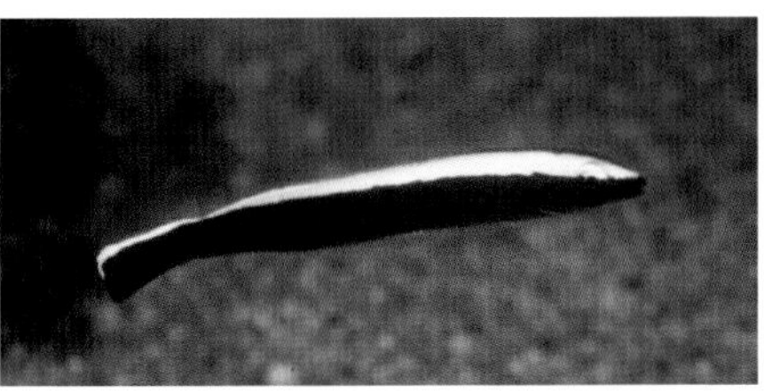

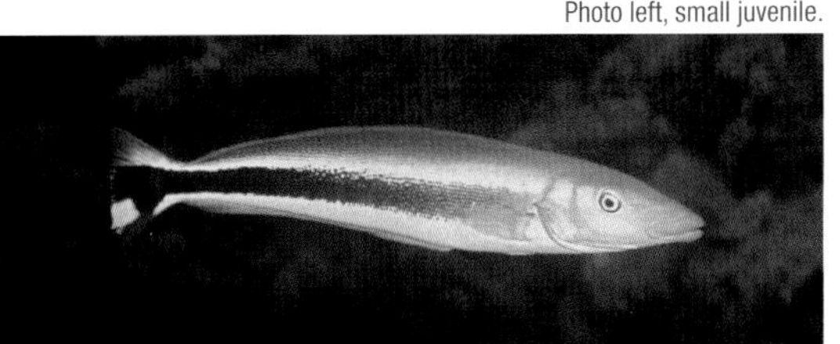

Green Tilefish
Hoplolatilus cuniculus

Uncommon, but usually occurs in numerous pairs where found. A rather plain looking species with greenish to light brown colour. Widespread Indo-Pacific, usually over 30 m depth. Length to 15 cm.

Blue-saddle Tilefish
Hoplolatilus fronticinctus

Found in deep water in the same area as the Green Tilefish. The whitish eyes and blue stripe, as well as a somewhat stocky body, distinguishes it from similar species. The tail looks black in deep water in the ambient light. Widespread Indo-West Pacific, but usually at moderate depths. Length to about 16 cm.

Blue Tilefish
Hoplolatilus chlupatyi

Found on open rubble-bottom habitats sloping away from steep walls. This species looks brilliant blue, even in deep water. Widespread Indo-West Pacific, but usually at moderate depths. Length about 12 cm.

REMORAS
ECHENEIDAE

A small family of four genera and eight species, all distributed globally in tropical and temperate seas. Four species have been reported from the Maldives and two, which are particularly common, have been included here. Remoras feature a sucker disc on top to the head, which has evolved from a spinous fin into series of laminae. They hitch rides on all kinds of oceanic creatures, including sharks, rays, turtles and large fishes. Diet comprises scraps from their feeding host, while some species eat parasites off their host.

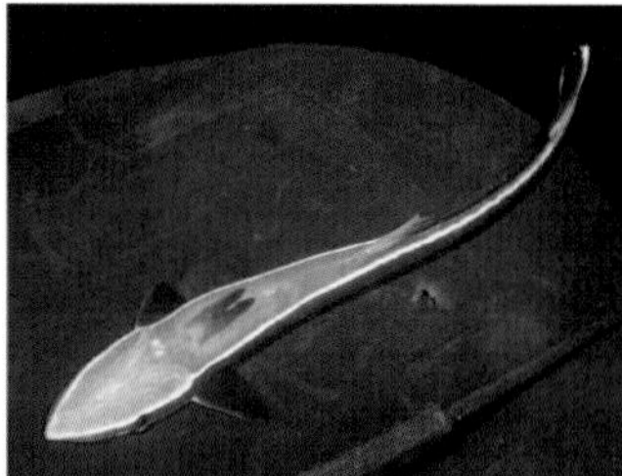

Slender Suckerfish
Echeneis naucrates

The most common species and most observed by divers in tropical seas. Juveniles can be found on many reef fishes and often swim by themselves in small groups. Adults are also seen without a host and may even try to hitch a ride with a diver. Usually identified by the broad black midbody stripe, but this may fade in large individuals. Length to 1 m.

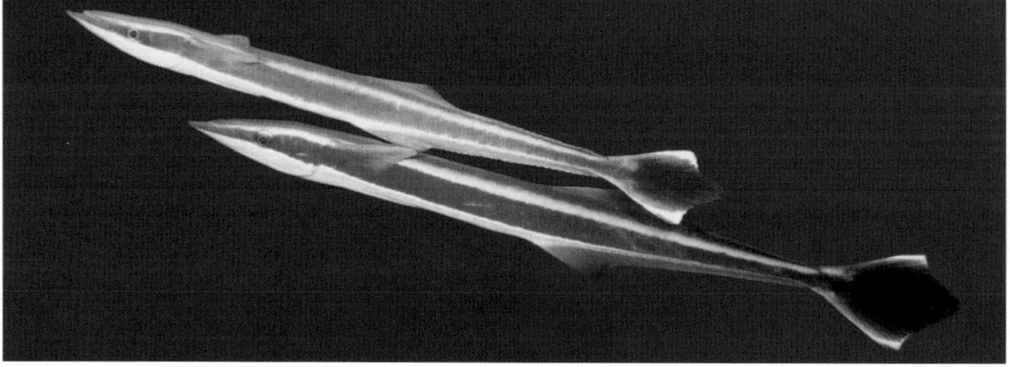

Short Suckerfish
Remora remora

Usually only seen attached to large sharks, this species is primarily oceanic and is occasionally carried inshore by its host. A rather stocky, plain-looking species with a very large pinkish grey disk. Widespread and ranges into temperate seas. Length is to 80 cm in temperate seas, usually smaller in tropical waters.

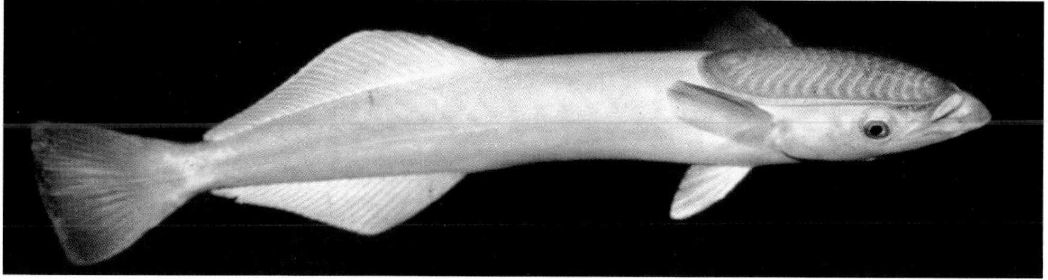

JACKS AND TREVALLIES
CARANGIDAE

A large tropical to warm-temperate family with approximately 25 genera and 140 species and about 20 species known from the Maldives. They are primarily pelagic and the number of known species will probably increase in time, as many species migrate and may be noticed or establish new populations in different locations. They are streamlined silvery fishes with a smooth skin, which features a series of bony scales along the tail, called scutes. They are fast swimming hunters; the smaller species feeding on zooplankton and the larger ones feeding on smaller fishes. However, in turn all species are hunted by the larger tunas or dolphins as well as being targeted by fishermen. Many species swim close to reefs, preying on those making mistakes when being distracted, or swimming too far from safety. Generally juveniles and small species school in shallow depths, while the larger species hunt solitary or in small groups to great depths.

Big-eye Trevally
Caranx sexfasciatus

A large and common species, that occurs singly or in small groups and sometimes in large schools along deep drop-offs. Often shows interest in divers. Juveniles found inshore, including in mangroves. Adults are rather elongated compared to similar species. Identified by the relatively large eyes and white tip on the dorsal fin. Widespread Indo-Pacific. Length to 85 cm.

Giant Trevally
Caranx ignobilis

The largest trevally, giants are often seen solitary along deep slopes but occasionally occur in small groups or schools in outer reef channels. Large adults identified by steep forehead. Juveniles can be found inshore, often hunting close to beaches. Widespread Indo-Pacific. Length to 1.7 m.

Blue-fin Jack
Caranx melampygus

Commonly seen patrolling reef slopes, often swimming near bottom feeders that disturb other fishes targeted by the jack. Occasionally seen in schools along the outer reef walls. Adult species are robust. Identified by blue fins and dark spots on upper half of the body. Widespread Indo-Pacific. Length usually to 70 cm, reported to 1 m.

Black Jack
Caranx lugubris

Inhabits clear coastal slopes and outer reef drop-offs. Usually seen solitary or in small numbers swimming close to reefs in moderate depths over 15 m. A dark looking species with a long streak of black scutes along the tail. Widespread in all tropical seas. Length to 80 cm.

Blue-spined Trevally
Carangoides coeruleopinnatus

A deep-bodied species found on inner reefs and in lagoons. Often occurs in silty habitats, along slopes or near large, remote coral bommies. Juveniles swim solitary, while adults are often in pairs. Variable in colour; juveniles are strongly banded and with age develop numerous yellow spots over the body. Widespread Indo-Pacific. Length to 40 cm.

Banded Trevally
Carangoides ferdau

Mainly found on sand slopes or along the bases to about 20 m deep. Occurs singly or in small groups and occasionally forms schools along deep drop-offs. Swims fast and low over the bottom to hunt prey and will follow other species, which disturb the bottom. Identified by a bluntly rounded snout and often has 5-6 dusky bars on the sides. Small juveniles are yellow with a dark band and often swim with jellyfish. Widespread Indo-Pacific. Length to 70 cm.

Yellow-spotted Trevally
Carangoides fulvoguttatus

Adults occur primarily in deep water and are usually seen in small groups well away from reefs, above the open sandy bottom and entering deep lagoons. Greenish on top and usually has some small scattered black spots on its upper sides. Large individuals often have several larger spots occurring centrally along the tail. Widespread Indo-Pacific. Length to 90 cm.

Island Trevally
Carangoides orthogrammus

Outside the Maldives, this species is known as the Thicklip Trevally. Usually seen solitary in the vicinity of deep water, along drop-offs or deep sand flats visiting large coral bommies. Adults have blue fins and a rather long tip on the dorsal fin. The body has several yellow spots scattered over the middle of sides. Widespread Indo-Pacific. Length to 60 cm.

Bar-cheek Trevally
Carangoides plagiotaenia

An inshore species usually found in moderately deep water along slopes or associated with shipwrecks. Often swims well away from reefs in current channels to hunt reef dwelling planktivores such as fusiliers or basslets. Usually seen solitary, but sometimes in small loose aggregations. Widespread Indo-Pacific. Length to 45 cm.

Golden Trevally
Gnathanodon speciosus

Adults live in deep water where they form schools and swim over the open bottom between distant reefs. Juveniles and semi-adults are often seen with large pelagic fish acting as pilot fishes, but also with turtles and even sea snakes. The distinctive yellow and black barred pattern remains to almost adult size, which becomes silvery with a black spot on the sides and may show faint banding on upper sides, with usually one band angled away from above the eye. Widespread Indo-Pacific. Length to 1 m.

Pilot Fish
Naucrates ductor

A pelagic species, usually seen swimming near the head of sharks or other large pelagics to feed on scraps. Juveniles are often seen with jellyfish or below floating offshore and inshore weed and other objects. Widespread in all tropical seas, ranging into warm-temperate zones. Length to 70 cm.

Rainbow Runner
Elagatis bipinnulata

A common pelagic species in the Maldives that occasionally visits reefs or enters deep lagoons. Swims in small to moderately sized schools in surface waters, as well as deep in the pursuit of food. Identified by its streamlined shape, yellow and blue stripes and isolated finlets on the tail base. Diet comprises mainly fishes but it will also take large zooplankton creatures that usually swim deep. Found in all tropical seas. Length to 1.2 m.

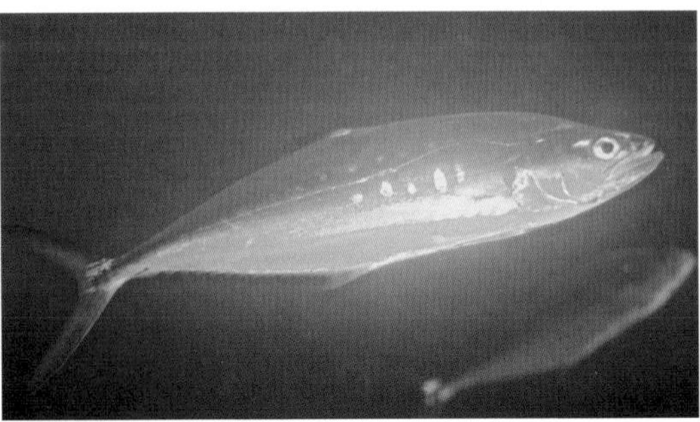

Double-spotted Queenfish
Scomberoides lysan

A common pelagic species, usually seen solitary swimming just below the surface along beaches and deep sided reef crests. Identified by a double row of 6-8 dark spots on the side; upper spots are small. Reported in depths of 100 m. Widespread Indo-Pacific. Length to 70 cm.

Big-eye Scad
Selar crumenophthalmus

A schooling species, often gathering in large numbers in sheltered inshore bays. Feeds primarily on zooplankton and recorded to depths in excess of 150 m. Generally a common species in coastal waters of continents and islands in tropical seas. Usually has a broad yellowish mid-lateral stripe. Length reported to 35 cm, usually less than 25 cm.

Mackerel Scad
Decapterus macarellus

Swims in tight groups in pursuit of zooplankton and occurs in various depths along reefs, from near surface, to almost 200 m depth. A schooling pelagic, common in the Maldives. A slender species, identified by a blue line along its side in natural light, and a small black 'ear' spot. Widespread in all tropical seas. Length to 32 cm.

Black-spotted Pompano
Trachinotus baillonii

Often seen in shallow waters near beaches, but also in current channels at lagoon entrances and outer reefs where swimming near the surface. Identified by slender shape, deeply forked tail and series of pupil-sized spots along the sides. Very common in the Maldives. Widespread Indo-Pacific. Length to 56 cm.

Snub-nose Pompano
Trachinotus blochii

Large adults are usually seen solitary in deep water around reefs. Juveniles swim in small schools along sandy beaches in very shallow depth and sometimes viewed in small waves rolling onto the beach. Identified by deep body, broadly rounded snout and deeply forked tail. Juveniles have bright yellow fins, becoming dull in adults. Widespread Indo-Pacific. Length to 65 cm.

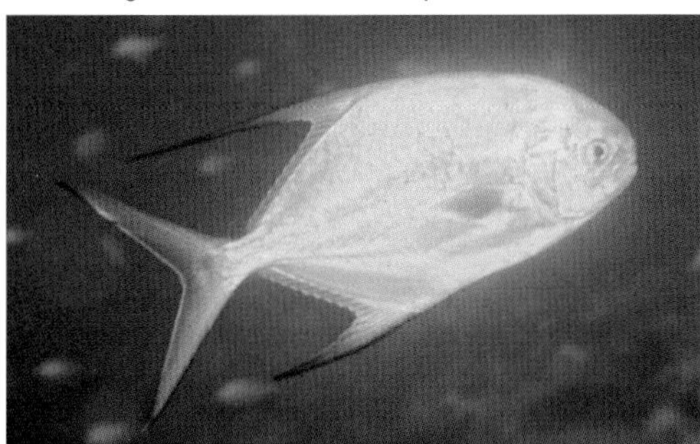

SILVER BATFISHES
MONODACTYLIDAE

A small Indo-Pacific family with three genera and about five species, only one of which occurs in the Maldives. They are deep-bodied, reflective and silvery fishes. The ventral fin is greatly reduced or rudimentary in some adults. Juveniles are mainly estuarine and some species can live in freshwater. Diet comprises plankton and floating algae.

Silver Batfish
Monodactylus argenteus

A schooling, shallow-water fish that occurs in protected lagoons, although in other areas, usually found near the mouth of rivers. A common mainland species, that occurs sporadically in the Maldives. Distinguished from Platax batfishes by diamond shape and silvery colour. Length is up to 12 cm.

PURSEMOUTHS
GERREIDAE

A moderately sized tropical to warm-temperate family with seven genera and an estimated 40 species, four of which are known from the Maldives. They are called silverbellies or silverbiddies elsewhere and mojarras in America. These fishes are silvery, deep-bodied fishes with a greatly expandable mouth. They are bottom feeders and usually travel alone or in small loose groups, swimming slowly with sudden stops in search of small invertebrates. Most are shallow water species but they may venture into greater depths; some are known to range to at least 50 m depth.

Oblong Pursemouth
Gerres oblongus

Commonly seen on shallow sand flats and slopes, adjacent to reefs and on the bottom of sand lagoons. Usually seen solitary, although others are often nearby. This species gets large and is more slender when adult compared to other silver bellies in the area. Found to depths of about 10 m. Widespread Indo-Pacific. Length to 30 cm.

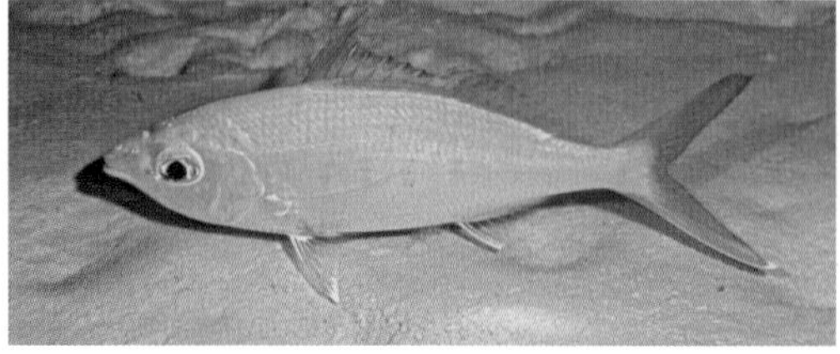

Black-tip Pursemouth
Gerres oyena

An inshore species often found in shallow waters along beaches and in estuaries swimming along reef edges with fine rubble and sand. The body is rather deep and has an elevated part of dorsal fin with a dark tip or margin. Widespread Indo-Pacific. Length to 20 cm.

Small-scale Pursemouth
Gerres acinaces

Mainly inhabits clear water sand flats near outer reefs, swimming adjacent to reefs over sparse rubble zones. Usually seen solitary from very shallow to over 20 m depth. A deep-bodied species, adults have a vertical series of dusky spots along the upper sides. Widespread Indo-Pacific. Length to 25 cm.

Short Pursemouth
Gerres abbreviatus

Inhabits inshore sand flats and sheltered bays to about 10 m depth. Enters very shallow depths and often seen at high tide in small spread out groups. A deep-bodied species with distinct yellow lower fins and a tall dorsal fin with a dusky tip. Length to 30 cm.

SPINECHEEKS
NEMIPTERIDAE

A moderately large family with five genera and at least 64 species, of which only one genus and three species known from the Maldives. Spinecheeks swim close to the bottom and pick small prey from the rubble and sand with their excellent eyesight. They typically swim short distances and will suddenly stop and study the ocean bottom for any movement of potential prey. Their diet mostly comprises worms and various small creatures.

Monocle Bream
Scolopsis bilineata

Usually found shallow in clear lagoons and protected reefs to 30 m depth. A common species found on, or near reefs on a rubble bottom. Adults occur in pairs, juveniles always solitary. Appearance is variable; Maldives fish usually lack yellow stripes and share similar colours with the venomous *Meiacanthus* blenny, a form of mimicry. Identified by a curved black-edged white stripe from below the eye to the mid-base of the dorsal fin. Widespread Indo-Pacific. Pacific fish are more yellow. Length to 20 cm.

Blue-stripe Spinecheek
Scolopsis xenochroa

A deep-water species in the Maldives, found on sand flats at 25+ m in clear water areas near outer reefs. Usually seen in small groups in rubble sand habitats with invertebrate growth such as seawhips. Colour is variable with habitat, being pale with little colour on white sand and more blue in reef habitat. Mainly West Pacific, ranging as far as the Maldives. Length to 20 cm.

Golden Spinecheek
Scolopsis aurata

Found in various habitats, from silty shallow lagoons, to deep sand flats well away from reefs. Usually seen in small loose groups, but forms schools in deep water. These schools occasionally enter a divers depth range to feed near reefs. Identified by pale stripe on the side. Indian Ocean, from Maldives ranging east to Java. Length to 23 cm.

Photo darker form: Java, Indonesia.

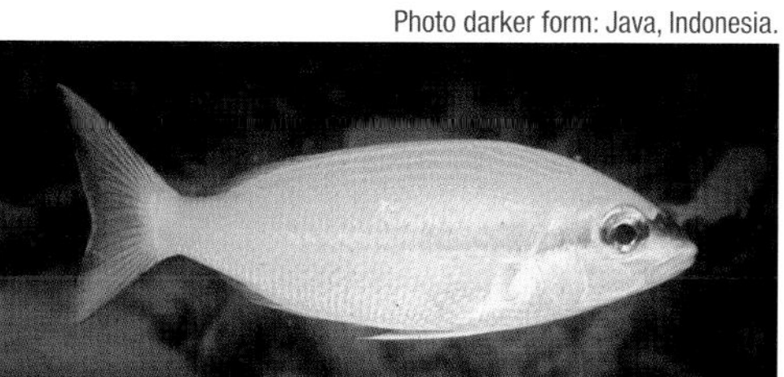

EMPERORS
LETHRINIDAE

A moderately large, Indo-Pacific family with five genera and about 40 species, 18 of which are reported from the Maldives. Some species are restricted to very deep water. Emperors are oval-shaped, medium sized fishes, with the largest to about one metre long, and important food fishes in some areas. They are bottom-dwellers, preferring sand and rubble bottoms, and feed on small invertebrates or worms. Their prey is targeted by sight or by taking mouth-fulls of sand, in areas with potential prey, which is then filtered through the gills. When adult, some of the larger species prefer feeding at night.

Orange-finned Emperor
Lethrinus erythracanthus

Usually found on silty lagoon reefs with rich algae on coral bases. Commonly observed on sheltered inshore reefs and in lagoons. Adults range to 120 m depth. Larger adults are usually solitary and easily recognised by the coloured fins that vary from deep yellow to bright orange, and their large mouth with fleshy lips. Juveniles are greenish. Widespread Indo-Pacific. Length to 70 cm, rarely over 50 cm.

Orange-stripe Emperor
Lethrinus obsoletus

Commonly found in deep lagoons to about 30 m depth. Adults are sometimes found in small loose groups and often feed in very shallow depth, juveniles on algae reefs. Variable in colour and quickly change colour with mood, from blotchy to pale. Identified by light orange stripe along lower sides. Widespread Indo-Pacific. Length reported to 60 cm, usually 45 cm.

Photo: juvenile, Australia.

Yellow-lip Emperor
Lethrinus xanthochilus

Enters sand slopes and flats adjacent to deep water. Adults are rather plain and recognised by their slender body and yellow lips. Usually seen solitary but occasionally in small groups. Juveniles inhabit seagrass beds. Widespread Indo-Pacific. Length is up to 60 cm.

Black-blotch Emperor
Lethrinus harak

An inshore species mainly found in protected waters, including seagrass beds. Often occurs in silty conditions. Usually found solitary, but occasionally congregate, probably when getting ready to spawn. They have a distinctive black blotch on the side, sometimes bordering with yellow. Small juveniles live amongst seagrasses and occur in mangroves. Widespread Indo-Pacific. Length reported to 60 cm, usually 40 cm.

Long-nose Emperor
Lethrinus olivaceus

Mainly a schooling species and occasionally seen along deep slopes on inner reefs. Shy in the Maldives. Found in shallow to deep water, reported to 185 m depth. A large fish, but rather slender with a long snout. Widespread Indo-Pacific. Length to 1 m.

Small-tooth Emperor
Lethrinus microdon

Occurs either individually or in small groups on coastal reef slopes, usually at the deeper end. Very similar to the Long-nose Emperor, but is much smaller and differs slightly in colour and scale arrangements on the body. Widespread Indo-Pacific. Length to 70 cm, usually to 50 cm.

Spangled Emperor
Lethrinus nebulosus

Adults form small loose groups in deep lagoons. Juveniles are found in estuaries and often in silty habitats with seagrass beds and in deeper areas with sponges. Colour varies but is usually yellowish, with a light blue centre on each scale. Widespread Indo-Pacific. Length to nearly 1 m.

Red-spot Emperor
Lethrinus lentjan

Adults occur in deep silty habitats and hover in small groups in reef shelters during the day to 50 m depth. They feed mainly at night. Juveniles occur in seagrass beds and are diurnal. The red spot on the gills at the margin identifies adult fish. Uncommon in the Maldives, mainly found in continental coastal waters. Widespread Indo-Pacific. Length to 50 cm, but usually much smaller.

Blue-line Large-eye Emperor
Gymnocranius grandoculis

Commonly found on sand slopes in protected areas of lagoons, inshore as well as near outer reefs. Swims well above the bottom to hunt invertebrates in sand, and excellent eyesight to spot prey from a long distance. Large adults develop blue lines on the cheek. Widespread Indo-Pacific. Length to 50 cm.

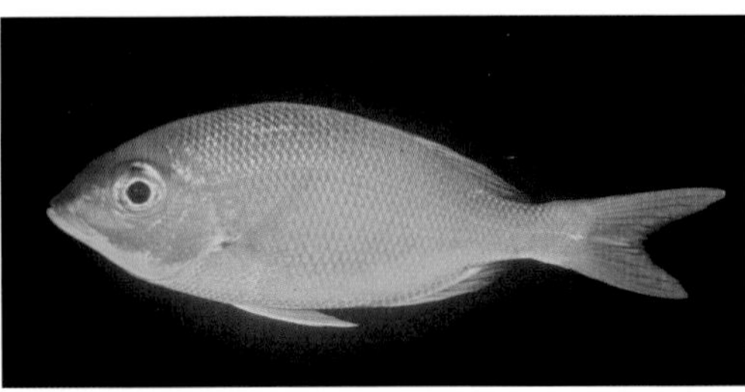

Blue-spotted Large-eye Emperor
Gymnocranius microdon

Occurs deep, in sandy lagoons swimming solitary in depths of about 15 m, but often with several other individuals. Adults develop blue spots over the snout and below the front of the eyes. Widespread Indo-Pacific. Length to 40 cm.

Large-eye Emperor
Gymnocranius sp.

An undetermined species; occurs in large lagoons with good coral growth. Usually swims over rubble and sand along reef margins. Length to about 45 cm.

Large-eye Bream
Monotaxis grandoculis

Adults typically drift in sheltered parts of the reef, often near current channels where they congregate during the day. Juveniles found in sandy lagoons, swimming just above the bottom in search of prey, along reef sections or over rubble. At night, adults feed on various bottom creatures. Large eyes and a bluntly rounded snout identify the species. Widespread Indo-Pacific. Length to 60 cm.

Gold-spot Emperor
Gnathodentex aurolineatus

A small schooling species; commonly seen along drop-offs or steep slopes from inner to outer reefs. Usually seen drifting near large caves during the day and then dispersing at night to feed on bottom invertebrates. Colour is variable, from almost silvery to dark brown or grey. The yellow blotch below the end of its dorsal fin identifies the species. Widespread Indo-Pacific. Length to 30 cm.

SWEETLIPS
HAEMULIDAE

A large family with 18 genera and about 120 species, including the sub-family grunts, which comprises primarily estuarine species. In the Maldives, sweetlips are represented with two genera and five species. The greatly thickened lip in adults characterizes this group. Juveniles look drastically different from adults and go through several changes in both looks and behaviour with growth. Juveniles are diurnal, while adults are mainly nocturnal. Diet changes with growth; juveniles feed on algae, as well as zooplankton and tiny mysids, whilst adults hunt various invertebrates and fishes.

Grey Sweetlips
Diagramma cinerascens

Adults are usually found in small groups, in deep water along reef edges and sheltering in low reefs during the day. Observed in depths of about 40 m. This species is similar to the closely related *D. labiosum* from Australia. Juveniles are a yellowish white colour with longitudinal black stripes. Probably widespread Indian Ocean. Length to almost 1 m.

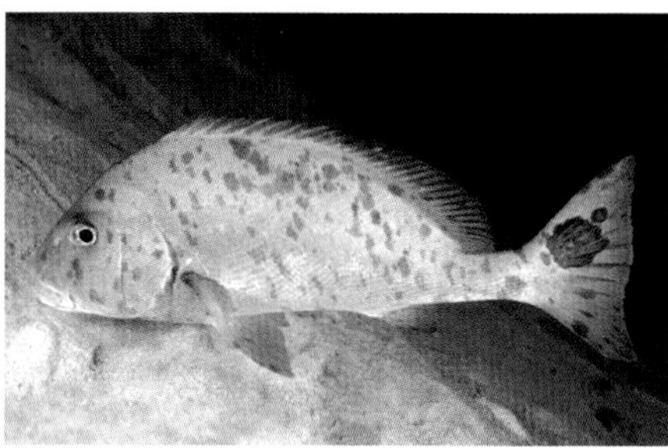

Giant Sweetlips
Plectorhinchus albovittatus

Large adults are usually found on the upper part of outer reef drop-offs, using large caves during the day. Often swims about openly in adjacent areas. Juveniles live in coastal waters but are rarely seen. Usually recognized by their large size, large lips and black fin markings. The name *Plectorhinchus obscurus*, which is often used for this species, is a junior synonym. Widespread Indo-Pacific. Length to at least 1 m.

Photos: adult right: Papua New Guinea; left juvenile: Java, Indonesia.

Brown Sweetlips
Plectorhinchus gibbosus

Common in the Maldives, usually found on sheltered reefs with large corals for shelter during the day. Depending on shelter space, found singly or in small groups. Juveniles are estuarine. They are mainly grey or brownish with indistinct dark barring on the head. Very similar to *P. nigrus* from the Red Sea. Widespread Indo-Pacific. Length to 75 cm.

Harlequin Sweetlips
Plectorhinchus chaetodonoides

Also called Spotted Sweetlips. Large adults are commonly seen in caves along inner reef drop-offs. Small juveniles occur in lagoons amongst staghorn corals and most commonly seen after the wet season. They have spotted patterns throughout all growth stages. Widespread Indo-Pacific. Length to 60 cm.

Photo, juvenile: Flores, Indonesia.

Oriental Sweetlips
Plectorhinchus vittatus

Commonly found in caves along drop-offs on outer reefs, usually in groups. Adults easily recognised by their yellow lips and horizontal black striped pattern. Juveniles are blotched. Widespread Indo-Pacific. Length to 50 cm.

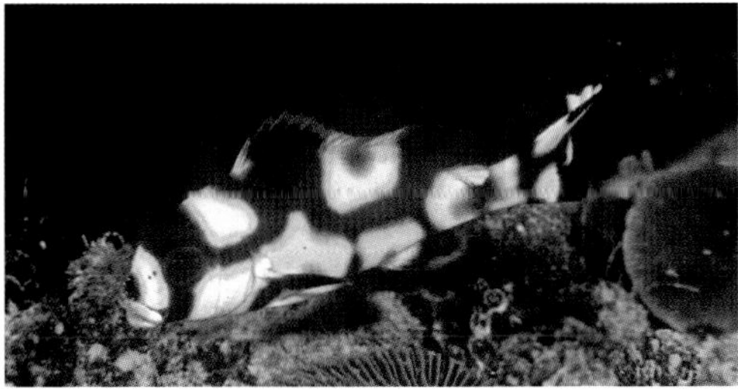

SNAPPERS
LUTJANIDAE

A large tropical family of 17 genera and over 100 species globally, of which 28 are recorded from the Maldives. Several records are doubtful and need to be verified. Some species are only found in very deep waters and are not included here. There are several sub-families. Those that are commonly seen by divers and are the most numerous are the LUTJANINAE, the benthic snappers. Adult fish live in moderate depths, some entering shallow reefs. Juveniles of many species occur inshore, some enter freshwater and often reach near adult size in shallow depths. Diet comprises invertebrates and fishes, usually taken from the bottom, but some form schools and additionally feed on zooplankton. ETELININAE are the Jobfishes and APSILININAE are the Fusilier Snappers. The latter are often mistaken for fusiliers (CAESIONIDAE).

Blue-striped Snapper
Lutjanus kasmira

Usually found in depths over 20 m, near deep channels between outer reefs and lagoons. Adults form large schools during the day, sheltering in reefs from strong currents. Juveniles usually in small groups inshore, often in silty habitats. Easily recognised by the blue lines, but often confused with *L. bengalensis*. Best distinguished by the yellow ventral fins and yellow below the lowest blue stripe. Widespread Indo-Pacific. Length to 35 cm.

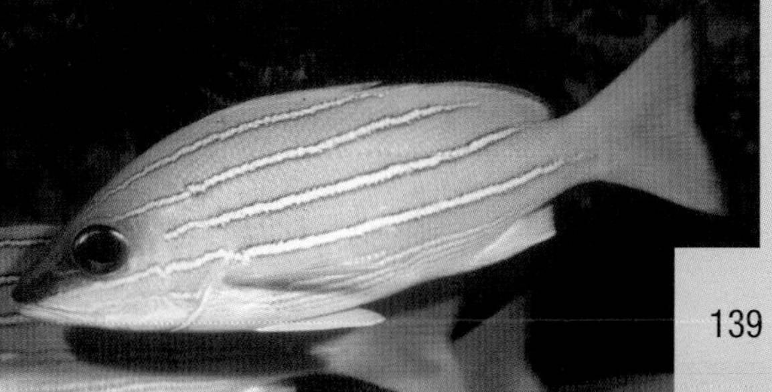

Bengal Snapper
Lutjanus bengalensis

An inshore species that forms small aggregations. Usually found in sandy or muddy lagoons around outcrops of dead coral or washed-in land debris. Mostly shallow, rarely deeper than 25 m. Easily overlooked because of the similar colouration to *L. kasmira* but lacks faint horizontal lines on the belly. Also, it is much less common in the Maldives. The Bengal Snapper is more common in continental waters and is widespread Indian Ocean, ranging to Indonesia. Length to 30 cm, commonly about 20 cm.

Yellow-striped Snapper
Lutjanus rufolineatus

Forms large dense schools during the day along sheltered coastal reefs, where common between 10 and 30 m. The yellow tail and many yellow horizontal lines on the body identify it. Occurrence in the Maldives needs to be verified. Previously confused with *L. boutton*, another West Pacific species that lacks stripes. A small species, length to 30 cm.

Indian Snapper
Lutjanus madras

Occurs in shallow outer reef surge zones in channels and under large coral plates. A flighty species and not commonly seen. Photographed snorkelling at 3 m depth, the only way to get close at the time. Colouration of the Maldives fish is unusual and identification needs to be verified. Mainland variations have thick yellow stripes and lack a black side spot. Common along the mainland from Sri Lanka to Indonesia, and ranging to the Philippines. Reported to 90 m depth. Length to 30 cm.

Photo left, spotless form: Java, Indonesia.

One-spot Snapper

Lutjanus monostigma

Adults shelter in the reef during the day, often singly or in small groups below short overhangs or caves along walls from about 10 m down. Commonly associated with shipwrecks. It hunts on the open bottom at night. Recognised by a silvery grey body and yellow fins, usually with a small black side spot. Widespread Indo-Pacific. Length to 60 cm.

Black-spot Snapper

Lutjanus ehrenbergii

A widespread coastal species usually found near freshwater run offs where it resides in large schools. Possibly a stray, arriving postlarvae with floating weeds in the wet season. Recognised by the large black spot and several thin lines, running below along the entire body. Widespread Indo-Pacific. Length to 35 cm.

Black-tail Snapper

Lutjanus fulvus

Occurs in coastal habitat in moderate depths. Juveniles occur in seagrass and mangrove areas, or algae dominated reefs in lagoons. Also seen entering freshwater elsewhere. Tail and dorsal fins darken with age and become black in adults. Identified by a narrow white margin on the tail and dorsal fins and yellow anal, pelvic and pectoral fins. Widespread Indo-Pacific. Length to 40 cm.

Humpback Snapper

Lutjanus gibbus

Adults often in dense stationary schools on sheltered inshore reefs, sometimes well above the bottom on the slopes. They disperse at night to feed on the bottom. Juveniles mainly found in seagrass habitats. Adults have a distinct concave head profile. Identified by forked caudal fin, that has a very broad upper lobe, which gives it its alternate name: the Paddletail. Widespread Indo-Pacific. Length to 50 cm.

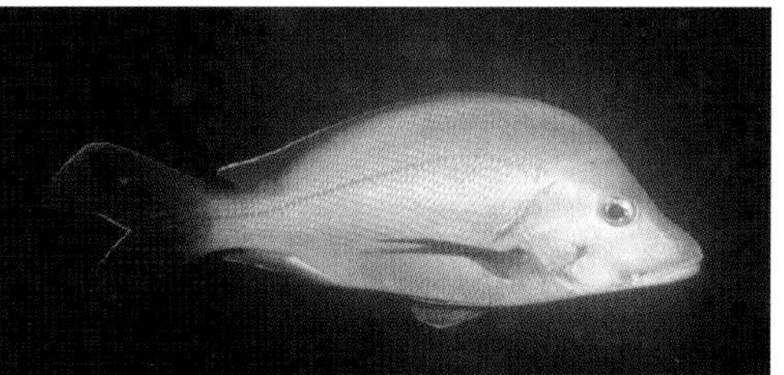

Mangrove Jack
Lutjanus argentimaculatus

Large adults occur along deep drop-offs between 40 and 120 m. Juveniles and sub-adults found inshore, often in silty habitats with small juveniles forming small aggregations when on reefs. Small juveniles are also found in mangrove estuaries and entering freshwater. Juveniles distinctly banded and have red fins when in freshwater, a pattern that is gradually lost with age. Widespread Indo-Pacific. Length to 1.2 m.

Photo below right, large adult: Guam; others: Flores, Indonesia.

Photo, sub-adult: Australia.

Red Emperor Snapper
Lutjanus sebae

Adults prefer deep water and are rarely seen by divers. Juveniles seen among long-spined urchins. Sub-adults in small groups in caves at the base of drop-offs or with remote outcrops of reef on deep sand flats. Large adults are uniformly red. Widespread Indo-Pacific. Length to 1 m.

Red Bass
Lutjanus bohar

Occurs along reef edges to about 70 m depth, from sheltered inshore habitats, to outer reef walls. Adults often travel in small groups, occasionally in schools. Juveniles solitary in lagoons, often with large staghorn coral patches on sand in a few metres depth. Small juveniles are sometimes mistaken for damselfishes. Distinguished from *L. argentimaculatus* by black on fins and notch in front of eyes. Common in the Maldives. Widespread Indo-Pacific. Length to 80 cm.

Two-spot Snapper
Lutjanus biguttatus

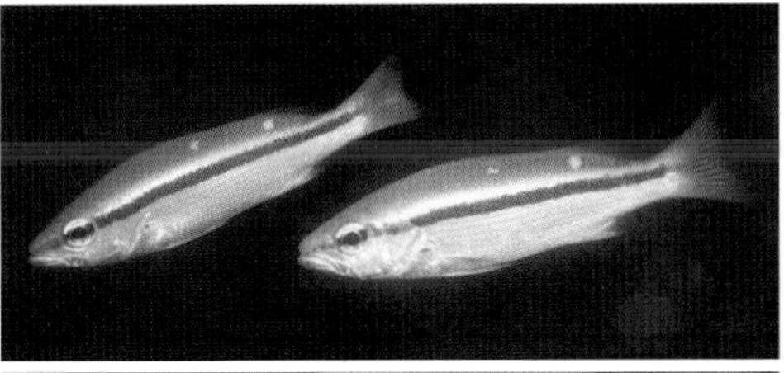

Inhabits sheltered inshore reefs and large lagoons with rich coral growth. Solitary or forming schools, slowly swimming low above the corals during the day. Disperses at night, usually swimming well above the bottom, which suggests feeding on zooplankton or mid-water fishes. Recognised by elongated shape, mid-lateral stripe and twin white spots. Occurs in West Pacific from New Guinea to Philippines and west to the Maldives. Length to 20 cm.

Photo top, juveniles.

Midnight Snapper
Macolor macularis

Inhabits protected reef slopes and walls with rich coral growth. Adults in caves or swim openly about and sometimes congregate in loose numbers in reef channels. Juveniles recognised by very long fins below and swim with feather stars, long-spined urchins and coral fans between 5 and 20 m. Widespread Indo-Pacific. Length to 60 cm.

Black Snapper
Macolor niger

Large adults often in small schools near reef channels adjacent to deep water. Small juveniles are solitary, swimming openly about, but close to reefs with rich coral growth. Often confused with *M. macularis*, but juveniles have short fins and adults lack the yellow iris and are plain grey to almost black. Common in the Maldives. Widespread Indo-Pacific. Length to 60 cm.

Green Jobfish
Aprion virescens

Swims high in the water column over open bottom or at distance along reefs. Usually hunts solitary for fishes and squid, including larger zooplankton animals. Recognised by elongated body, rounded head with eyes placed well back, and very large tail fin. Widespread Indo-Pacific. Length to 1 m.

Small-tooth Jobfish
Aphareus furca

Commonly seen solitary, occasionally in small groups, swimming close to reefs on inner and outer reefs to depths of about 70 m. It hunts fishes and invertebrates. A fork-tail species, with edges of gill plate dusky, showing two vertical bars, with adults sometime bright yellow over the top of the snout. Widespread Indo-Pacific. Length to 40 cm.

Fusilier Snapper
Paracaesio sordidus

Usually seen along deep drop-offs but easily overlooked by lack of colour. Depth range is reported between 100 and 200 m, but it rises to near the surface to feed. Photographed in 20 m depth. Caudal fin is very large and reddish, but looks dark grey with depth and the fish is well camouflaged against open water. Widespread Indo-Pacific. Length to 40 cm.

FUSILIERS
CAESIONIDAE

A moderately sized tropical family, that has four genera and about 20 species, 14 of which are known from the Maldives. In many areas, fusiliers form large schools and particularly in the Maldives, make up a large component of the open water reef species. Fusiliers have longitudinal patterns and are predominantly blue and yellow in colour. At night, these colours change completely and species resting in crevices may turn red. All fusiliers are planktivores and congregate in current areas along deep drop-offs, tidal channels or submerged reefs and feed at any depth where plankton is carried.

Thin-lined Fusilier
Caesio varilineata

A very common species in the Maldives, that schools over inner and outer reef flats. Often seen from boats as a stream of blue travelling through the water. Identified by the thin yellow lines running parallel along the sides and lack of black tips on the tail. Widespread Indian Ocean, ranging east to Bali, Indonesia and Red Sea. Length to 22 cm.

Gold-band Fusilier
Caesio caerulaurea

Uncommon in the Maldives, usually found in lagoon channels, forming small groups or mixed with other species. A single yellow band along the upper sides and dark streaks in the tail fin identify it. Widespread and generally common throughout the Indo-Pacific. Length to 25 cm.

Moon Fusilier
Caesio lunaris

Common in the Maldives, occurs in deep lagoons and along inner reefs walls. Adults form large schools and feed at various depths from the surface to 40 m depth. Adults are all blue in colour with distinctive black tips on the tail fin. Juveniles have a yellow caudal fin base. Widespread Indo-Pacific. Length to 35 cm.

Yellow-tail Fusilier
Caesio teres

Not a common species in the Maldives. Often seen singly in large lagoons and sometimes mixed with other species. Distinguished by the lack of lines or black fin tips and the yellow, which is mainly confined to the tail area, although it may extend over the back to the head. Widespread Indo-Pacific, very common in Indonesia. Length to 20 cm.

Yellow-back Fusilier
Caesio xanthonota

Common in the Maldives, forms large schools along inner reefs. Easily recognised by the yellow colour extending over the head and along the back to its tail, and the lack of black fin tips. Widespread Indian Ocean, ranging to southern Java, Indonesia. Length to 20 cm.

Yellow-banded Fusilier
Pterocaesio flavifasciata

Uncommon and was only known from southern Java until found in the Maldives, although no doubt widespread throughout the Indian Ocean. Appears closely related to *P. digramma* from the Pacific. Only known from outer reef habitats and seamounts. Length to about 25 cm.

Yellow-stripe Fusilier
Pterocaesio chrysozona

Rare in the Maldives, mainly found in continental waters of the Indian Ocean. A thick yellow line distinguishes it, running from the top of the eye to the caudal fin; the latter has distinct black tips. Widespread Indo-Pacific, common on inshore reefs in Indonesia and Australia. Length to 30 cm.

Broad-stripe Fusilier
Pterocaesio lativittata

Almost identical to *P. chrysozona* but the yellow stripe is slightly higher on the body and usually lacks black on the base of pectoral fins. Found in small groups in the Maldives. The Maldives record of another species, *P. tessellata*, appears to be based on a photograph of this species. Reported from Indian Ocean and Papua New Guinea. Length to 15 cm.

Banana Fusilier
Pterocaesio pisang

A moderately common species in the Maldives, found in lagoon habitats. Colour is variable from plain pale blue to almost red and tail with distinctive black tips. Generally a common widespread Indo-Pacific species, forming small groups along reef slopes, drop-offs and outer walls. Length to 16 cm.

Blue-dash Fusilier
Pterocaesio tile

A common outer reef species, that usually forms large schools along deep drop-offs. Recognised by a bright blue dash along the sides that varies in length when seen from different angles. It also has a dark streak on each lobe of the tail. Widespread Indo-Pacific. Length to 25 cm.

Striped Fusilier
Pterocaesio trilineata

A common Maldives species, but not reported until now. Mainly found in silty lagoons and inner reefs, forming moderate sized schools. Easily recognised by the trio of alternating light and dusky stripes along upper sides. Widespread Indo-Pacific, often common in coastal waters. Length to 16 cm.

Slender Fusilier
Gymnocaesio gymnoptera

Appears to be uncommon in the Maldives, but easily overlooked. A small slender species, lacking strong colours and often swims with unrelated similar shaped fishes. Mainly in deep lagoons along reef slopes. Widespread Indo-Pacific, and often found on outer reefs to moderate depths of about 25 m. Length to 15 cm.

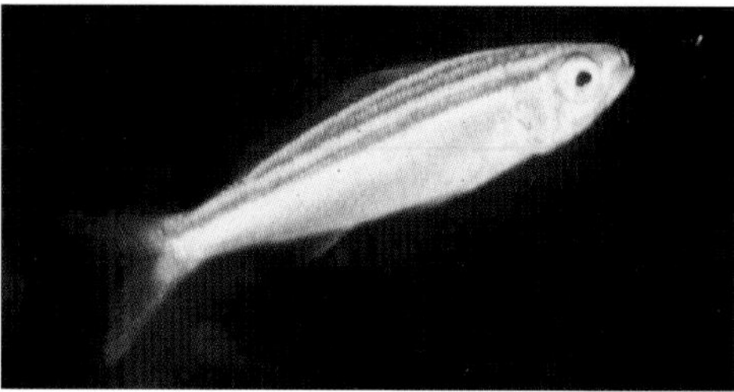

Dwarf Fusilier
Dipterygonotus balteatus

Moderately common, but swims well away from reefs and mainly schooling pelagic. Often swims with other similar shaped small pelagic fishes and easily overlooked. Widespread Indo-Pacific. The smallest fusilier, usually not much over 10 cm.

GOATFISHES
MULLIDAE

A moderately large family with six genera and at least 50 species, of which at least 10 are found in the Maldives. Readily identified by the pair of barbels below the mouth, which are used to probe the bottom for various invertebrates and small fishes. Most species are seen singly or in small groups around reefs but there are several small schooling species that prefer open substrate or often deep silty type bottom, but these are not well known.

Yellow-saddle Goatfish
Parupeneus cyclostomus

Inhabits inner and outer reefs from shallow reef crests to moderate depths, reported to 100 m. Adults often seen singly or in pairs, sometimes forming schools. Juveniles bright yellow and in the Maldives, the adults commonly retain this colour. A second colour variety is purplish-pink or bluish with gold saddle on top of the tail base. Widespread Indo-Pacific. Length to 38 cm.

Round-spot Goatfish
Parupeneus pleurostigma

In the Maldives, mainly found in deep water in 20+ m depth, on clean sand flats with rubble and invertebrate-rich areas. Easily recognised by a large black spot on middle of upper side followed by a large white patch. Widespread Indo-Pacific. Length to 30 cm.

Long-barbel Goatfish
Parupeneus macronema

Common in the Maldives on clear reef crests and on slopes in both inner and outer reefs, usually in small, loose groups. Identified by a thick black or red stripe along the head and body, separated from a black spot on the tail base by a large white patch. Feeds on rubble patches around dead parts of coral bases, from near intertidal to about 35 m depth. Widespread Indo-Pacific. Length to 30 cm.

Dash-and-Dot
Parupeneus barberinus

Usually seen along reefs on sand flats or slopes in depths over 10 m; reported to 100 m. Large individuals are usually solitary but accompanied by various wrasse species, eager to catch prey when bottom is disturbed. Distinguished by a black stripe, usually thin but with yellow above in more colourful specimens, and a large black spot on the tail base. Widespread Indo-Pacific. Length to 40 cm.

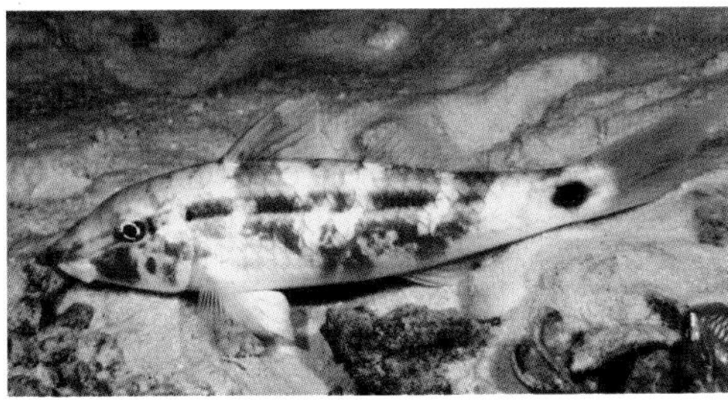

Yellow-spot Goatfish
Parupeneus indicus

Appears to be rare in most of the Maldives. Mainly occurs inshore on sheltered reefs with sand zones and in lagoons to about 25 m depth. Easily recognised by the bright yellow spot centrally placed along upper sides and black spot on tail base. Widespread Indo-Pacific. Length to 40 cm.

Double-bar Goatfish
Parupeneus trifasciatus

Common in various shallow, reef habitats with sand and rubble patches. Adults often seen resting on corals, while young are usually in channels on outer reef slopes. The double black band easily identifies this species. Widespread Indo-Pacific, some geographical variations or subspecies. Length to 30 cm.

Square-spot Goatfish
Mulloidichthys flavolineatus

Common in sheltered lagoons in the Maldives, usually forming active schools around remote large staghorn coral patches on the sand. Has a small black spot centrally on sides, usually followed by yellow stripe but this is pale in the Maldives due to habitat colour. The spot is missing at night. Widespread Indo-Pacific. Length to 40 cm, but usually much smaller in Maldives.

Yellow-stripe Goatfish
Mulloidichthys vanicolensis

A schooling species, that aggregates during the day in sheltered reefs. Sometimes mixed with blue-striped snapper. Uncommon in the Maldives. Length to 30 cm.

Schooling Goatfish

Upeneus taeniopterus

Commonly occurs in silty inshore habitats, seagrass beds and sandy lagoons, usually in schools that move along quickly while feeding. Identified by tail pattern and pale body colour with yellowish line. Widespread Indo-Pacific, mainly oceanic locations. Length to 30 cm.

Shiny Goatfish

Upeneus sp. 1

A small species, possibly *U. sundaicus*, that normally has a yellowish stripe along its side. This stripe may not show because of the white sand habitat in the Maldives, where most fish lack colour. Found in small groups on fine-sand flats in depths over 10 m. Length about 15 cm.

Bar-tail Goatfish

Upeneus tragula

Reported from the Maldives and appears to be rare. Usually found in various reef habitats from silty coastal harbours to outer reefs to depths of about 20 m. Found singly or small groups. Identified by stripe along side of body and two yellow spots in the dark tip-area of the first dorsal fin. Widespread and usually common Indo-Pacific. Length to 30 cm.

BULLSEYES
PEMPHERIDIDAE

A small family, comprising two genera and about 20 species globally. Both genera and at least three species occur in the Maldives. They are nocturnal fishes that school during the day, usually sheltering in caves and some are secretive in the back of dark, far-reaching caves or tunnels. A distinctive group of fishes by shape, with large eyes and a small triangular fin on the back, positioned just behind the head and the long anal fin below that reaches the tail fin. They float high above the bottom at night to hunt the larger zooplankton animals.

Greenback Bullseye
Pempheris vanicolensis

Occurs in sheltered inshore waters, harbours and shipwrecks, forming schools where space is available. Easily recognised by the black margin on the anal fin and black tip on the dorsal fin. Usually has a greenish shiny top and large adults appear reddish brown in natural light. Found to depths of at least 40 m. Common in the Maldives. Widespread Indo-Pacific. Length is to 15 cm.

Silver Bullseye
Pempheris schwenkii

Found mainly along outer reefs in caves. Usually in small groups and often mixes with other species. Fins are plain, only the dorsal fin has a dusky tip. It has a shiny back and sides are yellowish. Occurs in moderate depths, usually between 10 and 50 m. Widespread Indo-Pacific. Length to 15 cm.

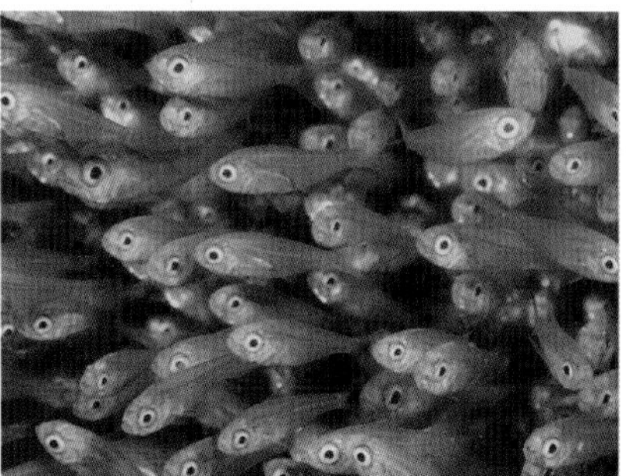

Yellow Sweeper
Parapriacanthus ransonneti

Usually found in large dense schools against reef walls or in caves and in deep clear lagoons around large remote coral bommies. Easily recognised by its behaviour and yellowish colouration. Often, other unrelated species, such as young cardinal fishes, swim amongst them for protection, taking on the same colour. Found in depths from 10 to at least 50 m. Widespread Indo-Pacific. Length to 10 cm.

RUDDERFISHES
KYPHOSIDAE

A small family with three genera and ten species globally. They are primarily subtropical or warm-temperate but two species occur widespread Indo-Pacific, including the Maldives. They feed primarily on algae and consequently live in shallow waters, often in turbulent high-energy zones where food is more abundant. Also known as drummers.

Snubnose Rudderfish
Kyphosus cinerascens

Adults swim in schools in shallows over reefs near tidal channels, or form smaller groups while feeding on floating algae at various depths in the currents. Sometimes found around shipwrecks to depths of about 30 m. Post larval stages swim under weed rafts and settle in intertidal zones. Recognised by the more elevated fins above and below the tail. Widespread Indo-Pacific. Length to 50 cm.

Brassy Rudderfish
Kyphosus vaigiensis

Occurs on inshore reefs with moderate currents in small groups or schools, often feeding in surface waters along the shorelines. Rarely goes deeper than 10 m. Sometimes shows an evenly spaced pattern of pale blotches over body and head. Widespread Indo-Pacific. Length to 50 cm.

BUTTERFLYFISHES
CHAETODONTIDAE

A large family with ten genera and about 120 species globally, of which 32 species are known from the Maldives. There are many closely related species that are morphologically almost identical. Colouration is often the best diagnostic feature. Juveniles can differ considerably in colour from the adult and usually have a proportionally much shorter snout. Diet comprises filamentous algae and various invertebrates, including live coral polyps. Most species target small creatures, plankton or pick on corals, and some specialise in particular foods. The plankton feeders may form large schools high above the bottom and the reef-pickers swim in pairs or small groups when adult, staying low on the bottom in search of food. Small juveniles are usually solitary and live secretively in corals or among boulders. Eggs and larvae are pelagic for several weeks. Habitats vary between species from shallow reef flats to deep outer reef walls, but the majority of species live in relatively shallow depths, rarely below 50 m depth. One species in the Maldives that lives very deep and usually to 100+ m: *Prognathodes guyotensis*, which is not included in this book.

Black Pyramid Butterflyfish
Hemitaurichthys zoster

A very common species in the Maldives. A schooling plankton feeder with very distinctive colouration and readily recognised by the broad white and black pattern on the body and head. Often feeds near the surface in large numbers, ranging to a depth of about 30 m. Restricted to western Indian Ocean. Length to 18 cm.

Yellow Teardrop Butterflyfish
Chaetodon interruptus

Found singly or in pairs and occasionally in small groups on shallow coral reefs. Feeds on small invertebrates, algae and some corals. Distinguished by a black spot on a yellow background. Differs from its Pacific sibling *C. unimaculatus* in colour and was previously considered a sub-species, but is obviously a valid species in its own right. Western Indian Ocean. Length to 20 cm.

Eclipse Butterflyfish
Chaetodon bennetti

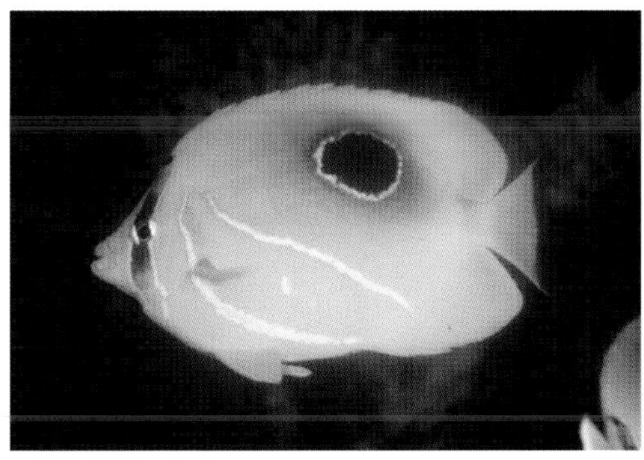

Adults usually swim in pairs close to reefs. Easily recognised from other yellow species by the large pale-edged black spot on the upper side and the pair of blue stripes running diagonally from the head to the anal fin. Often feed on coral-like anemones that carpet some reef areas, and also pick on coral polyps. Widespread Indo-Pacific. Depth range to about 30 m. Length to 18 cm.

Racoon Butterflyfish
Chaetodon lunula

Adults usually swim in pairs close to reefs, but are occasionally seen floating, almost motionless, high above reefs in still waters where other reef fishes congregate. The black and white face "mask" and diagonal black bar behind the head distinguish them. Occupies various habitats, feeding on a great variety of invertebrates to depths of at least 30 m. Widespread Indo-Pacific. Length to 20 cm.

Yellow Butterflyfish
Chaetodon andamanensis

Usually seen in pairs and occasionally in small groups, on reefs with rich coral growth to 10 m depth. Feeds mainly on coral polyps. Only known from Indian Ocean, from the Maldives to the Andaman seas. It was previously confused with the Blue-dash Butterflyfish *C. plebeius* from the eastern West Pacific. Length to 15 cm.

Pinstriped Butterflyfish
Chaetodon trifasciatus

Also called Red-fin or Purple Butterflyfish. Adults swim in pairs or small groups in the shallows of coral rich reefs, while the small, secretive juvenile occurs in coral thickets. They feed mainly on coral polyps. Have unique colour patterns and an obvious orange anal fin. Identified by the many dark stripes on pale yellow and bluish background, often with a black blotch on an upper stripe. Widespread Indian Ocean, ranging to Bali, Indonesia, then replaced by its Pacific sibling *C. lunulatus*. Length to 15 cm.

Chevroned Butterflyfish
Chaetodon trifascialis

Typically swims close to large plate-corals (*Acropora*) singly or in pairs, and juveniles tend to stay between the branches. Usually inhabits depths of about 15 m, rarely deeper. Identified by chevron lines along the body; juveniles with additional black over the body at the ends of dorsal and anal fins. Widespread Indo-Pacific. Length to 14 cm.

Brown Butterflyfish
Chaetodon kleinii

Mainly found on shallow reef flats and in lagoons but may venture into deep water. Usually forms small groups and lives in various habitats with rich algae growth. Juveniles often mix with small surgeonfishes to feed on algae and small crawling invertebrates. Identified by bars on head and varied brown to yellow-brown coloured body; adults with blue on the nape. Widespread Indo-Pacific. Length is to 12 cm.

Citron Butterflyfish
Chaetodon citrinellus

Inhabits shallow reef-flats, including surge zones, lagoons and harbours, but occasionally seen along deep walls. Usually swims in pairs in the Maldives when adult. Feeds on tiny invertebrates and algae. Identified by a pale yellow body, with a series of dusky to orange dots along the scale rows, and a black margin on the anal fin. Widespread Indo-Pacific. Length to 11 cm.

Spotted Butterflyfish
Chaetodon guttatissimus

Occurs among rich coral growth, often along steep slopes and walls, from reef crests to moderate depths over 30 m. When adult, it swims either singly or in pairs. Feeds on various small invertebrates and often picks worms from calcareous tubes. Identified by the dense spotting over the body, extending onto dorsal and anal fins. Indian Ocean, ranging to Bali, Indonesia. Length to 10 cm.

Black-back Butterflyfish

Chaetodon melannotus

In the Maldives, adults usually form pairs. They are not particularly common and mainly found in large lagoons with large coral formations to depths of about 20 m. Easily identified by the bright yellow fins, including ventral fins, which in similar species are white, and the dark diagonal lines over the body. Widespread Indo-Pacific. Length to 15 cm.

Pig-face Butterflyfish

Chaetodon oxycephalus

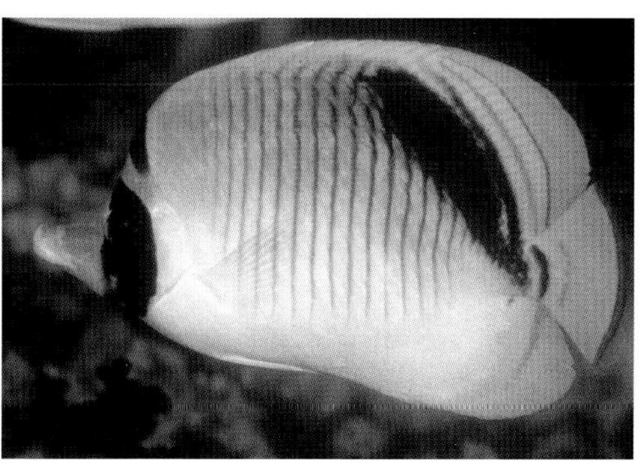

Swims in pairs when adult and juveniles remain secretive amongst boulders. Often overlooked because of its similarity with *C. lineolatus* which is better known and more widespread. Best recognised by the broken black band over the eye. Feeds on small invertebrates on the bases of corals and sometimes picks at coral polyps. Indo Pacific. Length to 25 cm.

Lined Butterflyfish

Chaetodon lineolatus

Often found in reef-channels on outer reefs, feeding on various invertebrates, including anemones and coral polyps. Adults usually travel in pairs and are found in depths of about 10 to 20 m, but may venture into deep water. Identified by a broad black band over the head and along dorsal fin base. It is the largest butterflyfish and often noticed because of its size. Indo-Pacific. Length usually to 30 cm, reported to 45 cm.

Double-saddle Butterflyfish

Chaetodon falcula

Occupies various habitats from lagoons to outer reef walls to 20 m. Adults form pairs, usually seen swimming low on reefs. Juveniles are solitary and secretive in reefs. Diet consists of various invertebrates, including anemones and coral polyps. Easily identified by double black saddle-mark over its back. An Indian Ocean species, replaced by the similar *C. ulietensis* in the West Pacific. Length to 18 cm.

Threadfin Butterflyfish
Chaetodon auriga

Inhabits lagoons and inner reefs often over sand and feeds on various invertebrates, including tubed or free roaming worms. Adults usually occur in pairs, and juveniles travel solitary. Readily identified by areas of diagonal dark lines running in opposite ways over the body that end in yellow chevron markings. Adults develop a long trailing filament from the dorsal fin. Widespread Indo-Pacific. Length to 24 cm.

Vagabond Butterflyfish
Chaetodon vagabundus

Occupies various habitats and has a broad diet range. Rare in the Maldives, usually seen in pairs. Identified by the black banding over the eye, the back of the body and over the tail fin. The dorsal and anal fins end in yellow, which distinguish this species from the similar *C. decussatus* (next species). Widespread Indo-Pacific. Length to 20 cm.

Blackened Butterflyfish
Chaetodon decussatus

Sometimes called Indian Vagabond Butterflyfish; readily identified by the large black area covering most of the back part of the dorsal fin and continuing down to the end of the anal fin. Uncommon in the Maldives, mainly seen on shipwrecks and usually in pairs; common in shallow continental coastal waters. Indian Ocean, ranging east to Flores, Indonesia. Length to 20 cm.

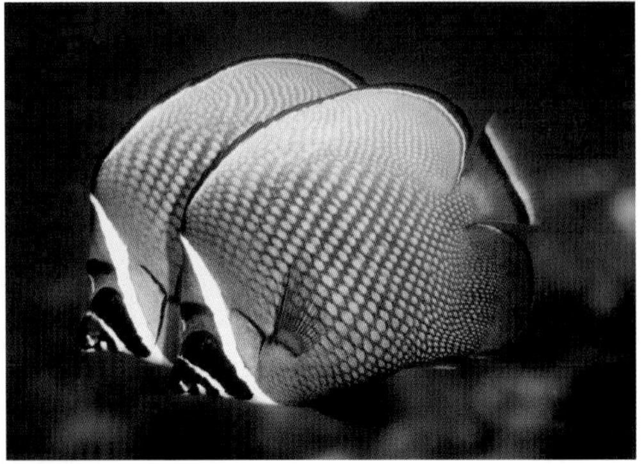

Head-band Butterflyfish
Chaetodon collare

Common in the Maldives and occurs in most habitats to depths of at least 35 m. A schooling species that also forms pairs at times, probably when preparing to spawn. Large schools often congregate on shallow reefs at about 6 m depth. Readily identified by its dusky colour, red tail fin and brilliant white bar behind the eye. An Indian Ocean species, ranging east to Bali where it is rare. Length is to 18 cm.

Triangular Butterflyfish
Chaetodon triangulum

Occurs mainly on shallow inner reefs with good coral growth but ventures to depths of about 25 m along walls. A common species in the Maldives, adults are usually seen in pairs picking on corals, and juveniles among coral branches. Identified by its deep body and black tail fin. An Indian Ocean species, replaced by the nearly identical *C. baronessa* in the Pacific, with both species occurring in Java, Indonesia. Length to 16 cm.

Yellow-head Butterflyfish
Chaetodon xanthocephalus

Occurs on reefs with good coral growth, usually shallow to about 20 m depth. Adults travel singularly or in pairs, while juveniles occupy shallow protected reef flats in silty lagoons. Feeds on invertebrates and algae. Adults identified by a rich yellow snout and distinctive colouration on dorsal and anal fins. Closely related to *C. ephippium* and hybrids are reported where the two species occur together. West Indian Ocean only. Length to 20 cm.

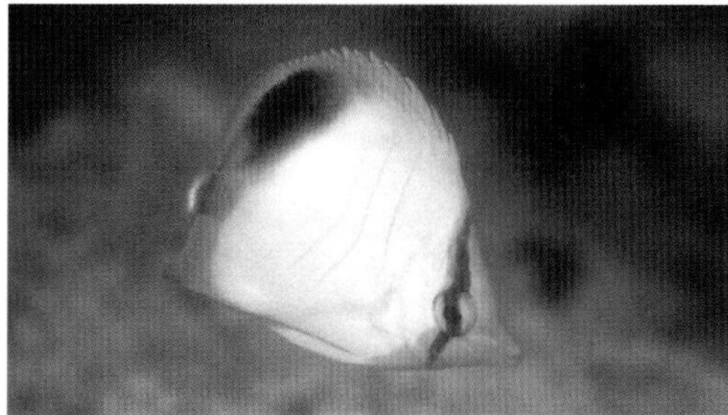

Meyer's Butterflyfish
Chaetodon meyeri

Mainly found on reef crests near outer reef walls, to depths of about 15 m. Adults swim in pairs and appear to be very territorial, which often results in fights in areas where common. A coral nibbler, that swims on rich coral growth reefs. Juveniles are solitary and secretive among the corals. Easily identified by the purplish body and thick diagonal black stripes. Widespread Indo-Pacific, common in the Maldives. Length to 20 cm.

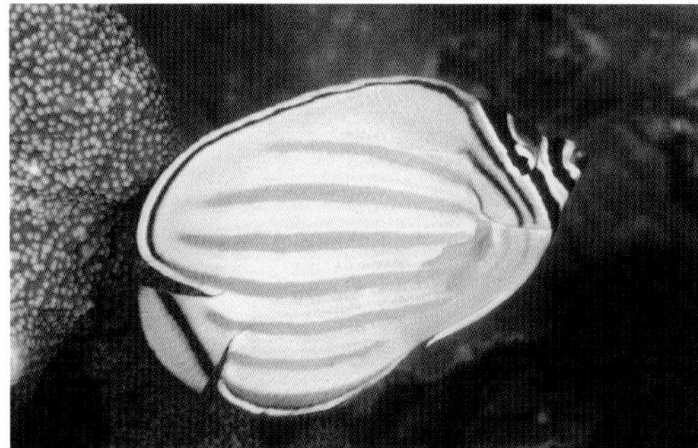

Ornate Butterflyfish
Chaetodon ornatissimus

Very rare in Maldives and only reported from a few reliable sightings. Generally common elsewhere in the Indo-Pacific, where it pairs and lives in rich coral growth areas to depths of about 20 m. Distinguished by brown-orange diagonal stripes. Length to 20 cm.

Madagascar Butterflyfish
Chaetodon madagaskariensis

Adults occur singly or in pairs, usually in moderate depths along outer reef walls to at least 50 m. Feeds on a great variety of small mobile invertebrates. Easily identified by the orange band over the ends of its dorsal and anal fins and the chevron lines on its body. One of a complex of several similar species and closely related to *C. mertensii* from the Pacific, but appears to be restricted to the west Indian Ocean. Length to 12 cm.

Indian Butterflyfish
Chaetodon mitratus

Occurs in depths below 50 m, either singly or in pairs. Rarely shallower, therefore not often seen by most divers using compressed air. Feeds on a variety of small mobile invertebrates. Readily recognised by the broad black diagonal bands running from the back and over the eye. Belongs to a complex of similar species of the Indo-Pacific that typically live in depths near the 100 m mark. Length to 12 cm.

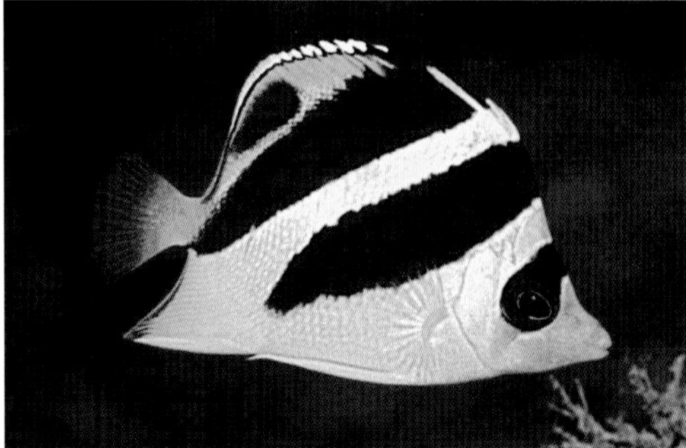

Long-nose Butterflyfish
Forcipiger flavissimus

Found on shallow inner reef to the upper part of outer reef walls to depths of about 30 m. Nearly always seen in pairs when adult. Picks tiny mobile invertebrates from narrow crevices on reefs and may pick on urchins. Very similar to the next species but snout is shorter and lacks the fine dark spotting in the white chest area. Widespread Indo-Pacific. Length to 22 cm.

Very-long-nose Butterflyfish
Forcipiger longirostris

Similar appearance and behaviour to the previous species, but has a longer snout and prefers deeper water. The length of snout is variable, but usually proportionally longer. Best distinguished by the fine black spots on its chest near the pectoral fins. Widespread Indo-Pacific. Length is to 22 cm.

Phantom Bannerfish
Heniochus pleurotaenia

Occupies shallow reefs to about 30 m depth. Adults form large schools in the Maldives, but in other parts of the Indian Ocean usually seen in pairs, ranging east to Java. Adults lack a banner, the distinctive dorsal spine that characterizes the genus, which is short in juveniles. Identified by its mostly brown and black colouration. Replaced by similar *H. varius* in the West Pacific, although both occur in Java, where the author observed a mixed pair of the species. Length to 17 cm.

Reef Bannerfish
Heniochus acuminatus

Found singly or in pairs but appears to be uncommon in the Maldives, where mainly found in depths of 20+ metres. Elsewhere often found on shallow reefs, ranging to at least 50 m depth. Juveniles are coastal and found in protected bays. They have a broad diet. Distinguished from Schooling Bannerfish by slightly longer anal fin and longer snout. Widespread Indo-Pacific. Length to 25 cm.

Singular Bannerfish
Heniochus singularius

Prefers rich coral growth areas and can be seen in various habitats from shallow reef crests to deep walls. Normally swims in pairs when adult, but is rather rare in the Maldives and often seen singly. Juveniles are usually found on protected inshore reefs. More elongate than other bannerfish and has a short banner. Widespread Indo-Pacific. Length to 30 cm, the largest of the bannerfishes.

Masked Bannerfish
Heniochus monoceros

Often found in caves along deep walls and slopes, in shallow waters to at least 50 m depth. Adults usually occur in pairs and feed on a mixed invertebrate and algae diet. Adults are best identified by the single black band that extends vertically from the ventral fins and belly to behind the start of the short white banner. Widespread Indo-Pacific. Length to 23 cm.

Schooling Bannerfish
Heniochus diphreutes

In the Maldives, this is a common schooling fish and is found in shallow lagoons to deep reef walls, venturing well beyond divers limits. Feeds primarily on plankton. Juveniles clean other fish from parasites, whilst adults will clean on occasions. Has a very short snout and the anal fin is shorter and more angular-shaped compared to Reef Bannerfish. Widespread Indo-Pacific. Length to 20 cm.

ANGELFISHES
POMACANTHIDAE

A large family with seven genera and over 80 species, of which at least 14 are known from the Maldives. Some are very rare and more discoveries can be expected. Small species are secretive and easily overlooked. They differ from the closely related butterflyfishes in having a clearly visible spine on the lower corner of the gill plates. The large *Pomacanthus* species have juvenile stages that are similar to each other: black with many white lines on the body and electric blue in the fins. They change at almost half adult size and take on the completely different colouration of the adult forms. This change occurs rather quickly and changing forms are rarely seen. The small *Centropyge* species show little change with growth and generally become more colourful when adult. Most species feed on mixed algae and invertebrates. Some prefer algae, especially when juvenile, and others may specialise on sponges. Only *Genicanthus* are plankton feeders. Eggs and larvae are pelagic for several weeks, and post-larvae settle in specific habitats that relate to diet. Most species live shallow and some species range to about 50 m.

Regal Angelfish
Pygoplites diacanthus

Also called Empress Angelfish in the Maldives. Common on Maldives reefs and although mostly seen solitary, usually occurs in loose groups. Small juveniles live secretively in caves. They feed primarily on sponges and are found on most reefs from shallow crests to almost 80 m. Identified by alternating dark-edged white and orange crossbars. Widespread in the Indo-Pacific, but there are two forms between the Indian and Pacific Oceans. The difference is noticeable in the colour of their heads: grey in the Pacific and orange in the Indian Ocean. Length is to 25 cm.

Three-spot Angelfish
Apolemichthys trimaculatus

Adults occur solitary or in small groups on reef crests and slopes to about 30 m depth, but mostly inhabit shallow depths in the Maldives. Small juveniles are usually seen on deep slopes. Adults readily identified by their bright yellow colour, black spot on the forehead, broad black margin on the anal fin and blue lips. Small juveniles are all yellow with a black line over the head and a distinctive black spot towards the back. They feed on ascidians, sponges and algae. Widespread Indo-Pacific. Length to 26 cm.

Photo, small juvenile: Mabul, Malaysia.

Smoke Angelfish
Apolemichthys xanthurus

Also called Yellowtail Angelfish, but this name also applies to several other angelfishes. Adults usually seen in pairs when deep, but singly in shallower parts of its depth range, where less common. Seems to prefer depths over 30 m with open flat reef and low ledges with sponge and soft coral growth. Recognised by the blackened fins, followed by the yellow tail. Restricted to western Indian Ocean. Length to 15 cm.

Hybrid Angelfish
Apolemichthys xanthurus x trimaculatus

Formerly known as *A. armitagei*, this fish is a natural hybrid that occurs in places where the two parent species co-exist. Varies in colour, looking more or less like one of the parent species. Usually seen solitary in depths of about 20 to 30 m and is moderately common in the Maldives. Most specimens seen by the author were about 20 cm long.

Blue-face Angelfish
Pomacanthus xanthometopon

This large beautiful fish is easily approached in the Maldives. Normally seen singly along reefs with caves in shallows, as well as along deep walls. Adults recognised by their obvious colours and yellow 'mask' covering the eyes. Juveniles, although rarely seen, are similar to other juveniles in the genus, except vertical lines are almost straight. Widespread Indo-Pacific. Length to 36 cm.

Emperor Angelfish
Pomacanthus imperator

Also known as Imperial Angelfish. Common in the Maldives. Both adult and juvenile seen solitary at various depths, but juveniles usually deep in caves or large sponges. Feeds on various invertebrates, including sponges and juveniles pick parasites from other fishes in cleaning stations with shrimps. Juveniles identified by circling patterns. Widespread Indo-Pacific, but the west Pacific fish developed trailing filament on dorsal fin. Length to 38 cm.

Half-circled Angelfish
Pomacanthus semicirculatus

Rare in the Maldives. Post-larvae usually settle in very shallow depths on rocky reef with good algae growth. Adults prefer outer reef walls and are often seen on shipwrecks in depths over 30 m. Juveniles Identified by their semi-circle vertical lines over the body. Widespread Indo-Pacific. Length to 35 cm.

Blue-ringed Angelfish
Pomacanthus annularis

Included here on the basis of a sight record by Herwarth Voigtmann. The adult was seen in deep water. Common in mainland waters and often found on silty reefs. Juveniles in very shallow depths, often on jetty pylons. Distinguished by diagonal blue bands on side, circular blue ring above the gill cover and a white tail. Length to 45 cm.

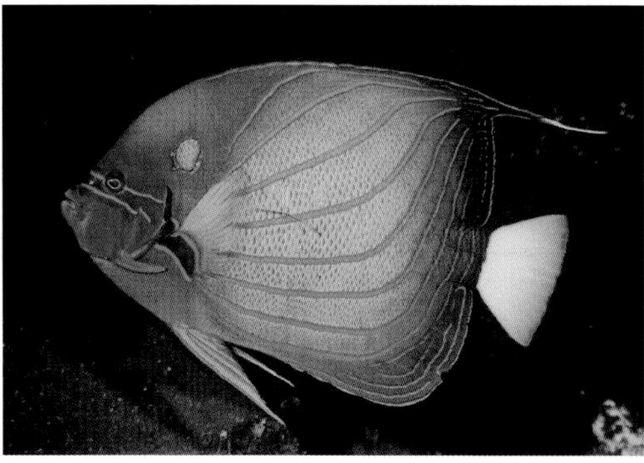

Many-spined Angelfish
Centropyge multispinis

Occurs in silty and shallow lagoons on coral bommies as well as deep along outer reef walls. Often swims in small groups when feeding on algae. A dark looking species showing little colour other than electric blue margins on the fins. The most common small angelfish species in the Maldives. Widespread and common in the Indian Ocean. Length to 14 cm. Seen in lagoons, but usually to about 10 cm.

Moonbeam Angelfish
Centropyge flavipectoralis

In the Maldives, this species was observed between 20 and 40 m on mixed rubble-sand reef with sparse sponge and soft coral growth. Adults singly or in small groups. Easily overlooked because of its similarity to the previous common species. Best recognised by the yellow pectoral fins on the sides. Indian Ocean. Length to 10 cm.

Coral Beauty
Centropyge bispinosa

Rare in the Maldives, occasionally collected by aquarists. Elsewhere, lives in a great depth range, from shallow rich coral lagoons to deep drop-offs to at least 60 m depth. Varies in colour, often more orange in deep water and more blue in shallows, but generally looks blue in natural light. Widespread Indo-Pacific. Length to 10 cm.

Eibl's Angelfish
Centropyge eibli

Rare in the Maldives, occasionally collected by aquarists. Inhabits shallow reefs with soft coral and hydroid growth to a depth of about 25 m. Appearance is variable, mainly light grey with thin vertical lines and a dusky to black tail. Sometimes has orange markings on the head or below its vertical lines and on the anal fin and. Indian Ocean only, ranging east to Bali. Replaced by similar *C. vroliki* in the Pacific. The two species occur together in some areas where they commonly produce hybrids. Length to 10 cm.

Indian Cherup Angelfish
Centropyge acanthops

Rare in the Maldives, sought after and occasionally collected by aquarists. Occurs on coral rich reefs where seen feeding on algae along the bases. Readily identified by the bright orange head and back, and blue below. Reported from depths between 10 and 40 m. Restricted to western Indian Ocean. Length to 8 cm.

Damsel Angelfish
Centropyge flavicauda

Rare in the Maldives, but easily overlooked and is usually mistaken for a White-tailed Damselfish. Occurs on rubble zones at the base of reefs, usually in 10-20 m depth but reported to 60 m. Feeds primarily on algae and settling invertebrate growth. Young are dark brown to black, adults with a bluish sheen and the tail is usually whitish. Widespread Indo-Pacific. Length to 8 cm.

Lyre-tail Angelfish
Genicanthus caudovittatus

Observed on deep outer reef walls, usually in 40+ m depth. Occurs in invertebrate-rich habitats, such as in caves or ridges at the base of drop-offs. Feeds on zooplankton, as well as benthic invertebrates. Seen in small loose groups of females with a single male. Males have a barred body-pattern. West Indian Ocean and Red Sea. Length to 20 cm.

BATFISHES
EPHIPPIDAE

A small family with five genera and about 10 species, of which three species from the genus *Platax* occur in the Maldives. Juveniles are extremely tall finned and gradually change with growth to an almost round, profiled fish. Small juveniles are pelagic and float with land debris, such as leaves, near the surface or with sargassum weeds during the wet season. They form small groups and often settle in harbours under jetties. Adults can be solitary or in groups and prefer deep water, but enter shallow water to feed. Diet comprises bottom invertebrates and zooplankton and they are sometimes seen nibbling jellies.

Rounded Batfish
Platax orbicularis

Adults usually solitary but sometimes school. Juveniles generally in small groups near bottom. Pelagic juveniles mimic browned tree leaves. Juveniles best recognised by two dark spots opposite each other on the tail, at the end of the body fins. The adult has yellowish pectoral fins on the sides. Widespread Indo-Pacific. Length to 50 cm.

Tall-fin Batfish

Platax teira

Also known as Longfin Batfish. Adults solitary or in small groups. Best recognised by a black blotch on the side below pectoral fin, which is part of the broad dark side band, and a short dark bar on the anus that is usually visible but may fade in adults. Tiny juveniles have very long dorsal, anal and ventral fins and float below surface debris, forming groups when they find each other. They often settle under jetties and swim mid water. Widespread Indo-Pacific. Length to 60 cm.

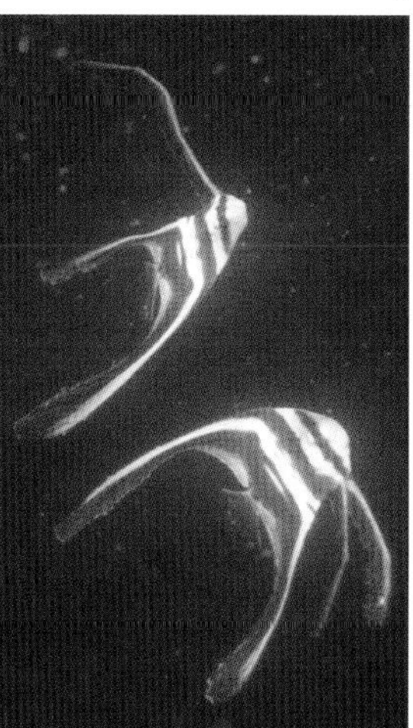

Boer's Batfish

Platax boersii

Only recently recognised as a valid species and previously confused with others. A semi-adult specimen was observed at close range by the author. Adult is very similar to the Rounded Batfish and juvenile is similar to the Tall-fin Batfish. As an adult, Boer's Batfish has a very short mouth and appears to be flat-faced, whilst juvenile identified by the tall but somewhat triangularly vertical fins. Appears to be widespread Indo-Pacific. Length to at least 50 cm.

HAWKFISHES
CIRRHITIDAE

A moderately large family with nine genera and 35 species, mainly Indo-Pacific (only three are known from the Atlantic), of which six genera and eight species are known from the Maldives. Hawkfishes vary in shape from compressed and high bodied, to stocky or elongate. They are best recognised by the little filamentous tufts attached to the tip of each spine in the dorsal fin. They are carnivores that perch themselves on corals to watch out for small prey such as shrimps or juvenile fishes. The various species live on reef crests, surge zones, deep current-channels or in black corals. Some are territorial, while others form small groups.

Longnose Hawkfish
Oxycirrhites typus

Usually seen individually amongst black coral bushes, but often occur in pairs. Rests on sponges or large fan corals, and feeds on small creatures and floating plankton. Easily recognised by the elongated snout and colouration. Moderately common between 15 and 35 m in the Maldives. Widespread Indo-Pacific. Length to 10 cm.

Spotted Hawkfish
Cirrhitichthys oxycephalus

Very common in the Maldives, occurs almost anywhere on reefs from shallow lagoons to deep along walls. Usually rests on top of small coral heads. Colour is variable, from purple-brown to bright red with depth. Identified by the uniformly blotched pattern and small spots in the tail fin. Widespread Indo-Pacific. Length to 9 cm.

Coral Hawkfish
Cirrhitichthys falco

Uncommon in the Maldives, but common in most other parts of the Indo-Pacific in clear water reefs on crests and slopes to 45 m depth. Identified by a series of red-brown saddles tapered ventrally, mostly red spots on its near-white body, and the large spots in the tail fin. Length is to 65 mm.

Blotched Hawkfish
Cirrhitichthys aprinus

Rare in the Maldives, primarily a mainland species of coastal waters and harbours. Sometimes occurs in deep water with sponges. Could be mistaken for the Spotted Hawkfish that has a similar but smaller spotted body pattern with spots on the tail; whereas the tail is plain in the Blotched Hawkfish. Widespread tropical Indo-Pacific. Length to 12 cm, usually to 9 cm.

Two-spot Hawkfish
Amblycirrhites bimacula

Uncommon but secretive that could easily be overlooked. Typically lives inside reefs in holes that are dark or shaded, usually shallow surge zones to about 15 m depth. Has a blotched pattern but lacks spots in the fins. A dark eye-size spot on the gill behind the eye and a second one below the soft dorsal fin, identify it. Widespread Indo-Pacific. Length is to 75 mm.

Lyre-tail Hawkfish
Cyprinocirrhites polyactis

Uncommon in the Maldives. Lives in current prone channels and rises above the ocean bottom to feed on plankton. Unlike other hawkfish, it has a lyre-tail, which serves it better for swimming in currents. Sometimes mistaken for a basslet that also feeds the same way. Usually rests on sponges or coralline algae bommies in depths from 10 to 50 m. Length is to 65 mm, excluding the filaments on its tail.

Ring-eye Hawkfish
Paracirrhites arcatus

Also called Horseshoe Hawkfish. Adults occur singly, sometimes in pairs, in small coral heads on exposed, upper reef slopes. Recognised by an elliptical ring extending from behind the eye, three orange streaks on the lower edge of the gill cover and a white streak on the sides. The main body colour ranges from light green to bright red. Widespread Indo-Pacific. Length to 14 cm.

Forster's Hawkfish
Paracirrhites forsteri

Also known as Freckled Hawkfish. A common Maldives species that has several colour variations. Best identified by the numerous dark spots on the head. Occupies reef crests and slopes, usually shallow to about 20 m depth, but may venture deeper. Widespread Indo-Pacific. Length is to 20 cm.

White-spotted Hawkfish
Cirrhitus pinnulatus

Also known as Stocky Hawkfish as it has a much lower and less compressed body. Probably common in the Maldives, but typically lives in very shallow surge zones (to 6 m) where it clings to the reef in currents where few divers or snorkellers are able to go, unless conditions allow. Feeds on various small creatures and has a blenny-like appearance. Best recognised by the series of white blotches that may appear yellow under water. Widespread Indo-Pacific. Length to 25 cm.

DAMSELFISHES
POMACENTRIDAE

A very large family with an estimated 30 genera and 300 species globally, most of which are tropical but some can be found in sub-tropical to warm-temperate seas. They are well represented in the Maldives with about 50 species presently known, and more can be expected. They are dividable into several groups and are treated here as such.

ANEMONEFISHES
POMACENTRIDAE-1

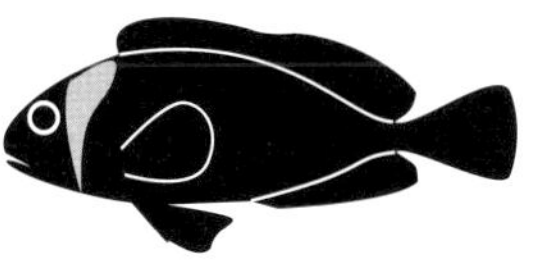

Anemonefishes are specialised damselfishes that have adapted to living in a symbiotic relationship with anemones, to such extent that they are rarely seen away from their host. There are about 30 species, all except one in the genus *Amphiprion*. Three species are known from the Maldives but anemonefishes can be found throughout most of the Indo-Pacific region. Of the 1000 or so anemone species, only ten play host to these fishes. The greatest diversity of the family is found in the New Guinea region. Each fish species has a preference for particular anemones but some are fussier than others and may live in several species depending on their availability and habitat. The anemone does not sting the fish as it recognises it as being part of itself. Anemonefishes feed on food drifting past and their diet comprises zooplankton; however, they may also occasionally feed on algae growing around coral bases nearby.

Blackfoot Anemonefish
Amphiprion nigripes

The Maldives own anemonefish, not known from anywhere else except nearby Sri Lanka. A common species easily recognised by the single white bar over the head and black lower fins. Only known in one host anemone, *Heteractis magnifica*. Occupies reef crests and slopes to depths of about 15 m. Length to 10 cm.

Photo below left by Peter Craig, showing black lower fins; right, freshly laid eggs on coral rubble.

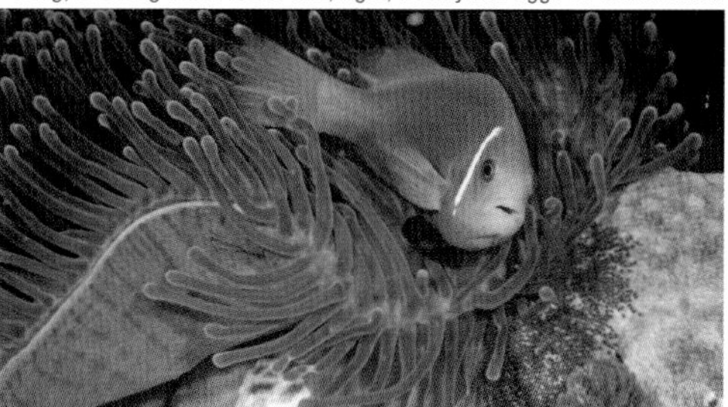

Yellow-tail Anemonefish
Amphiprion sebae

Usually occurs at moderate depths in the Maldives on sand and rubble flats in clear water to 35 m depth. Recognised by the long all yellow tail. Lives in host anemone *Stichodactyla haddoni*. Widespread on mainland reefs along northern Indian Ocean, ranging to Java, Indonesia. Length to 14 cm.

Clark's Anemonefish
Amphiprion clarkii

Common in most reef habitats. Highly variable in colour, depending on the geographical area and host anemone. The only species known to live with all host anemones. In the Maldives, Clark's Anemonefish is typically coloured as shown in the photographs below. Distinguished from previous species by more narrow white bars. Widespread Indo-Pacific. Length to 14 cm.

HUMBUGS
POMACENTRIDAE-2

All belong in a small genus with nine species, three of which are found in the Maldives. They are stocky small species, many of which are broadly banded, hence the name Humbug. They often occur in schools amongst corals and some juveniles live in or near tentacles of anemones and amongst the long spines of urchins.

Humbug Damsel
Dascyllus aruanus

A common species in lagoons among various branching corals. Adults often found among staghorn coral, while juveniles among *Acropora* coral heads, which provide more shelter for small fish. Feeds on zooplankton in loose schools above corals during currents. Easily identified by the black and white banding. A similar species *D. melanurus*, has a black tail but is not known from the Maldives. Widespread Indo-Pacific. Length to 8 cm.

Indian Humbug
Dascyllus carneus

Forms small schools around branching *Acropora* coral heads on sheltered reefs, from a few metres depth to almost 30 m. Feeds on zooplankton above corals and will quickly dive amongst the coral branches at any sign of danger. Identified by an almost white body and the single dark band over its head. Widespread Indian Ocean, east to Java, Indonesia, replaced by sibling *D. reticulatus* in the Pacific. Length to 6 cm.

Three-spot Humbug
Dascyllus trimaculatus

Commonly found in most reef habitats, mainly on shallow reef crests and slopes with tall coral growth to 20 m depth. Juveniles have three large white spots and often group together in large anemones. A white spot on the forehead and a similar spot on each side of the body that gradually fades with age distinguish adults. Readily identified by the black colour. Widespread Indo-Pacific. Length to 12 cm.

PULLERS
POMACENTRIDAE-3

A single large genus *Chromis* with over 80 species, many of which were only recently discovered and at least 13 of these species occur in the Maldives. Most are schooling species that live on shallow reef crests, slopes and walls where the current carries zooplankton, either from oceanic or lagoon origins. Some live in very deep water only.

Green Puller
Chromis viridis

Usually occurs in large schools where lagoon currents run across reefs, in particular on crests, which have very large colonies of dense branching corals that can accommodate numerous individuals. Mainly occupies inner reefs to about 10 m depth. Colour is a plain light green, although males turn a golden-yellow shade when nesting. Widespread and common throughout Indo-Pacific. Length to 8 cm.

Blue-green Puller
Chromis atripectoralis

Often overlooked because of its similarity to the Green Puller, but is much less common in the Maldives. Distinguished by the black spot at the base of the pectoral fins. Occurs inshore on reef slopes, usually in loose groups, to depths of about 20 m. Widespread Indo-Pacific. Length to 10 cm.

Swallow-tail Puller
Chromis ternatensis

One of the most common pullers in the Maldives, often forming large schools that fill the water column above reefs when feeding on zooplankton. Occurs in most reef habitats with branching corals exposed to currents, to about 25 m depth. Has a plain body, which is yellowish in the Maldives, and strong black margins along outer rays and on upper and lower margins on the tail. Widespread Indo-Pacific, although there are some colour variations. Length to 10 cm.

Buff Puller
Chromis xutha

Seen singly or in small loose groups along drop-offs in or near caves. Feeds on zooplankton close to reefs and mainly lives in clear water habitats to about 30 m depth. Plain light brown in colour, with long filaments on the tail when adult. Only known from the western Indian Ocean. Length to 75 mm.

Pemba Puller
Chromis pembae

Occurs in outer reef habitats, usually in depths between 20 and 50 m. Seen singly or in small, scattered groups and feeds on zooplankton. Variable dark brown to yellow colour and identified by the yellow marginal band in its spinous dorsal fin and white ventral fins. West Indian Ocean and Red Sea. Length to 75 mm.

Two-tone Puller
Chromis dimidiata

Occurs in clear water habitats from 5 to 30 m depth, usually at about 10 m in small caves or crevices. Usually seen singly in reefs and stays close to the ocean bottom. Easily recognised by its partly black body and white tail colouration. Widespread Indian Ocean, ranging to southern Java, Indonesia. Length to 7 cm.

White-finned Puller
Chromis flavipectoralis

Occurs in clear lagoons and inner reefs on walls and reef slopes with rich coral growth. Usually seen solitary and adults in moderate depths along walls in 20+ m. Juveniles found shallow in rich coral areas. Identified by the white ventral fins. Only known from Maldives to Java, Indonesia, reported from shallow depths, outside Maldives. Length to 8 cm.

Deep-reef Puller
Chromis delta

Seen in clear water reefs, mainly in caves along inner and outer reef walls, from 15 to 40 m depth, although reported to 80 m. Occurs in small loose groups, staying close to the bottom. Common where found. Identified by dark grey body, abruptly changing to white at the tail base, and long double filaments at tips of fin. Widespread Indo-Pacific. Length to 7 cm.

Twin-spot Puller
Chromis elerae

Moderately common on steep reef walls, in coastal to outer reefs where large caves with rich invertebrate growth are available. Often swims upside down near the ceilings of large overhangs in small loose groups. Usually found deep from 20 m down. Identified by its generally dark grey colour and the pale twin spots on the tail base. Widespread Indo-Pacific. Length to 65 mm.

Scaly Puller
Chromis lepidolepis

Species is rarely noticed because of its lack of colour or distinctive pattern. Inhabits reef crests and slopes on inner and outer reefs, usually solitary or in small loose groups, to about 20 m depth. Mainly light greenish grey colour and its only distinguishing feature is a vertical black bar in its eye. Widespread Indo-Pacific. Length is to 8 cm.

Double-bar Puller
Chromis opercularis

Inhabits inshore reef crests to depths of about 10 m, while on outer reefs, more shallow. Prefers current prone reefs and feeds high above the bottom on zooplankton. Widespread Indo-Pacific but numerous geographical variations that often look like completely different species. This photograph shows the typical Maldives fish. Length to 12 cm.

Weber's Puller
Chromis weberi

Occurs on inner reef crests and slopes to depths of about 25 m. A common but dull species not often noticed. Mainly a plain greenish grey colour and sometimes has yellowish sides. Best identified by the double dark bar on the head and dark tips on the tail fin. Widespread Indo-Pacific. Length to 10 cm.

Black-fin Puller
Chromis nigroanalis

Usually seen solitary in moderate depths along outer reef walls between 20 and 40 m. A deep-bodied, bluish grey species named for the large black area on the anal fin. Widespread Indian Ocean, ranging to Java, but generally rare. Length to 11 cm.

Black-edged Puller
Chromis nigrura

A moderately common but small species, found on reef crests with rich coral growth, and often on outer reefs with moderate surge down to about 30 m depth. Recognised by the yellow tail and dark blue-black anal fin. Widespread Indian Ocean, mainly oceanic locations and not yet known from Indonesia. Length to 55 mm.

DAMSELS
POMACENTRIDAE-4

This group comprises the species generally called damsels. The genus *Pomacentrus* is the largest with 53 species distributed throughout the Indo-Pacific; six of which are found in the Maldives. The genus *Neopomacentrus* comprises 13 species and only one is recorded from the Maldives. The genus *Amblypomacentrus* was thought to contain only one species, but recently a new species was found in the Maldives. The genus *Chrysiptera* has 25 species, of which four are found in the Maldives. Most of these species associate with coral reefs and stay close to the bottom.

Blue-yellow Damsel
Pomacentrus caeruleus

Common in the Maldives, and readily noticed by the bright blue colour of its body and yellow lower fins and tail. Occurs in small groups on shallow, clear water reef crests with mixed rubble and good coral growth. Appears to be restricted to western Indian Ocean, replaced by a similar species in the east Indian and Pacific Oceans. Length to 8 cm.

Azure Damsel
Pomacentrus pavo

Common on large remote bommies on sand in deep lagoons. Forms small to large aggregations and darts in and out of holes. Colour is highly variable and ranges from pale green to bright blue. Often an ear spot shows, either dark or reflective green. Widespread and generally common in coastal habitats of the Indo-Pacific. Length to 10 cm.

Scribbled Damsel
Pomacentrus nagasakiensis

Although moderately common in the Maldives, this species seems to have been overlooked until now. These photographs represent the first records for the Maldives and Indian Ocean. Generally occurs deep on sand flats over 20 m, but commonly found around remote coral heads in those habitats. Identified by black pectoral fin base and ocellus on rear part of dorsal fin. Formerly, only known from the West Pacific between Japan and Australia, but now seems widespread. Length to 10 cm.

Indian Damsel
Pomacentrus indicus

Common in the Maldives, and juvenile usually noted for the bright orange colour over the top of its body. This marking gradually reduces with size and adults are typically dull coloured. Found from shallow inshore to outer reef habitats and adults ranging to deep water to 40 m depth. Distributed throughout central Indian Ocean. Length to 11 cm.

Philippine Damsel
Pomacentrus philippinus

Moderately common in clear inner and outer reef channels and along drop-offs with caves and overhangs, usually in depths between 10 and 40 m. Most often seen solitary and easily recognised by the bright yellow tail, the typical form in the Maldives. Widespread west Pacific, ranging west to the Maldives. Length to 10 cm.

White-tail Damsel
Pomacentrus chrysurus

Inhabits shallow reef crests and slopes and in the Maldives, usually found on outer reef flats with moderate surge in 6 to 15 m depth. Juveniles have orange over the head and part of its body. Adult has a prominent white tail, not always evident in juveniles. Widespread west Pacific, ranging west to the Maldives. Length to 9 cm.

Regal Damsel
Neopomacentrus cyanomos

A common continental species, which usually occurs in coastal, reef habitats. Mainly grey with a distinctive, small white spot at the end of the dorsal fin base. The spot is less obvious in large individuals, which develop long angular to filamentous lobes at the ends of the dorsal, anal and tail fins. Widespread Indo-Pacific, some geographical variations. Length to 10 cm.

Lyretail Damsel
Amblypomacentrus breviceps

Common in silty lagoons at about 35 m depth, where photographed. Seen on the open bottom with rubbish used for refuge and nesting, as is typical for the genus. A new discovery for the Maldives and the photograph included here represents the first record for the species, which was thought to be restricted to the west Pacific. Length to 10 cm, which includes the filamentous parts on the tail.

White-saddled Damsel
Chrysiptera biocellata

A common species in the Maldives found on shallow inshore waters, still lagoons and harbours, often on silty reefs with lots of coral rubble, and in seagrass areas with rubble patches. Rarely found deeper than 5 m. Identified by the white bar, which is slightly forward from the centre of body. Widespread Indo-Pacific, but some geographical variations. Length to 11 cm.

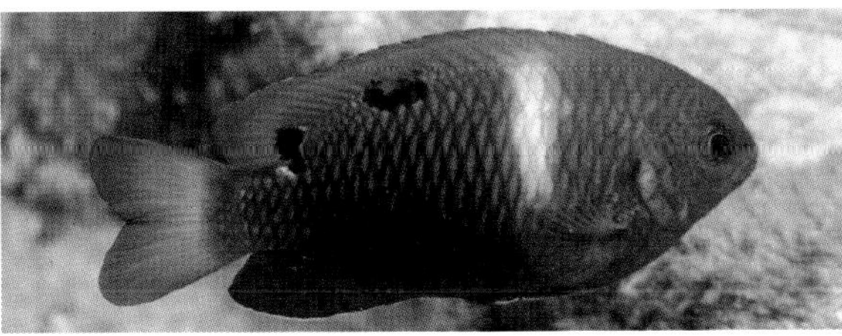

Surge Damsel
Chrysiptera brownriggii

As the name suggests, this fish is common on surge reefs. Found mainly on outer reef flats with channels and good algae growth, less common where coral becomes prolific. There are two distinctive colour forms, which look like two different species, but are probably sex related; one is dull with white bands, the other has a bright blue band along the top of its body. Widespread Indian Ocean. Replaced by similar *C. leucopoma* in the West Pacific. Length to 8 cm.

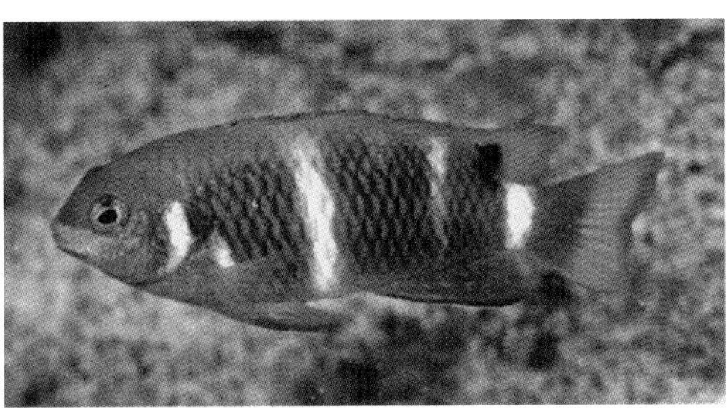

One-spot Damsel
Chrysiptera unimaculata

Inhabits shallow inshore reefs and harbours. A territorial species that occurs in large numbers and spread out over preferred habitats, such as dead coral pieces used along break waters in harbours. Usually has a black spot at base of the last few dorsal rays. In the Maldives, recognised by the yellow pectoral fins. Widespread Indo-Pacific, but one of the most variable damsels with so many geographical forms; it seems like several different species are involved. Length to 85 mm.

Pale-blue Damsel
Chrysiptera glauca

Mainly occurs in intertidal zones and often seen in silty habitats, rarely deeper than a few metres. Has a patchy occurrence in the Maldives, but is common where found. Adults identified by a plain blue-grey colour. Juveniles are brighter blue and have a thin iridescent blue line along upper sides from behind the eye to below the dorsal fin. Widespread Indo-Pacific. Length to 10 cm.

Fusilier Damsel
Lepidozygus tapeinosoma

The single species in this genus is commonly found in lagoons and inner reefs in the Maldives. Usually occurs in small to large schools around coral heads and feeds on zooplankton, high above the bottom. A slender species with a metallic green body, which changes colour when feeding or when in reefs, and usually darkens when going into holes. Males show a broad white band when guarding eggs. Widespread Indo-Pacific. Length is to 10 cm.

SERGEANTS
POMACENTRIDAE-5

A group of deep-bodied damsels that usually have a broadly banded pattern or several stripes, like those used on shoulder pads in the armed forces to show rank, hence the common name, Sergeant. Some species occur abundantly in their favourite habitat, while others prefer small groups, however all mainly occur inshore. The genus *Abudefduf* comprises 18 species, of which five are recorded from the Maldives, and just one species in the Atlantic. The genus *Amblyglyphidodon* comprises seven species and two of these are known from the Maldives.

Sergeant Major
Abudefduf vaigiensis

Very common in the Maldives, from inshore to inner reefs and often forms large schools in various depths to about 20 m. A community spawner, the eggs are deposited on flat surfaces and guarded by the parents, and usually timed in phase with the full moon. Easily recognised by the colour pattern and five dark bars. Widespread Indo-Pacific. Small juveniles often under floating sargassum weeds and distributed over great distances. Length to 15 cm.

Yellow-tail Sergeant
Abudefduf notatus

Occupies coastal reefs and often seen in freshwater run offs. It schools and can often be seen swimming along reef slopes, well away from reefs. Eggs are deposited inside caves, unlike open surfaces used by other sergeant species. Easily identified by five white bars and yellow tail. Widespread Indo-Pacific. Length to 20 cm.

Nine-band Sergeant
Abudefduf septemfasciatus

A very shallow water species found in sheltered bays with large boulders, rock or concrete structures, such as those used in harbours for breakwaters. Juveniles occur in intertidal zones and in rockpools. There are six bands on the body, one on the tail and two on the head that may not always show. The upper parts of bands are often extra dark, distinguishing it from other similar species. Widespread Indo-Pacific. Length to 20 cm.

Black-spot Sergeant
Abudefduf sordidus

Occupies inshore reefs, rubble and boulder slopes and often around jetties in harbours. Small juveniles often become stranded in pools on low tides. Has broad bands and the pale inter-spaces between bands are much narrower. A black spot on top of the tail base is usually obvious. Widespread Indo-Pacific. Length to 20 cm.

Scissortail Sergeant
Abudefduf sexfasciatus

Doubtfully reported from the Maldives, possibly an expatriate from the mainland in the northern atolls or from a different origin south of the equator, depending on currents. Usually common where found; inshore reef crests with rich soft coral growth. Widespread Indo-Pacific, along continental waters of the Indian Ocean. Length to 15 cm.

White-breasted Sergeant
Amblyglyphidodon leucogaster

Found on inshore to outer reef habitats and usually seen solitary in areas with rich coral growth. Reported to 45 m depth. Widespread Indo-Pacific, but with several geographical variations. In the Maldives, mainly a greenish colour with a dark bar on the cheek. Length to 12 cm.

Green Sergeant
Amblyglyphidodon batunai

A recently described species from Indonesia, commonly found in sandy lagoons with staghorn coral patches to about 10 m depth. Usually occurs in small groups and swims above the corals to feed on zooplankton. Colour is plain greenish and lacks any distinctive features. Length to 15 cm.

FARMER DAMSELS
POMACENTRIDAE-6

This group of damsels is associated, to various degrees, with algae habitats. Some feed on algae as part of their diet, while others promote the growth of algae by devoting most of their time to clearing areas and keeping invaders at bay. The genus *Plectroglyphidodon* comprises nine species restricted to the Indo-Pacific, five of which are found in the Maldives. The genus *Stegastes* has over 30 species globally, of which four are known from the Maldives.

Jewel Damsel
Plectroglyphidodon lacrymatus

Found in various reef habitats with good algae growth, including exposed, shallow outer reef slopes where algae may be dominant. An aggressive and territorial species. Easily recognised by bright blue spots when juvenile, or bright eyes when adult. Common in the Maldives. Widespread Indo-Pacific. Length to 10 cm.

Narrowbar Damsel
Plectroglyphidodon dickii

Inhabits coral reef crests with mixed rich coral and algae growth around coral bases. Often found in surge zones on outer reefs in shallow depths, ranging to about 10 m depth. Sometimes in small loose groups sharing large coral formations. Readily identified by the black bar near the tail, followed by white colour in juveniles and yellow in large adults. Widespread Indo-Pacific. Length to 10 cm.

Johnston's Damsel
Plectroglyphidodon johnstonianus

Inhabits clear water reefs, usually restricted to outer reef slopes but only known from a few sightings in the Maldives. Found on shallow reef crests with rich coral growth, rarely deeper than 10 m. Similar to Narrowbar Damsel but black bar is wider and not defined at the edges, and may also be absent; and generally more yellow with some blue on the head and in eyes. Widespread Indo-Pacific. Length to 9 cm.

White-band Damsel
Plectroglyphidodon leucozonus

Typically found in shallow water, high energy zones and not often observed by divers unless conditions allow. Rarely occurs deeper than 5 m. Mainly brown with a pale band across the body. The band is broad and distinctive in juveniles but narrows with age and sometimes becomes barely visible. Widespread Indo-Pacific. Length to 16 cm.

Sharp-eye Damsel
Plectroglyphidodon imparipennis

Occurs on clear outer reefs on shallow surge slopes, usually in depths less than 3 m. Tail colour varies from plain to bright yellow. The eye is white and has a short vertical black bar. Widespread Indo-Pacific, with several geographical variations. A small species, length to 60 mm.

White-banded Gregory
Stegastes albifasciatus

Uncommon in the Maldives. Found in high surge zones on outer reef slopes in the northernmost atolls, usually in a few metres depth. Generally all dark in colour, but sometimes has a broad pale band, a blue spot on each scale in the dark area, and a distinctive black spot at end of the dorsal fin base that has white in front of it. Widespread Indo-Pacific, but highly variable with several geographical colour forms that seem like other species. Length to 15 cm.

Indian Gregory
Stegastes fasciolatus

An undetermined species, that occurs on algae rich reefs in lagoons and on inner reefs. Indian Ocean form looks quite different from Pacific *S. fasciolatus* as a juvenile and adult. Juveniles have a yellow tail and a black spot heading the dorsal fin. Usually seen solitary and probably occurs throughout the Indian Ocean. Length to about 10 cm.

Blunt-snout Gregory
Stegastes lividus

Commonly occurs in lagoons amongst large staghorn coral patches to 7 m depth. Best recognised by the spot at the tail fin base, which is outlined with iridescent blue, and light coloured chest. Usually seen in small loose groups. Aggressive towards other fishes and even divers while caring for eggs. Widespread Indo-Pacific. Length to 16 cm.

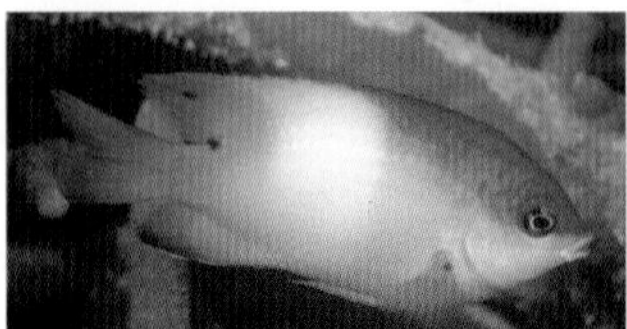

Dusky Gregory
Stegastes nigricans

Prefers inshore areas and silty lagoons or harbours. Usually found in rocky or dead coral reef habitats, and algae reefs to about 10 m depth. Colour is variable, usually plain with a dark spot on the top of its tail. Widespread Indo-Pacific. Length to 14 cm.

BARRACUDAS
SPHYRAENIDAE

This primarily tropical family comprises a single genus with about 20 species globally, of which six are reported from the Maldives, but there are several possible errors. For example, *Sphyraena novaehollandiae* is a temperate Australian species. Predatory fishes, recently reclassified and now placed closely to species such as tunas. Some species school in open water and are occasionally seen near the reef, such as *S. genie*, the Black Tail Barracuda (see Page 4). Some species only visit reefs at night. The most commonly observed species in the Maldives is the Great Barracuda, which is included here.

Great Barracuda
Sphyraena barracuda

Usually seen solitary, swimming along deep slopes and occasionally entering shallow depths. Generally occurs in depths over 10 m and occasionally travels in small groups. Juveniles live in sheltered inshore habitats, including mangroves. Widespread in all tropical seas and in some regions forms large schools. Reported to 100 m depth. Length to 1.9 m.

MULLETS
MUGILIDAE

A large family with about 15 genera and over 70 species globally, three of which are recorded from the Maldives. They are coastal, inshore fishes found in estuaries, harbours and often entering freshwater. Schools are frequently seen on the surface close to shore over shallow sand flats, occasionally dipping down to feed on the sand surface.

Warty-lip Mullet
Crenimugil crenilabis

A schooling species found in sheltered bays and probably the most observed species by divers. They swim at various depths along reefs to about 20 m depth, and feed by scooping the upper layer of sand or mud to filter various food items, including tiny animals and algae. Widespread Indo-Pacific. A large species to a length of 40 cm. Also in the Maldives, is the very similar Bluespot Mullet, *Moolgarda seheli*, which has a deeper forked tail fin and is more estuarine.

Fringe-lip Mullet
Oedalechilus labiosus

In the Maldives, this species is commonly found in small groups within harbours and protected bays that often have silty conditions. They swim near the surface around jetties and rocks and have a rather blunt pointed snout compared to other Maldives species. Widespread Indo-Pacific. Length to 25 cm.

WRASSES
LABRIDAE

One of the largest families of reef fishes as presently defined with more than 60 genera and 400+ species worldwide, of which 27 genera and at least 66 species occur in the Maldives. No doubt more will be discovered over time. Many species undergo tremendous colour changes with growth and changes in sex. Usually each individual starts adulthood as a female and becomes part of a group dominated by a male, which is normally the largest individual. The most dominant female is next in line and changes sex to reign over the rest of the group. Sizes range from a few centimetres to two metres as adults. Although all species are diurnal, the various groups either sleep under sand, in crevices or simply on the bottom. As there are a number of distinctively different groups, based on both looks and behaviour, each is treated here separately with a brief introduction to simplify basic information.

SAND WRASSES
LABRIDAE-1

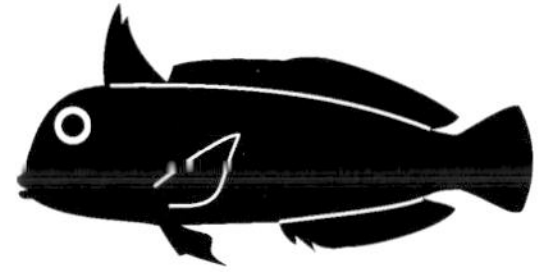

A large number of wrasses are associated with sand, where they bury themselves to escape danger or to sleep. The various species occupy different habitats, ranging from open sand flats to small patches surrounded by reefs. The wrasses, which have adapted to living on open sand flats, are known as razor fishes or knife fishes. They are strongly compressed, thin and have a sharp keel-like forehead that enables them to bury in the sand with speed and ease. Some can swim for a long distance through the sand by vibrating their bodies. Normally, these fishes have a special patch of sand, or sometimes several patches, already prepared for them to bury amongst, in which the coarse and sharp pieces have been removed. Small juveniles are often brightly coloured and look completely different to the adults. Those on sand may be yellow or green, and even have white phases, while those visiting reefs are red or have distinctive patterns of lines and spots. Males can also differ considerably from females. The genera included in this section are a mix from a taxonomic point of view and may belong to several different tribes. The majority of genera are placed in the Julidines and Novaculines, but *Cheilio* is placed on its own in Cheilionines.

Batu Rainbow-wrasse
Hemicoris batuensis

A common lagoon species also found on sheltered sandy reefs, usually in small loose groups. Juveniles occur on algae and rubble patches, or seagrass patches to about 30 m depth. There is little change with growth or between the sexes. Widespread Indo-Pacific, although some geographical variations. Closely related to *H. variegata*, which is Red Sea only. Length to 20 cm.

Queen Rainbow-wrasse
Allocoris formosa

Occurs at moderate depths, adults at about 30 m, often in sand channels between reefs with rubble on the bottom. Juveniles found at shallow depths, usually on sand patches. The large male is solitary and has a large territory, which it defends against neighbouring males. They feed on various small creatures, often caught by turning over pieces of rubble with their snout.. West Indian Ocean, moderately common in the Maldives. Length to 50 cm.

Photo below right, male.

African Rainbow-wrasse
Allocoris cuvieri

Adults in small loose groups usually with a large male in the area, on shallow reefs with sand channels or rubble patches. Small juveniles occur on exposed reefs close to surge zones and adults in waters to about 20 m depth, although occasionally they venture deep. Indian Ocean species, common in the Maldives, ranging to northern Java and overlapping in range with the Pacific sibling *Coris gaimard*, previously called *Coris africana*. Length to 35 cm.

Ringed Wrasse
Hologymnosus semidiscus

Inhabits shallow reef crests and slopes to about 25 m depth, usually over sand and rubble areas. Small juveniles often occur in small groups, adults seen solitary with the male patrolling a very large territory. Photographing a male can be difficult. It is best to find a female first and wait for the male to check her out. There are several changes with growth. Large males are green and sometimes show a pale band during display. Juveniles have black over most of the lower half of body and head. Widespread Indian Ocean and Red Sea. Length to 40 cm.

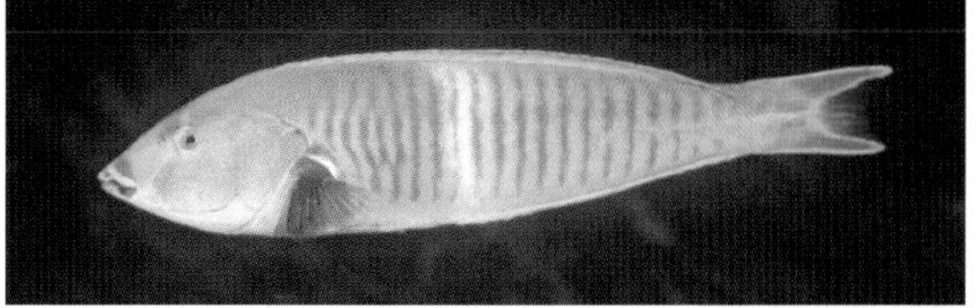

Photo middle, female.

Narrow-banded Wrasse
Hologymnosus doliatus

Occurs in clear outer reef habitats, deep sand flats on rubble zones below drop-offs and slopes, or areas near large bommies. Several, about 12 cm long, were seen and photographed along a reef edge on sand. Rare in the Maldives and this represents the first record. Small juveniles have horizontal lines, which gradually change into a barred pattern in the adult. Males are predominantly bluish and have a pale zone behind the pectoral fin. The fish is more elongate than most wrasses. Widespread Indian Ocean. Length to 30 cm.

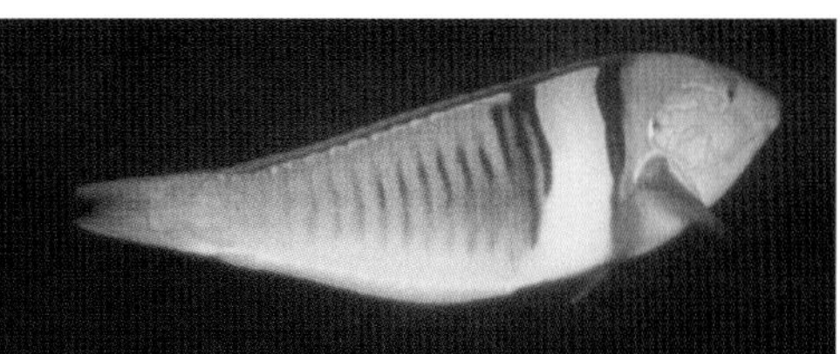

Cigar Wrasse
Cheilio inermis

Occurs in intertidal zones to about 20 m depth. Not often observed by divers and lives mainly in seagrass areas. This makes the species rare, as many seagrass areas are suffering due to resort and island development. Very elongate and usually greenish grey in colour. Sometimes has a yellow phase when in soft corals, but this form is rare in the Maldives. Widespread Indo-Pacific. Length to 48 cm.

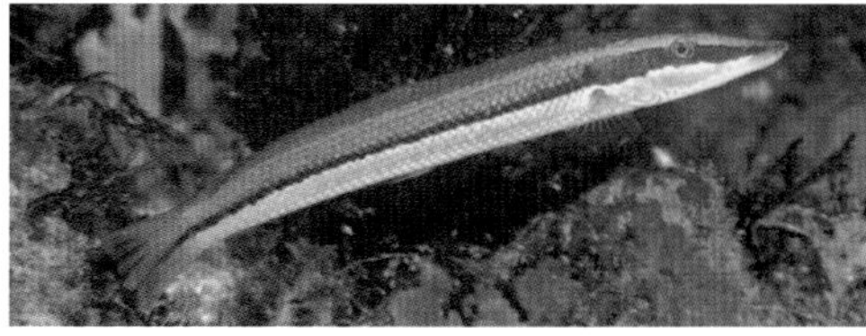

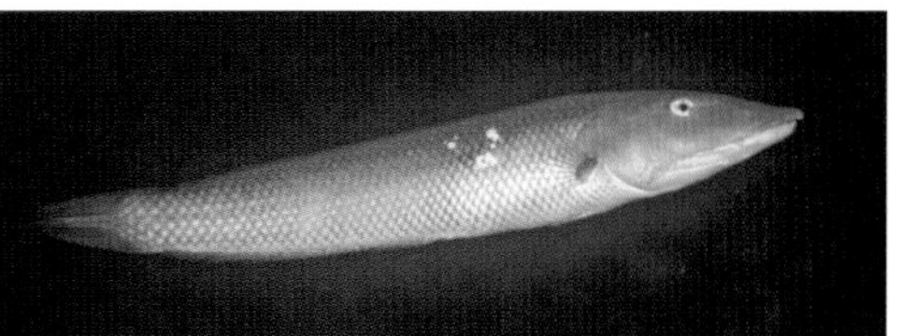

Knife Wrasse
Cymolutes praetextatus

Occurs in small loose groups on shallow sand flats and near seagrass beds. Common in the Maldives, usually in depths less than 10 m. Appearance is variable in colour to suit habitat. Usually has a tiny dark spot, like a speck of dirt, on the upper part of the tail base. Indo-Pacific. Reported length to 20 cm, although this is probably based on other species in the genus, as the largest ever seen by author is about 10 cm.

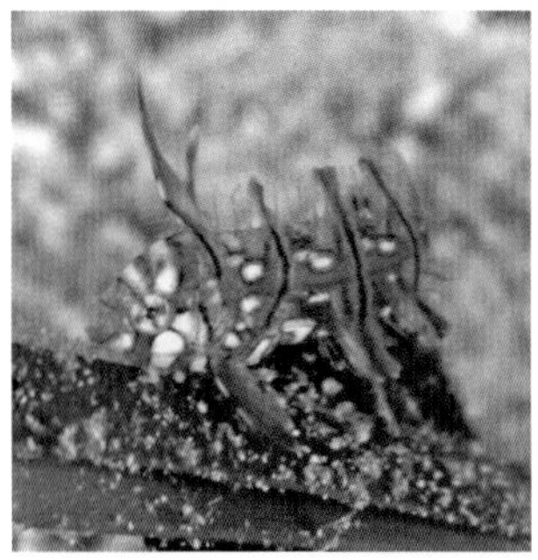

Reindeer Wrasse
Novaculichthys taeniourus

Also called Rockmover Wrasse. Typically found on rubble reef and sand flats with rubble ridges, from shallow surge zones to deep water, observed to 45 m depth. Identified by white bar across base of tail when adult. Adults nearly always swim in pairs, juveniles remain solitary. They lift and turn large rubble pieces to catch small creatures underneath, such as crabs. When in pairs they take turns, usually one fish lifts rubble, while the other catches prey. Widespread Indo-Pacific. Length to 25 cm.

White-blotch Razorfish
Xyrichtys aneitensis

A common species on sand often spread out in groups with each individual having its own prepared sand patch to bury in. It quickly dives into sand when approached. Shallow to at least 40 m depth. Small juveniles vary significantly in colour from white, green, brown or black, becoming sandy coloured with vertical bars with age. Adults have a large white blotch on sides. Widespread Indo-Pacific. Length to 20 cm.

Blue Razorfish
Xyrichtys pavo

Adults usually occur on deep sand slopes, in excess of 50 m. Several individuals were observed by the author in depths between 15 and 40 m. Easily overlooked because of its habitat and shyness. Small juveniles have greatly extended first dorsal fin spines, which resemble the stem of a leaf. The first two spines are separate from the rest, but connected by a membrane when the fish is small. Juveniles are variable in colour, from green to brown and develop false eyes in the dorsal fin. Male is plain blue and has a small distinctive spot on its sides. Widespread Indo-Pacific. Length to 30 cm.

Pink Wrasse
Pseudocoris yamashiroi

Adults occur in small groups over deep sand flats near reefs or around bommies. They swim high above the bottom to feed on zooplankton. Dark-edged caudal fin lobes distinguish them. Small juveniles also form small groups but stay close together near reefs or bommies. Small juveniles are bright pink and become paler with age. Seen in the Maldives to 35 m depth. Widespread Indo-Pacific. Length to 16 cm, but about 12 cm in the Maldives.

Photo left, male; right, juvenile.

Blue-nose Wrasse
Pseudojuloides kaleidos

Uncommon and lives on rubble reef slopes and flats in 20 to 35 m depth. First discovered in Malé Atoll, but now known from Indonesia as well. Females are a brownish pink colour and juveniles have a pale yellow snout-tip. Males change from the female colouration within a week to gaudy colours. Indo-Pacific, known distribution is sporadic, but is probably widespread. Length to 10 cm.

SAND-REEF WRASSES
LABRIDAE-2

This group of wrasses is mainly found on reefs, but burrow in the sand to sleep. Some of the members within this group could be included in the previous group as they are mainly sand-dwellers, but belong in a large genus of which most other members are typical reef dwellers. All the species form loose groups of females, dominated by a single male that has a section of the reef as his territory. Nearly all species feed on the bottom on small invertebrates, although some include algae in their diet. Only the genus *Leptojulis* feeds in the water column on plankton. None of the species grow large and all are about 10 to 20 cm long. They are quick and rely on speed and reef coverage to escape danger and bury in the sand to sleep. Juveniles and females are often similar, but males are usually very different in colour. Previously, many male and female forms where thought to be different species. The genus *Macropharyngodon* has ten species, two of which occur in the Maldives. *Halichoeres* was once used as a 'catch-all' genus, but it now comprises only a few species and is separated into a large number of different genera, including *Biochoeres*, *Platyglossus*, *Hemitautoga*, *Octocynodon* and *Hemitautoga*, all of which have representatives in the Maldives.

Splendid Leopard Wrasse
Macropharyngodon bipartitus

Occurs in clear reef habitat with rich invertebrate growth. Juveniles and females are often feeding together in small groups on rubble reef. Males are so different from the females and could easily be mistaken for separate species. All phases are readily identified by colour. A common but beautiful Maldives species with restricted west Indian Ocean distribution. Also known as the Divided or Vermiculate Wrasse. Depth range is 3 to about 30 m. Length to 13 cm.

Photos: above left, juvenile; left, females; below, male.

Ornate Leopard Wrasse
Macropharyngodon ornatus

Lives on rubble reef in small groups. Ranges in depth from shallow reef-crests to about 30 m. Differences between the sexes is not as great as in most other species in the genus. Identified by rows of pale spots on side and reddish fins. Colour patterns of both sexes are diagnostic. This species is uncommon in the Maldives. Indo-Pacific, ranging to Flores, Indonesia. Length to 11 cm.

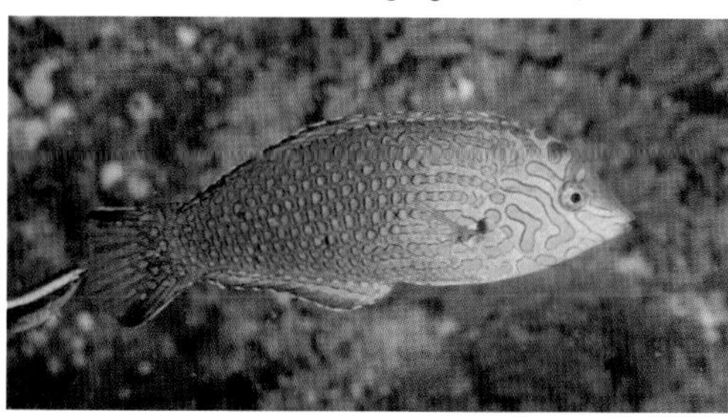

Lemon Meringue Wrasse
Biochoeres leucoxanthus

Common in the Maldives, often seen in small groups on sand and rubble and along reef edges. Usually found in depths over 20 m and often individuals are seen following goatfishes that disturb the sand, for an easy feed. Readily identified by the bright yellow backs and white below. Indian Ocean, ranging east to Java, Indonesia. Length to 12 cm.

Indian White Wrasse
Biochoeres trispilus

Prefers deep walls where seen in small groups. Occurs on sandy rubble patches on the bottom of large overhangs, usually in depths over 20 m. Appears to be white in natural light at the depth it occurs in, because water filters out its red colour. It was originally discovered in the Maldives, but ranges east to southern Java, Indonesia. Replaced by sibling *B. pallidus* in the Pacific. Length to 12 cm.

Adorned Wrasse
Biochoeres cosmetus

Common in the Maldives on shallow rubble patches to about 20 m depth, sometimes deeper. Usually seen in small loose groups swimming close to the bottom. Pale green with pink lines. Juveniles and females have a double black spot in dorsal fin. West Indian Ocean only, similar to B. ornatus from the Pacific. Length to 12 cm.

Vrolik's Wrasse
Platyglossus chrysotaenia

A common species in protected reefs and lagoons with areas of heavy coral growth. Less numerous on outer reefs and typically occurs in small loose groups to about 20 m depth. Identified by greenish colour, female with numerous lines from the snout to tail and male with a series of pale blotches or short bars on the body at the dorsal fin base. Widespread Indian Ocean, replaced by sibling *P. melanurus* in the Pacific. Length to 12 cm.

Dusky Wrasse
Platyglossus annularis

Moderately common in the Maldives. Adults swim close to reef and found in shallow surge areas to deep reefs and shipwrecks. Juveniles are secretive in the reef and almost black with thin longitudinal lines and a large blotch in the dorsal fin. This changes gradually to the green and gold coloured male. Widespread Indian Ocean. Length to 18 cm, usually 15 cm.

Clouded Wrasse
Octocynodon nebulosus

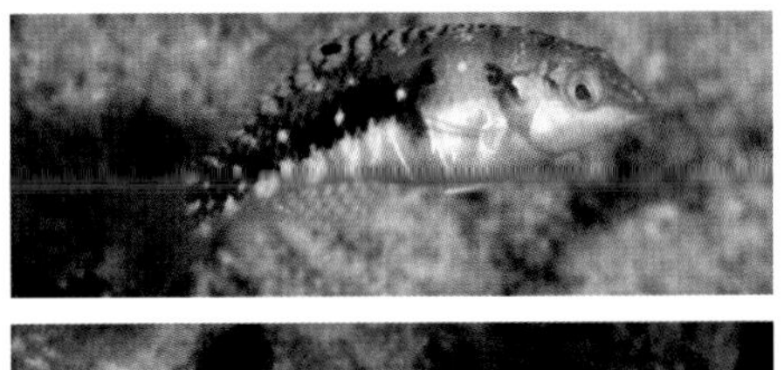

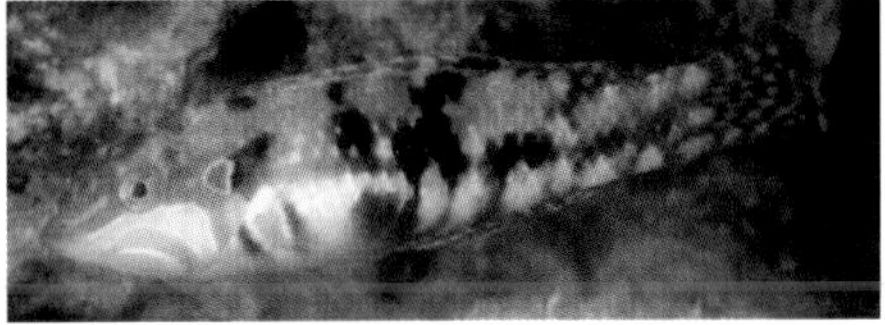

Not commonly observed in the Maldives and only seen in shallows. Prefers shallow surge zones with algal reef but also occurs on rubble in harbours. Colour is highly variable, depending on habitat, from green to brown or pink, usually with a pink patch on the belly. Male has pink band on cheek. A widespread and common continental species of the Indo-Pacific. Found to 40 m depth in some areas. Length to 12 cm.

Zigzag Wrasse
Hemitautoga scapularis

Common on sand flats on reef edges or in lagoons. Often follows goatfishes or emperors to feed on creatures that emerge when these fishes disturb the sand. Usually occurs in loose aggregations with a single large colourful male in charge. Very pale in colour in the Maldives and usually has a short black line following the eye. Depth range is great, from intertidal to at least 50 m. Widespread Indo-Pacific. Length to 15 cm.

Checkerboard Wrasse
Hemitautoga hortulanus

Occurs in shallow lagoons and reef slopes to about 25 m, occasionally deeper. Adults usually singly, swimming well above reefs. Males have large territory; females variously distributed over reef. Adults whitish with a yellow tail, a single yellow saddle below spinous dorsal fin and a black spot on upper tail fin base. Widespread Indo-Pacific, but some colour differences between Indian Ocean and Pacific, with both forms found in Bali. Length to 25 cm.

Sri Lankan Wrasse
Halichoeres zeylonicus

A common species found on deep sand flats with rubble patches and remote bommies, often far away from reefs. Swims in loose groups with male dominating. In the Maldives, prefers depths of 25+ m. Identified by broad yellow stripe on the middle of the side and male with a black spot. Widespread Indian Ocean, replaced by similar *H. hartzfeldi* in Pacific. Ranges of the two species overlap in Bali. The species are identified by different cheek patterns. Length to 15 cm.

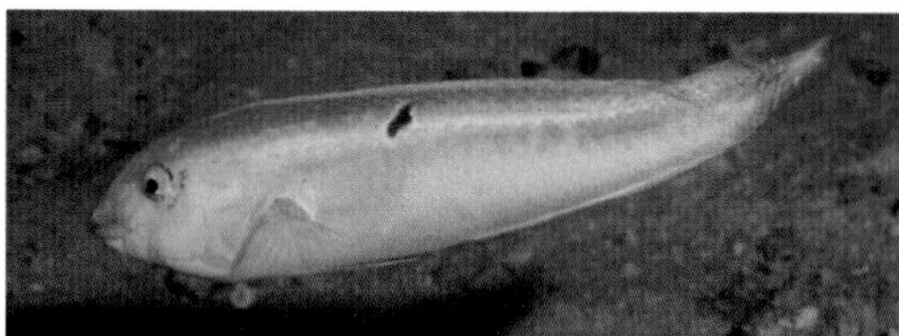

Blue-spot Wrasse
Leptojulis cyanopleura

Photograph below-right represents the first record for the Maldives. Lives on deep open sand flats away from reefs around remote coral bommies and could easily be overlooked. Occurs elsewhere in shallow coastal waters as well as deep. Several small groups were found in different atolls, in depths of about 30 to 40 m. A slender species, females are pale with a dark mid-lateral stripe, while males have a reflective blue spot in the dark band behind pectoral fin. Widespread Indo-Pacific. Length to 12 cm.

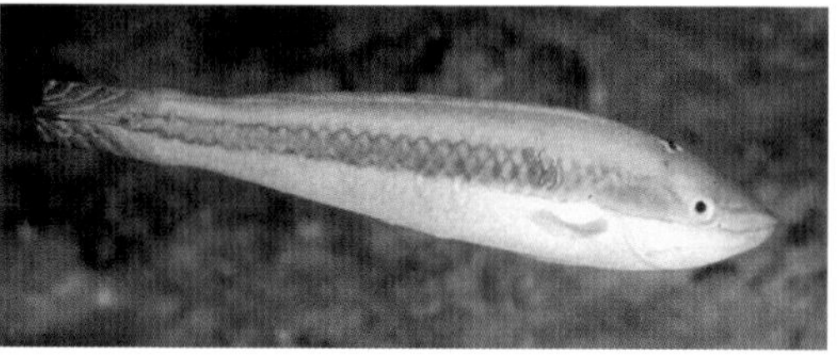

Blue-lined Wrasse
Stethojulis albovittata

Common in most reef habitats, usually found at shallow depth, swimming in small but loose aggregations above reef. Males swim fast mainly using the pectoral fin. Males identified by the lower line, which bends upwards over the pectoral fin base and curved blue stripe on cheek, females by the bright yellow cheek. Indian Ocean, east to Java, Indonesia. Replaced by nearly identical *S. bandanensis* in the Pacific. Length to 14 cm.

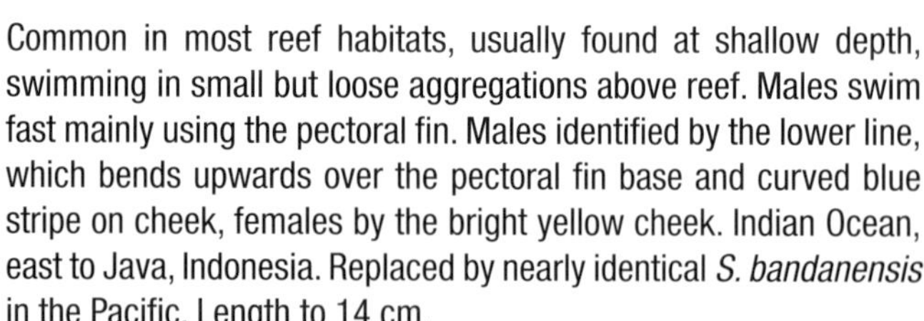

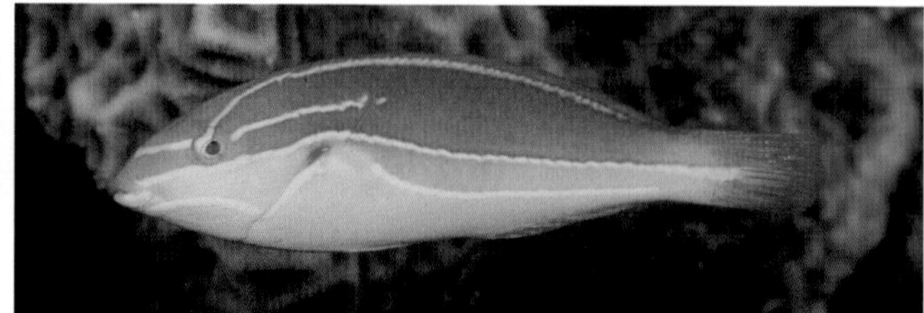

Silver-streaked Wrasse
Stethojulis strigiventer

Moderately common in lagoons and near seagrass beds, often in silty conditions. Inhabits shallow reefs, usually in depths less than 10 m. Swims in small aggregations and males nearly always on the move. Small juveniles seen in seagrasses or algaes. A slender species compared to other members of the genus. Females are distinguished by white streaks along the belly. Males are similar to Blue-lined Wrasse (previous page), but lack blue stripe on cheek. Juveniles are green. Widespread Indo-Pacific. Length to 12 cm.

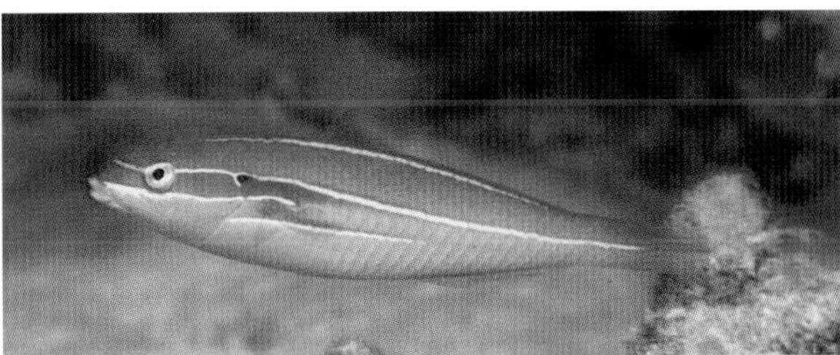

Blue-ribbon Wrasse
Stethojulis trilineata

Mainly found on outer reef slopes and along upper parts of drop-offs with rich coral growth, including surge zones. Often swimming through gutters or channels. Seems less territorial than most wrasses as several males are often seen close together. Found shallow to about 15 m depth. Three long blue lines along the body identify males; one is along the dorsal fin base and two run onto the tail fin, another shorter line runs below the eye. Females are dark above with numerous small white spots and white below. Widespread Indo-Pacific. Length to 14 cm.

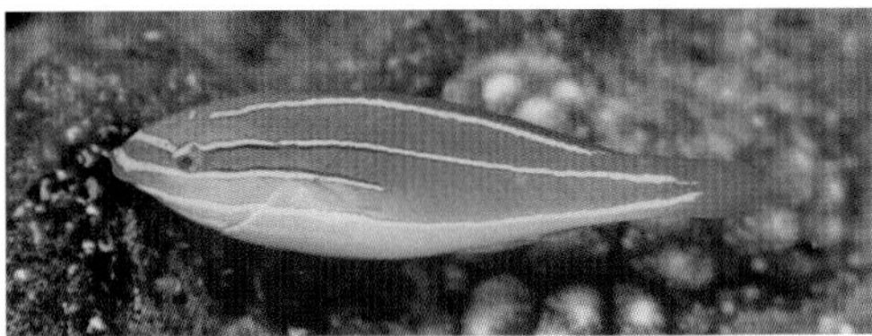

Diamond Wrasse
Anampses caeruleopunctatus

Not common in the Maldives. Mainly seen on reef crests adjacent to deep water, mostly in surge prone areas with mixed algae and coral habitat. Usually small groups of females are observed. Large males are territorial, often venturing deep to about 30 m. Females have a bright blue spot on each scale. Large males become deep bodied and are mostly blue, showing a pale band over the body just behind the head. Widespread Indo-Pacific. Length to 30 cm.

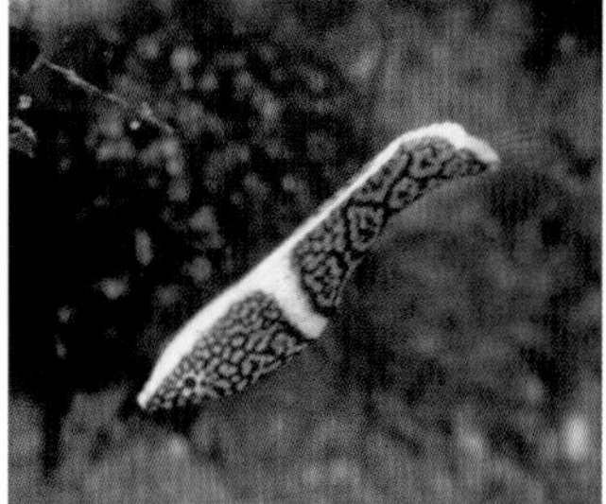

White-dashes Wrasse
Anampses lineatus

Deep-water habitat, along walls or rich coral-rock shelves in 25+ m depth. Uncommon and seen singly, or in small numbers. Could be mistaken for a juvenile Speckled Wrasse (next species) except it has a white tail, and spots on body are elongated to dashes forming lines in adults. Indian Ocean, ranging to Bali, Indonesia, where its Pacific sibling *A. melanurus* also occurs. Length to 12 cm.

Speckled Wrasse
Anampses meleagrides

Also called Yellow-tail Wrasse. Females usually noted for their distinctive colouration, often swimming in small loose groups in coral rich areas. The white spots and yellow tail easily identify them. Males are colourful and usually brighten when displaying to the female. Tail pattern gives the appearance of having pointed tail fin lobes. Mainly found on shallow reefs to about 20 m depth. Indo-Pacific. Length to 22 cm.

Yellow-Breasted Wrasse
Anampses twistii

Usually seen solitary in rich coral reefs or along steep walls, swimming close or through the corals, to depths of at least 25 m. Small juveniles have false eyes at the end of dorsal and anal fins and often swim with head down so the side on view looks more like the face of a larger fish. Large adults are recognised by yellow below eye level from the mouth to belly, dark-edged pale spots and ocellus at the rear of dorsal and anal fins. Indo-Pacific. A widespread species, but not particularly common anywhere. Length to 16 cm.

Chisel-tooth Wrasse
Pseudodax moluccanus

Often seen in caves along deep drop-offs to at least 40 m depth. Small juveniles are secretive in crevices and may clean other fishes from parasites. Adults feed on encrusting invertebrates, by hacking into protective cover of their prey with strong chisel-like teeth. Juveniles are black with two blue horizontal bands on sides. Adults become spotted, usually with yellow on the mouth. Widespread Indo-Pacific. Length to 25 cm.

CLEANER WRASSES
LABRIDAE-3

A small group of specialised fishes, especially the genus *Labroides* that spend much of their lives removing parasites from other fishes. Tiny post-larvae juveniles settle in caves or crevices and their colour pattern, combined with their dance-like swimming, is immediately recognised by other fishes. Adults often work in pairs and use special places on the reefs, known as cleaning stations. Different kinds of fish come to the cleaning stations for inspections and the removal of itchy parasites. Towards the end of the day, it can get very busy with many customers lining up to be serviced. Occasionally, rarely seen pelagic fishes come to the station. Many other wrasse species clean on occasions, or only when juvenile and vary their diet with coral polyps. Juveniles of the genera *Labrobsis* and *Labrichthys* clean regularly, but adults only engage in the behaviour part time or not at all. The genus *Labroides* comprises five species, two of which occur in the Maldives; *Labrobsis* has six species, of which one occurs; and *Labrichthys* has a single species.

Blue-streak Cleaner Wrasse
Labroides dimidiatus

Inhabits shallow lagoon reefs as well as deep on coral bommies to at least 40 m depth. Juveniles are solitary, adults usually occur in pairs. Small juveniles are all black with an iridescent blue line. Adults become white on the belly and in some populations have yellow over the back. A common species in the Maldives and the most famous. Widespread Indo-Pacific. Length to 10 cm.

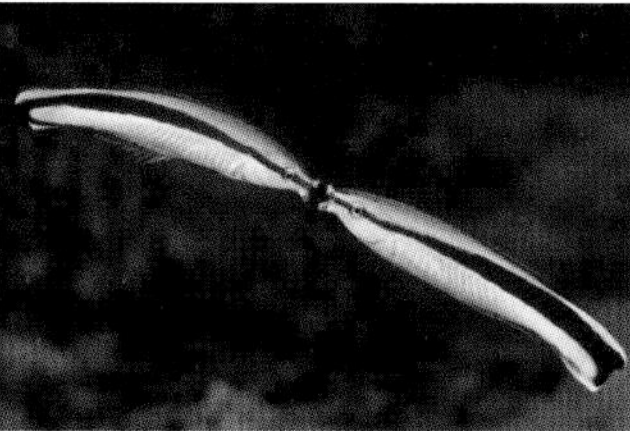

Two-colour Cleaner Wrasse
Labroides bicolor

Nearly always seen singly. Adults often swim in the open and clean large fishes high above the bottom, covering large sections of reef. Juveniles remain in caves along walls. Moderately common in the Maldives with a large depth range to at least 50 m. Adults are readily identified by the abrupt change in colour on the body and tail from dark blue to almost white or yellow. Widespread Indo-Pacific. Length to 15 cm.

V-tail Tubelip Wrasse
Labropsis xanthonota

Lives in rich coral habitat near outer reefs. Mainly shallow in 6 to 25 m depth. Juveniles and females swim in small groups with similar sized individuals, dominated by a territorial male. Juveniles 'clean' other fishes, adults feed mainly on coral polyps. Females and juveniles are easily identified by the dark body, which is light on top – this is usually the other way around in fishes – and the male has an unusual 'V' tail and a long dash on the rear edge of the gill cover. Indo-Pacific. Length to 10 cm.

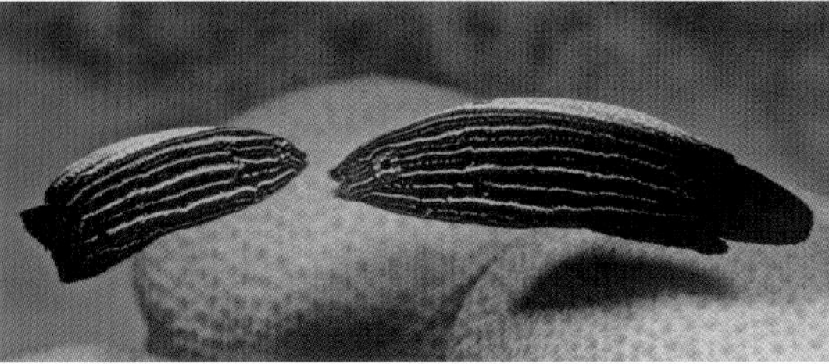

Tube-mouth Wrasse
Labrichthys unilineatus

Occurs in rich coral reefs from silty lagoons to outer reef crests, often swims through large branching staghorn corals. Thin blue lines on the sides distinguish them. Males are greenish and usually show a large pale area on body just behind the head. Juveniles are black with a white mid-lateral line. Common in the Maldives. Widespread Indo-Pacific, with some geographical variations between oceans. Indian Ocean fish grow larger and have proportionally much longer ventral fins, while the Pacific fish are bluer. Length to 20 cm.

LUNATE-TAILED WRASSES LABRIDAE-4

This group includes the genus *Thalassoma*, usually round-headed fishes that swim strongly with their pectoral fins and the long-snouted *Gomphosus* genus that is closely related. Their pectoral fins, directly situated behind their short head, often feature bright colours in the male. The tail in adults becomes strongly lunate and this is often accentuated by the transparency on part of the fin or the development of long fin tips. Some other wrasses have lunate tails; however, they are not usually a distinctive feature. Some juvenile and female fishes school, while the male is often solitary. In some species, the male may share reef flats with other males and fight regularly. Diet comprises a great variety of creatures picked from the bottom, as well as plankton. They are mainly opportunistic feeders and some species follow other fishes that disturb the sand, such as goatfishes, to snare an easy prey. The colour changes between juveniles and sexes are gradual and not as dramatic as in most other wrasses.

Bird Wrasse
Gomphosus caeruleus

Mainly occurs on shallow reef crests and often along the top of deep walls. An unusual member of this group as it has a greatly extended snout when adult. In small juveniles, the snout is relatively short. Commonly seen in the Maldives swimming in rich coral growth areas, usually with several females and a male nearby. Colour is variable between different stages, although their long snout easily identifies adults. Indian Ocean only, replaced by the similar *G. varius* east of Java, Indonesia. Length to 25 cm.

Two-tone Wrasse
Thalassoma amblycephalum

Juveniles and females form large groups, with each group comprising individuals of a similar size, that roam reef flats often in shallow turbulent surge zones. Males venture to at least 30 m depth. A slender species, that feeds on plankton as well as bottom creatures. Males are variable in colour but usually have a green head with broad pale band just behind it; females are similar to juveniles, white with a broad black stripe on the sides and over the back. Widespread Indo-Pacific. Length to 16 cm.

Six-bar Wrasse
Thalassoma hardwicke

Occurs on shallow to deep drop-offs and usually swims along the top of reefs in small loose groups. A common species in the Maldives that often follows divers in case they disturb the bottom, ready to grab unsuspecting prey. Colour is pale green with a series of dark-green to pink, or black saddles over the back. Juveniles are more banded, with bands extending to the belly region. Widespread Indo-Pacific. Length to 20 cm.

Jansen's Wrasse
Thalassoma jansenii

Prefers surge zones in the Maldives, adjacent to outer reef walls and commonly seen in gutters to 10 m depth. Occurs in small aggregations with a large male in charge. Colour is mainly black, with head half-white below and white extending along the body until tapering away below the anal fin. Males turn on pale yellow bands across the body. Widespread Indo-Pacific, but several geographical variations. Length to 20 cm.

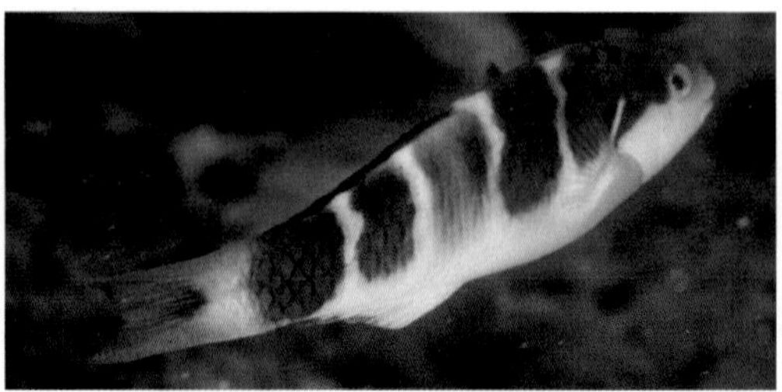

Moon Wrasse
Thalassoma lunare

Occupies various habitats from shallow lagoons to outer reef walls to about 35 m depth. Usually seen in small groups and can become very inquisitive toward divers. Identified by magenta central part of pectoral fin. Males are variable from dark green to bright blue and pink bands radiating from the eye, with tail fin often yellow. Juveniles are green to brown and have a large round spot in the dorsal fin. Common throughout Indo-Pacific. Length to 22 cm.

Ribbon Wrasse
Thalassoma schwanenfeldii

Common in the Maldives but prefers shallow surge zones where few divers go. Especially likes areas where coral plates (*Acropora*) are prolific with some algae growth below, near reef channels and rubble areas. Usually in depths between 6 and 10 m. Males swim quickly over large areas of reef. Identified by the red or deep pink bands on the cheek that is absent in similar species. Widespread Indo-Pacific. Length to 15 cm.

Photos: male left and female below.

Surge Wrasse
Thalassoma purpureum

A flighty species that lives almost exclusively in the shallow surge zone that typically features on the outer reefs of the Maldives. Rarely seen in depths over 10 m. Usually occurs in groups of females and sometimes several males. Male identified by ornate pattern with green cheek and large size. One of the largest in the genus but also the most shy – a challenge to fish photographers. Widespread Indo-Pacific. Length to 25 cm.

SMALL-MOUTHED WRASSES LABRIDAE-5

A large group of mostly small-sized planktivorous wrasses but only a few are known from the Maldives. The majority of species are less than 10 cm long when fully grown. An interesting feature is a divided eye-cornea that enables them to focus separately on tiny prey in front of the mouth, as well as normal viewing. Most males swim about frantically and have fancy colours used to display to females or other males. In many species, the brightest colours are present in the fins, which can be erected suddenly to have the greatest impact. As a result, these species are known as 'flasher wrasses'. Where common, adults form large schools and feed on plankton high above reefs or well away from walls, usually during currents. Small groups of juveniles are often seen along reef edges above the rubble bottom where they sleep, and in the evening, adults can be seen swimming in and out of their small holes as a safety check. Small juveniles are more secretive on coral rubble than reef. Most juvenile species of the genera *Cirrhilabrus* and *Paracheilinus* look alike, and are typically brown with a white tipped nose. The genus *Cirrhilabrus* has over 30 species, two of which are known from the Maldives; *Paracheilinus* has about 10 species, with one in the Maldives; and *Pseudocheilinus* has six species, three of which known from the Maldives.

Exquisite Wrasse
Cirrhilabrus exquisitus

Found on shallow reef crests to deep bommies on sand flats, to at least 40 m depth. The only common species of this genus in the Maldives. Males often form small groups, busily displaying to each other. Displaying males show blue spots and lines, have pink on the face and yellow to orange coloured tails. Females are mainly reddish with a white patch on the snout. Juveniles are brown, changing to green with growth. Widespread Indo-Pacific, but the Pacific form are quite different and may warrant separate species status. Length to 11 cm.

Photos: left female, right male.

Rosy-scaled Wrasse
Cirrhilabrus rubrisquamis

Mainly found along drop-offs in invertebrate rich habitats with caves and ledges to at least 50 m depth. Primarily a deep-water species, but female was photographed shallow. Sometimes occurs in small groups on rubble patches below reef overhangs. Generally light pink all over and scales on the front half of body have dark pink edges. Females have thin whitish lines running along upper sides. Only known from the Maldives and Chagos Archipelago. Length to 65 mm.

Photos: left female, right male.

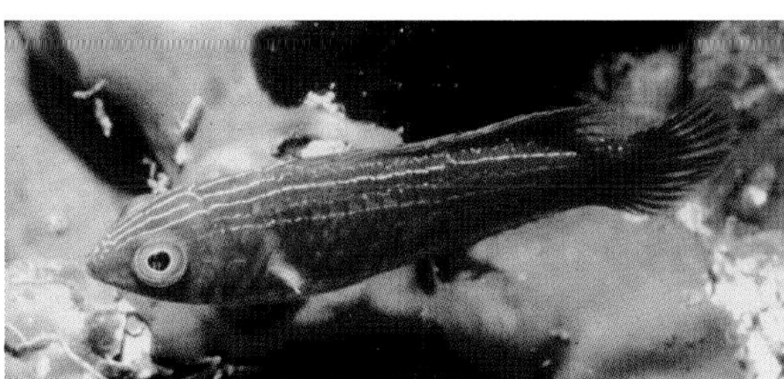

McCosker's Wrasse
Paracheilinus mccoskeri

Usually occurs in small groups on rubble pieces on sand along the bottom of reefs, in 20+ m depth. Single males are usually seen displaying to females only. They rise only short distances above the substrate when feeding on zooplankton. An extended ray on the dorsal fin readily identifies males. Females are plain without an extended ray. It is an Indian Ocean species that doubtfully ranges to Indonesia. Pacific siblings are considerably different in colour; males have a yellow anal fin and usually have a double extended ray on the back fin. Length to 65 mm.

Photos: Left displaying male; right juvenile.

Pin-striped Wrasse
Pseudocheilinus evanidus

Moderately common in the Maldives on shallow protected reefs but ranges to deep water along walls with rubble patches below large overhangs, to at least 40 m depth. A small secretive fish. Orange to pink-brown in colour and sometimes faintly banded. Best identified by the whitish streak extending from mouth and along the cheek. Widespread Indo-Pacific. Length to 8 cm.

Eight-line Wrasse
Pseudocheilinus octotaenia

Occurs in clear inner to outer reef habitats, usually in moderate depths along drop-offs at the bottom of large caves with rich invertebrate growth. Widespread Indo-Pacific. Length to 12 cm.

Six-line Wrasse
Pseudocheilinus hexataenia

A common and colourful small fish, that swims in rich coral areas and rubble reef, often in small groups. Remains under the cover of reefs, but is very active and often noticed by divers. Depth range is 3 to 20 m, but rarely deeper. Readily identified by a mauve body, sometimes greenish above, with many orange lines and a small spot on the upper edge of tail base. Widespread Indo-Pacific. Length to 60 mm in the Maldives, 85 mm in Indonesia.

CAVE WRASSES
LABRIDAE-6

A small group of interesting little fishes adapted to living in the back of dark caves. Divers need a torch and have to be on the look to find them, as they don't like light and quickly hide. Turning off the light will usually bring them back and as divers get used to the dim light the fishes can be observed. They usually occur in pairs and utilise the various holes and tunnels in the back of caves to move about and pick tiny prey from the bottom. There is a single genus and two of the known three species occur in the Maldives, where both are common.

White-banded Possum Wrasse
Wetmorella albofasciata

Occurs on inner and outer reefs, along walls in the back of large caves and overhangs at all divable depths. The white radiating lines from inside the eye identifies the species. The lines crossing the body are always white and the line before the tail is at an angle. Widespread Indo-Pacific. Length to 55 mm.

Yellow-banded Possum Wrasse
Wetmorella nigropinnata

Seen in caves in deep lagoons as well as outer reef walls. Adults usually occur in pairs, and the juvenile singly. Juveniles and females have four white bands, but males lose their central body bands and the remaining two bands turn yellow. Widespread Indo-Pacific. Length to 65 mm.

MAORI AND THICKLIP WRASSES LABRIDAE-7

This group includes the largest wrasses. They are the large-scaled and thick-lipped species that associate with reefs. Many are noticed by divers because of their size and behaviour, especially the Napoleonfish, which easily get accustomed to divers. There are some problems with the scientific names of the smaller *Cheilinus* species and the genus is in need of revision. Some authors use *Oxycheilinus* for the more slender species. Most species are seen solitary in various habitats of the reef. Small species stay close to the ocean bottom and the larger species often swim in open waters, well away from reefs. Small juveniles of most species are very secretive and rarely seen. They live amongst the rubble or weeds and sleep in narrow crevices or caves. Diet comprises small invertebrates but some species prey primarily on juvenile fishes. Genus *Epibulus* has one widespread species and possibly a second species ranging from the Philippines to eastern Papua New Guinea; *Cheilinus* has seven species, five of which occur in the Maldives; and *Hemigymnus* has two species, both in the Maldives.

Sling-jaw wrasse
Epibulus insidiator

Occurs in lagoons and protected reefs to about 20 m depth. It has a highly protrusible mouth that can be greatly extended into a suction tube to catch prey. Variable in colour, sometimes, bright yellow all over. Small juveniles are secretive in corals and look remarkably like possum wrasses or small juvenile Banded Maori Wrasses. A common species in the Maldives. Widespread Indo-Pacific. Length to 30 cm.

Banded Maori Wrasse
Cheilinus fasciatus

Inhabits lagoons and inner reefs, and usually swims along reef margins over rubble zones to depths of at least 30 m. Identified by the broadly banded pattern over the body. Males have a large red area over the head. Small juveniles occur in corals and look remarkably like possum wrasses. Widespread Indo-Pacific. Length to 35 cm.

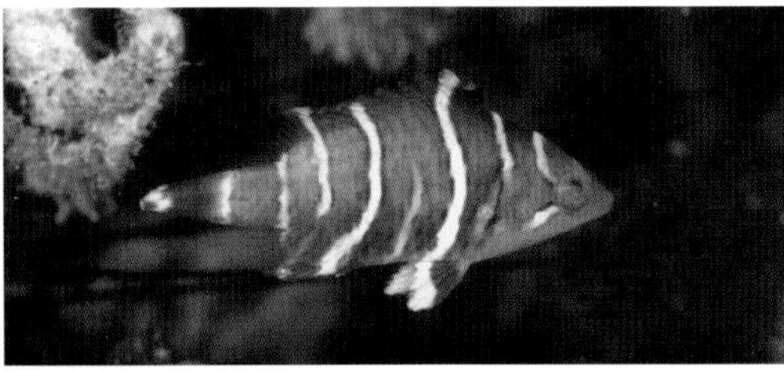

Triple-tail Maori Wrasse
Cheilinus trilobatus

Adults occur mainly on shallow protected reefs to about 10 m depth, often in silty inshore conditions. Juveniles found in algae reef habitat. Usually seen singly, but occasionally in loose groups. Fine pink spotting and scribbles on the head identify them. Juveniles have numerous thin vertical lines and a series of dark spots mid-laterally towards the tail. Widespread Indo-Pacific. Length to 40 cm.

White-dotted Maori Wrasse
Cheilinus chlorourus

Mainly found in shallow lagoons and harbours on rubble or around bommies. Adults occur in small loose groups dominated by a large male, juveniles singly in corals. The white spots on the body can identify it, usually one on each scale and often with a series of white saddles over the back. Common in the Maldives. Widespread Indo-Pacific. Length to 35 cm.

Napoleonfish
Cheilinus undulatus

Also known as Humphead Maori Wrasse and Giant Maori Wrasse, the best-known member of the genus and a favourite with many divers. Large males are distinguished by their huge size and hump on the forehead. Seen swimming singly along deep walls and often resident on shipwrecks. Juveniles have a pair of dark diagonal stripes through the eye. Small juveniles live in weedy areas and are rarely seen. Generally, greenish in colour, with a dark vertical bar on each scale that forms vertical lines. Widespread Indo-Pacific. Length to 2 m.

Photos: above right, juvenile; below, female; below right, large male.

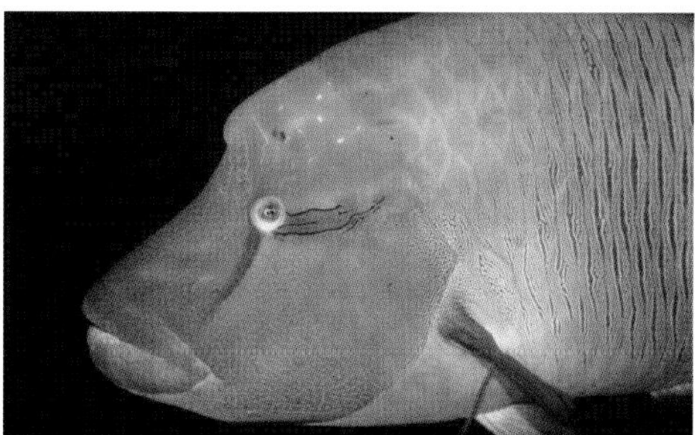

Point-head Maori Wrasse
Cheilinus oxycephalus

A small secretive species in lagoons and reef crests seen swimming amongst corals, but rarely out in the open. Colour is variable, from greenish grey to brownish red and adults usually with fine white speckles over the head. Deep-bodied for the genus, and has a pointed snout. Common in the Maldives, but easily overlooked. Widespread Indo-Pacific. Length to 17 cm.

Cheek-line Maori Wrasse
Cheilinus digrammus

Usually seen solitary and often swimming high above the bottom. Occurs on almost every reef habitat to depths of about 30 m. Pale green to reddish brown in colour. Males have pink scribbles on the head and many oblique lines on the cheek and gill cover. Sometimes curious towards divers. Moderately common in the Maldives. Widespread Indo-Pacific. Length to 35 cm.

Photo left, male. below, female.

Oriental Maori Wrasse
Cheilinus rhodochrous

Previously known as *Cheilinus orientalis*. Found mainly on clear water reefs and along drop-offs to 45 m depth. Small juveniles are often seen in crinoid featherstars or black coral bushes. Similar to the Cheek-line Maori Wrasse but usually show a broad dark band along the body, and are much smaller. Widespread Indo-Pacific. Length to 20 cm.

Photos: above left, juvenile; left, large male; right, female.

Thin-line Maori Wrasse
Cheilinus arenatus

A deep-water species, occasionally seen along outer reef walls, in rich invertebrate habitat with soft coral and seawhips, usually in 20 m depth. Appears to live solitary but little is known about this species. Identified by pale body and thin reddish midlateral line along the sides. Indian Ocean, ranging to west Pacific. Length to 15 cm.

Little Maori Wrasse
Cheilinus bimaculatus

Mainly inhabits shallow surge-zones with good algae growth, or deep on rubble with algae cover. Males develop filaments at the tips and centre of the tail, with a prolonged filament on the upper lobe. Females have a more rounded tail. Colour is variable from green to brown red. Widespread Indo-Pacific. Length to 15 cm, one of the smallest in the genus, but in the Maldives the largest seen was about 10 cm.

Photos: Left, male; right, female.

Banded Thicklip Wrasse
Hemigymnus fasciatus

Adults often seen in small loose groups in shallow depth on reef crests and slopes. Juveniles are secretive in rubble reef, and small ones often amongst urchin spines. Variable in colour from green to black, and the body is always banded. Males change colour on the face during courtship, showing a black horse-shoe shaped mark on the cheek. Widespread Indo-Pacific. Length to 30 cm.

Half-and-Half Wrasse
Hemigymnus melapterus

Occurs on most reef habitats. Juveniles are secretive in rubble reefs, adults swim openly over reefs. Surprisingly, shy in the Maldives compared to elsewhere. Photographs at close range could only be taken where fish were used to divers. Small juveniles are green with a broad white band centrally, that changes abruptly from a front white half to back black half, and have a yellow to orange tail. Adults mainly spotted and have thick lips. Common in the Maldives. Widespread Indo-Pacific. Length to 50 cm.

HOGFISHES
LABRIDAE-8

Hogfishes are the most wide-ranging among wrasses, with some species living in temperate waters, but most are absent from oceanic locations or represent a different species. Only two species are commonly encountered in the Maldives, both wide-ranging in the Indian Ocean. Juveniles often engage in cleaning activities, usually working in small groups in caves or around coral bommies. Diet comprises small-shelled invertebrates, especially shrimps, but also worms. The genus *Bodianus* comprises about 35 species, four of which are known from the Maldives. Some species are restricted to very deep water and could occur in the Maldives. The related large genus *Choerodon* is completely absent and appears to be restricted to continental waters. A new, second species of the only recently described genus *Terelabrus* was photographed by Jörg Aebi.

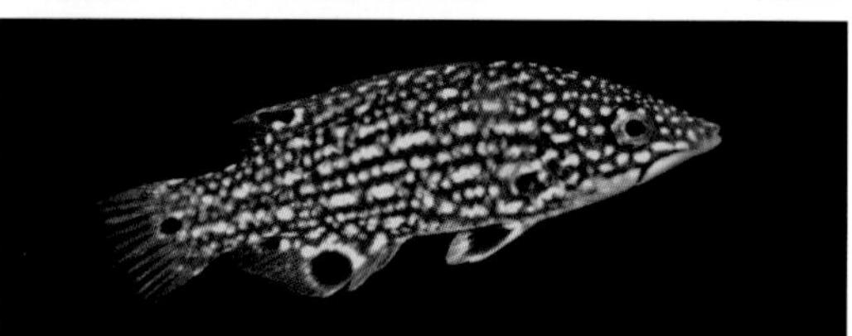

Diana Hogfish
Bodianus diana

Occurs on shallow reef crests as well as deep along walls to at least 50 m depth. Juveniles regularly clean other fishes from parasites. Adults are reddish to dark brown with a series of pale yellow or white spots. Large adults have red fins. Found only in Indian Ocean, the most common hogfish in the Maldives, ranging east to Java, Indonesia. Replaced by sibling Pacific species in Bali and rest of the Pacific, recently named *Bodianus dictynna*. Length to 25 cm.

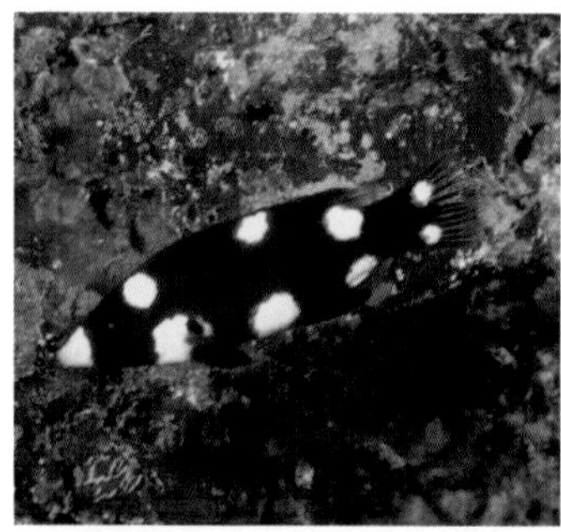

Coral Hogfish
Bodianus axillaris

Also known as Axilspot Hogfish. Usually seen solitary, swimming through reefs in caves or overhangs along slopes and walls. Sometimes shallow, but usually between 10 and 30 m depth. The white spotted black females get large in the Maldives compared to other areas, eventually changing to the half-dark and half-light male pattern. Identified by large black spot on dorsal, anal and base of pectoral fins. Common in the Maldives. Widespread Indo-Pacific. Length to 20 cm.

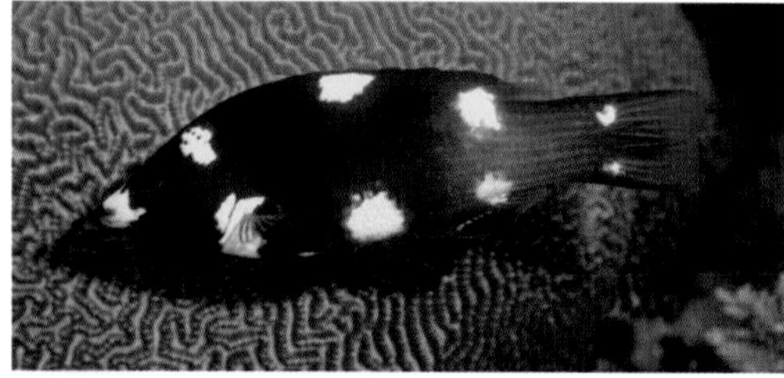

Lyre-tail Hogfish
Bodianus anthioides

Mainly occurs on coral rich reefs along walls adjacent to deep water. Usually seen solitary, swimming close to reef in 10 to 40 m depth. Small juveniles occur in large black coral bushes and sponges. Easily identified by its distinctive colour pattern and lunate tail. Widespread Indo-Pacific. Length to 22 cm.

Saddle-back Hogfish
Bodianus bilunulatus

Occurs in outer reef habitat, usually at moderate depths. Rare in the Maldives, probably found deep compared to continental waters. Juveniles inhabit rich rubble zones on deep slopes. Identified by a black saddle below rear of dorsal fin, juveniles with black rear of body. Widespread Indo-Pacific, with some geographical variations. Length to 40 cm.

Yellow Hogfish
Bodianus bimaculatus

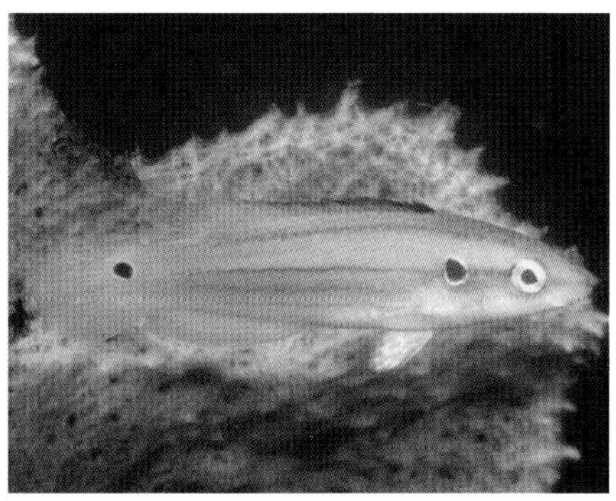

A small deep-water species, which occurs at different depths depending on location. In Bali, Indonesia, as shallow as 20 m, while in most other areas only below 40 m. Usually seen on rubble patches on the bottom of large overhangs along walls. Swims in small groups close to the bottom. Identified by bright yellow colour, males with thin orange lines. Uncommon in the Maldives. Indo-Pacific. Length to 10 cm, usually much smaller, about 6 cm.

Red-lined Hogfish
Terelabrus sp.

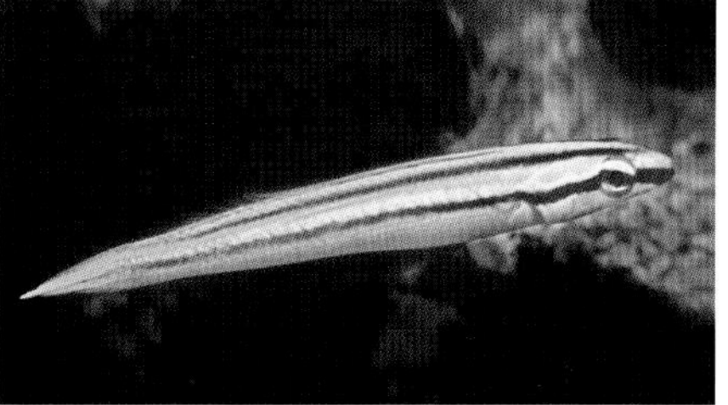

A new discovery in the Maldives, its Pacific sibling, *T. rubrovittatus*, which is reddish in colour with a yellow line, was only recently described as a new genus and species. Most specimens were found in depths in excess of 60 m. Length to about 10 cm.

PARROTFISHES
SCARIDAE

A large tropical family with nine genera and about 80 species globally, 23 of which are recorded from the Maldives. They are amongst the most noticed fishes on reefs because of their large size and bright colours. Most parrotfishes have dental plates, rather than individual teeth, fused to form a beak-like structure well suited for scraping algal food from the surface of reefs. Some are common and, by eating the algae and hard coral materials, they contribute greatly to the reef building process. This becomes evident when the fishes discharge their processed matter in a cloud of white dust, which sinks to the bottom. Adults often school and feed together on shallow reef flats on high tides. They travel along reef edges and some move considerably great distances between feeding sites during the day and sleeping places at night. Juveniles are solitary or form small groups, depending on the species. Seagrass species commonly form large schools at all sizes. Colour can change dramatically with growth or between sexes and often the only way to connect their stages to a species is by seeing the intermediates or the interactions between male and female. Females usually form their own schools and spawning activities occur near dusk. Typically, groups gather at reef corners and release their eggs and sperm simultaneously near the surface with out-going tides. Diet comprises algae, seagrasses or other vegetation and some species additionally take invertebrates, including coral polyps.

Two-colour Parrotfish
Cetoscarus bicolor

Occurs along reef slopes and upper parts of drop-offs, from shallows to about 30 m. Juveniles, male and female differ considerably from each other. Juveniles are solitary in rich coral growth, lagoons to outer reefs. Adult males usually occur on reef slopes on outer reefs. The white body and orange band over the head, readily identify juveniles. Males are bright green with pink markings. Common in the Maldives. Widespread Indo-Pacific. Length to 90 cm.

Humphead Parrotfish
Bolbometopon muricatum

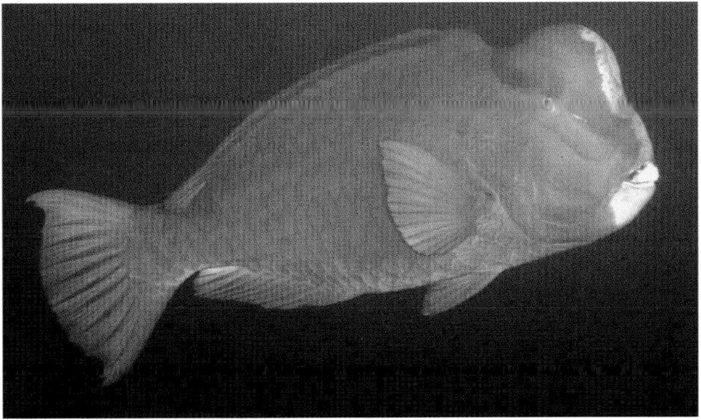

A schooling species often seen travelling in close packs along reef slopes and edges. They stop occasionally for feeding sessions by scraping large coral heads. Colour dull greenish grey and large adults develop a large hump on their head. They sleep at night in caves and crevices of reefs or shipwrecks in about 15 to 30 m depth. Widespread Indo-Pacific. The largest of all parrotfishes, length to 1.2 m.

Longnose Parrotfish
Hipposcarus harid

Occurs on inner reefs and deep lagoons to outer reefs, often in silty conditions. Males are usually solitary, females in small groups. Juveniles secretive in staghorn corals in lagoons and best recognised by the central red stripe along sides. The long shape of the snout best identifies adults. West Indian Ocean and Red Sea and replaced by sibling *H. longiceps* in the Pacific. Length to 60 cm.

Sheephead Parrotfish

Chlorurus strongylocephalus

Commonly occurs on inner reef crests with rich coral growth and rubble zones. Females often in small groups with a large male nearby. Females have distinctive colouration, males are best identified by the steep, blunt head shape and colour around eye and on the cheek. Widespread Indian Ocean, ranging to southern Java, Indonesia. Replaced by *S. microrhinos* in Pacific. Length to 70 cm.

Ember Parrotfish

Scarus rubroviolaceus

Mainly seen along deep slopes and drop-offs on inner to outer reefs, often openly swimming in groups, to depths of about 35 m. Females are distinctly marked with an irregular dark pattern and reddish colour, males best identified by the blunt snout and head colouration. Widespread Indo-Pacific, juveniles expatriate into sub-tropical waters. Length to 70 cm.

Bridled Parrotfish
Scarus frenatus

Occurs on reef slopes and drop-offs, mainly in outer reef habitats. Males usually seen solitary, females may form small groups sometimes mixing with other species. Males distinguished by abrupt colour change to pale green on lower half of head that continues along the body to the tail, females by the brown to pink fins. Widespread Indo-Pacific. Length to 47 cm, usually much smaller.

Photo below, juvenile.

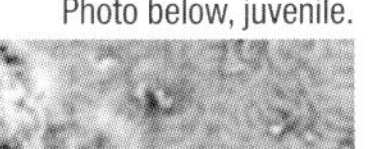

Shabby Parrotfish
Chlorurus sordidus

Occurs in various reef habitats, adults mainly seen on clear inner and outer reef slopes and along top of deep drop-offs, juveniles in seagrass beds and shallow lagoons to protected inner algae reefs, where usually forming small groups. Colour pattern readily identify both sexes, males overall green colour with a pale tail base and bluish cheeks, females darker with white tail. Widespread Indo-Pacific. Length to 40 cm.

Five-saddle Parrotfish
Scarus scaber

Commonly inhabits large lagoons with coral slopes and inner reefs, often in silty conditions. Usually seen in small groups of mixed sexes. Readily identified by colour patterns, distinct in both sexes, females with three saddle bars on back, males with overall greenish colour and pale side patch behind pectoral fin. West Indian Ocean. Length to 35 cm. Similar to *S. dimidiatus* in the Pacific.

Three-colour Parrotfish
Scarus tricolor

Commonly seen along deep outer reef walls, and on clear inner reef slopes. Usually in moderate depths from 10 to 40 m. Males identified by long green stripes on head, above and below eyes, which are usually short in similar species. Female has dark body, sometimes almost black, with yellow eye and pinkish brown tail. Widespread equatorial waters of Indo- Pacific. Length to 40 cm.

Rosy-cheek Parrotfish
Scarus psittacus

Found in various reef habitats from silty inshore reefs to outer reef walls. Highly variable in colour, in the Maldives, males are often bright yellow along base of dorsal fin and over the back. The cheek is mostly pink. Widespread Indo-Pacific. One of the smallest species, length to 30 cm.

Green-face Parrotfish
Scarus prasiognathos

A common species on outer reef slopes, often in large groups of females, as well as males. The latter are easily recognised by bright green on the cheek and snout. Females are dark with white spotting as shown in the photograph. Mainly Indian Ocean, but ranges along the continent to southern Japan. Length to 60 cm.

Dusky Parrotfish
Scarus niger

Inhabits clear inner reef crests to outer reef drop-offs at various depths to about 30 m. Males look very dark in natural light and have a distinctive green band behind the eye. Females are reddish brown below, and sides bear a lined pattern. However, colour patterns with regards to lines and band behind eye varies greatly throughout its Indo-Pacific range. Length to 40 cm.

Green-snout Parrotfish
Scarus viridifucatus

Occurs on inshore reefs and clear lagoons with rich coral and rubble zones. Usually seen solitary on reef crests or swimming with other species to feed together. Females dark and very plain, males distinguished by large green patch around mouth almost reaching the eyes. Widespread Indian Ocean, ranging to Bali and Sulawesi, Indonesia. Length to 25 cm.

Green-blotched Parrotfish
Scarus quoyi

An inshore species, primarily found on reef crests and slopes and occasionally on outer reefs, often in silty habitats. Form large schools of mixed sexes. An almost entirely purplish head with green around the mouth extending in a band to the eye identifies males. Widespread Indo-Pacific. Length to 40 cm.

Black-tip Parrotfish
Chlorurus capistratoides

Inhabits clear inner to outer reef crests with coral boulders rich in algae growth, usually shallow in surge zones. Females broadly banded and pectoral fins yellow. Males have pink bars on most body scales, with short green lines above, below and behind the eyes. One of a complex of similar species, probably widespread Indian Ocean, ranging to Bali, Indonesia. Length to 40 cm.

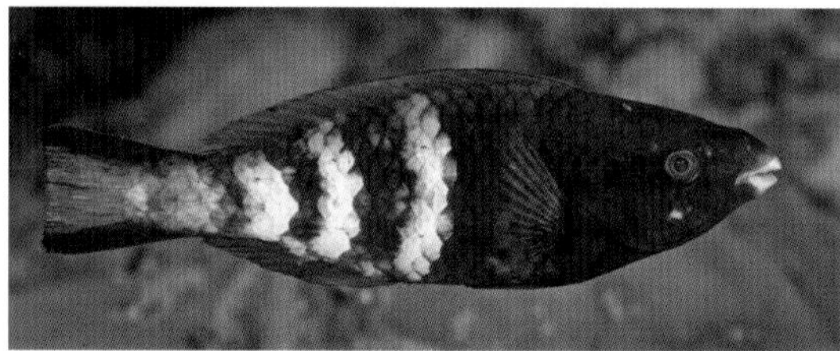

Bartail Parrotfish
Scarus caudofasciatus

Occurs in clear outer reef habitats, usually in depths over 20 m. Males are rather flighty. Females distinctly patterned with broad white bands on back half of body, males mainly green with thick blue stripes over snout and along fin margins, and long tail fin lobes. Only known from western Indian Ocean. Length to 50 cm.

Eclipse Parrotfish
Scarus russelii

Commonly found on outer reef slopes in 6 to 15 m depth, usually near edge of deep water. Males are solitary and large individuals distinguished by yellow patch following the mouth and a half - dark, half - light body colour. Females are banded. Only known from the west Indian Ocean. Length to 50 cm.

Happy Parrotfish
Scarus festivus

Inhabits clear water, mainly inner reefs. In the Maldives, it is inconspicuous and uncommon until fully grown. Male has a rather blunt head and distinctive banding across the top and above the eyes, and below the mouth leading towards the eye. Widespread Indo-Pacific, but mainly in continental waters of Asia, ranging to southern Japan. Length to 45 cm.

Blue-barred Parrotfish
Scarus ghobban

Occurs on inshore reefs with adults usually in depths of 15 to 40 m where common. Sometimes in small groups. Juveniles on algae reef habitat. Males are green to blue, have large scales with a yellow margin, sometimes showing pale vertical bands; more pronounced in the brownish females. Juveniles similar to adults but banding is more pronounced and follow twin white spots in Indian Ocean population. Widespread Indo-Pacific. Length to 75 cm

---

Spinytooth Parrotfish
Calotomus spinidens

Seen inshore, usually in seagrass habitat channels or adjacent slopes to about 25 m depth. Often swims amongst weeds and is well camouflaged. Eats seagrasses and algae, including invertebrates living on them. *Calotomus* spp. differ from most other parrotfishes by having separate outer teeth (rather than fused beaklike). Brownish or green with two series of spaced white spots along upper sides. Widespread Indo-Pacific. Length to about 30 cm.

Starry-eye Parrotfish
Calotomus carolinus

Habitats range from inner to outer reef crest in channels and around large coral heads. A dull looking species usually not noticed. Males are dusky grey-brown, greenish over back, and with red lines radiating from eyes. Mainly scrapes algae from dead coral bases. Widespread Indo-Pacific. Length to 40 cm.

Seagrass Parrotfish
Leptoscarus vaigiensis

Commonly occurs in seagrass beds, usually in very shallow intertidal zones. Seen swimming in groups during feeding sessions, mainly consuming seagrass leaves, including algae and invertebrates growing on them. Mainly green, males with white mid-lateral line. Widespread Indo-Pacific. Length to 35 cm.

GRUBFISHES
PINGUIPEDIDAE

A moderately large mostly tropical family with at least four genera and 60+ species, four of which are known from the Maldives. They are called sandsmelts in Africa, and also known as weevers or sand perches elsewhere, even though they do not look like smelts or perches. These bottom fishes are commonly seen on or near reefs, especially in rubble zones. Tropical species are found on shallow reef crests and slopes, but in cool temperate seas they mostly occur very deep and are only known from trawls. Some of the reef species have very similar colouration and can be difficult to identify. Several species appear to be undescribed. The adult and juvenile stages are very similar and differences between sexes are small, usually with some additional markings on the cheek or lips of the male. Grubfishes are diurnal and dig into the sand under solid pieces of rubble or reef to make shelter and to escape danger, or to sleep. Diet comprises small animals and zooplankton.

Maldivian Grubfish
Parapercis signata

Inhabits clear sand habitat in lagoons and on sand flats along reef edges, near large remote coral heads, on rubble or sand to at least 50 m depth. Usually in small groups, spread out in the area and occasionally pairing. Colouration is distinctive, with sandy colour and dark first dorsal fin. Only known from the Maldives, where common. Length to 13 cm.

Black-tail Grubfish
Parapercis hexophtalma

Occurs in large sandy lagoons and open sand slopes between reefs, including silty habitats. Usually shallow to about 15 m depth. Small juveniles have an almost fully black tail, reducing from the margins to a proportionally smaller area in adults. Body is very pale with a series of small dark spots; the lowest series is black and more defined. Widespread Indo-Pacific. Length to 25 cm.

Thousand-spot Grubfish
Parapercis millepunctata

Commonly found on algae reefs with mixed sand and coarse rubble from lagoons to outer reef slopes, in very shallow water to about 15 m depth. In the Maldives this species is distinguished by the series of dark blotches along the body and the white streak in the tail fin. Elsewhere, there are several similar species. Widespread west Pacific, ranging into Indian Ocean as far as the Maldives. Length to 14 cm.

Lyre-tail Grubfish
Parapercis schauinslandii

A rare species in the Maldives and only a few seen in deep water at 35 m, on a sandy channel with rubble bottom. Often swims well above the bottom to feed in currents on zooplankton. Tail is very distinctive with the elongated tips. Generally in depths of 10 to at least 50 m often occurs in small groups. Widespread Indo-Pacific, common in Indonesia. Length to 18 cm.

Photo: top right, juvenile; lower, adult male: Bali, Indonesia.

SAND DIVERS
TRICHONOTIDAE

A small Indo-Pacific family with a single genus and at least eight species, one of which is known from the Maldives, but more can be expected. They typically occur in groups on sand slopes with slow tidal currents and feed on zooplankton at particular times. They quickly dive into the sand when approached.

Long-rayed Sand Diver
Trichonotus elegans

Inhabits clear water sand slopes in the Maldives, between 5 and 20 m depth. Swims in large groups, often with many males together displaying the long filaments in the dorsal fin to each other. Smaller females and juveniles swim closely together when feeding. When no current is running, they are usually all buried in the sand slopes. A widespread species originally described from Japan but occurs commonly throughout Indonesia. These photographs represent the first record for the Maldives. Length to 18 cm, usually about 15 cm.

TRIPLEFINS
TRIPTERYGIIDAE

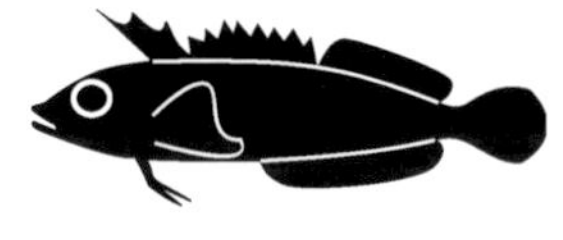

A large family of mostly small tropical fishes (some grow much larger in sub-tropical seas) with over 20, perhaps 30 genera, and probably about 200 species. Most species are undescribed and because of their small size and similarly camouflaged colours, they are difficult to work on. These fishes are blenny related and characterised by three separate dorsal fins. They are also known as threefins. Sometimes the male displays bright colours prior to spawning and a few have permanent distinctive colouration. Most species are a few centimetres long and live among algal reef habitats in crevices of cave walls. Possibly about 10 species are in the Maldives but few are commonly observed and only two are included here. Their diet comprises small animals, both benthic and zooplankton.

Maldives Triplefin
Helcogramma maldivensis

Inhabits clear water reefs, often on coral outcrops along steep slopes or drop-offs in depths from about 6 to 35 m. Often found in small groups on sponges or smooth corals. The distinctive colouration of stripes and spots makes this one of the few species to be easily recognized. Only known from Maldives and Sri Lanka. Length to 40 mm.

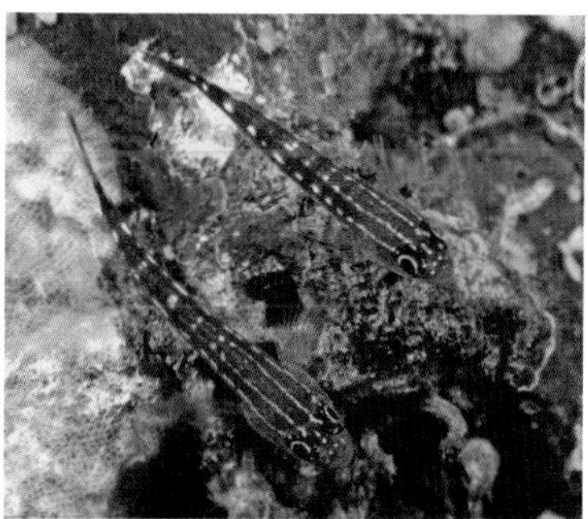

Green-head Triplefin
Helcogramma sp.

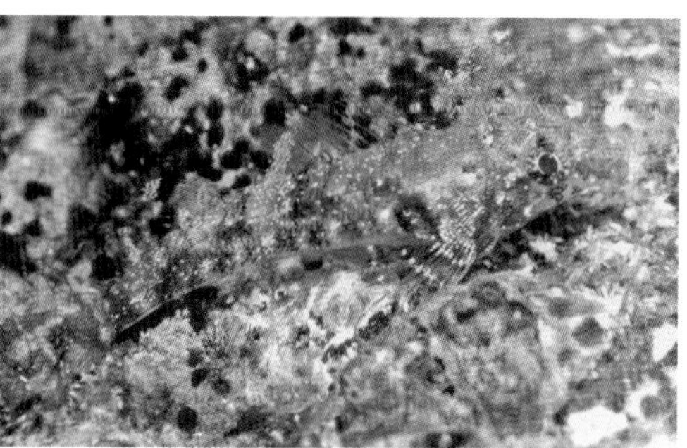

An undetermined species. Usually found in algae on sheltered reefs, at the bases of corals, or in caves along slopes and drop-offs. There are many similar species in this genus and with well over one hundred estimated species, several more can be expected in the Maldives, most of which are undescribed. Length of this species, about 40 mm.

BLENNIES
BLENNIIDAE

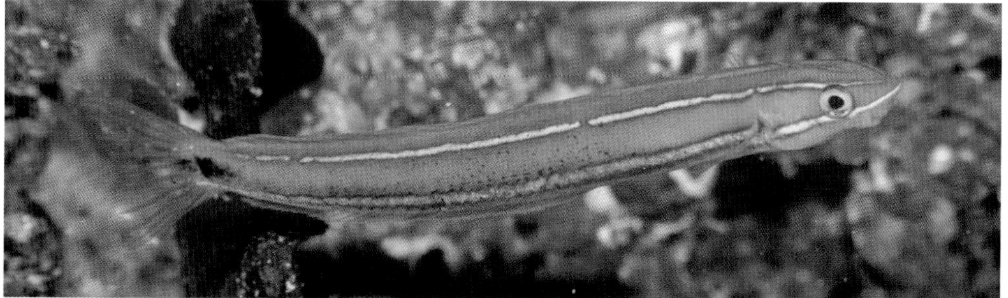

A very large family comprised of several distinctive groups or sub-families with more than 50 genera and about 350 species globally. They are divided here into two groups, the free-swimming, and those usually resting on the bottom.

SABRETOOTH BLENNIES
BLENNIIDAE-1

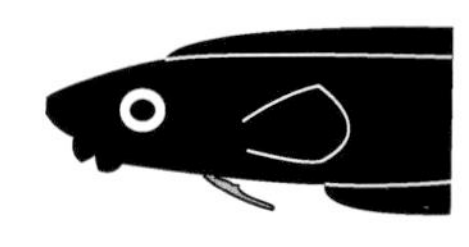

A group of slender and usually boldly marked species, that swim above the bottom when in pursuit of food. They retreat to holes in the reef to escape danger, for nesting, or to sleep. The sabretooth blennies have long sabre-like teeth in their lower jaw, venomous in some, that point forward when the mouth is wide open. Some harmless fishes, including some other blennies, mimic the venomous species that are respected by predators that target small fishes. Diet comprises various zooplankton and some species specialise in feeding on parts of other fishes, as explained in the species accounts.

Smith's Venomous Blenny
Meiacanthus smithi

Occurs on sheltered clear reef habitats including large coral rubble with mixed algae and coral growth, and soft bottom habitat with sponges and rich invertebrate growth. Usually seen solitary, shallow to depths of 35 m. Identified by black stripe on dorsal fin and oblique black band over the eye. Feeds on small invertebrates. Widespread Indian Ocean from Maldives to southern Indonesia. Length to 75 mm.

Imposter Blenny
Plagiotremus phenax

Occurs on sheltered reef habitat, usually shallow on reef flats with large corals. Mimics *Meiacanthus smithi* and is easily overlooked. Best distinguished by the lack of dark stripe over the eye, which is distinct in the *Meiacanthus.* Attacks other fishes, biting fins and scales. Widespread Indian Ocean from the Maldives to southern Indonesia. Length to 60 mm.

Mimic Blenny
Plagiotremus tapeinosoma

Also known as Piano Blenny. Seen singly or in small numbers, but often swims with similar shaped planktivores and attacks large fishes that swim close by. It takes bites from fins, scales or mucus, in a 'hit and run' fashion and quickly disappears in the reef when chased by an angry victim. Also bites divers, especially snorkellers going up to the surface. Shallow protected reefs. Widespread Indo-Pacific. Length to 12 cm.

Tube-worm Blenny
Plagiotremus rhinorhynchos

A moderately common species along inner reef slopes with mixed algae and coral growth. Uses empty tubeworm shells in the reef for shelter and nesting. Males guard eggs, and entice the female to nest by courting in a dance like motion, but gets rather rough, as females often bare scars. Variable in colour, from orange to almost black, and has two blue lines. Widespread Indo-Pacific. Length to 12 cm.

False Cleanerfish
Aspidontus taeniatus

Occurs on sheltered reef slopes and crests, usually in mixed invertebrate and algae habitats. Adults are usually seen in small aggregations, feeding on the bottom. Juveniles, until almost fully grown, remain solitary and are busy impersonating the cleaner wrasse *Labroides dimidiatus*. It differs by having a more pointed snout and longer dorsal and anal fin bases. Unlike the cleaner wrasses, that eat parasites from other fishes, the blenny bites bits from other fishes, such as the fins. Large adults do this part time only, and feed mainly on the reef itself, on invertebrates and algae. Widespread Indo-Pacific. Length to 12 cm.

Lance Blenny
Aspidontus dussumieri

Rare in the Maldives. Mainly seen inshore and often in silty habitat with rocky algae reefs, on crests and slopes, usually solitary in depths to 20 m. Identified by the long body and smooth black stripe along upper sides. Sometimes have filaments on the tail fin. It uses empty tubeworm tubes for shelter. Feeds on zooplankton and may bite other fishes. Widespread Indo-Pacific. Length to 12 cm.

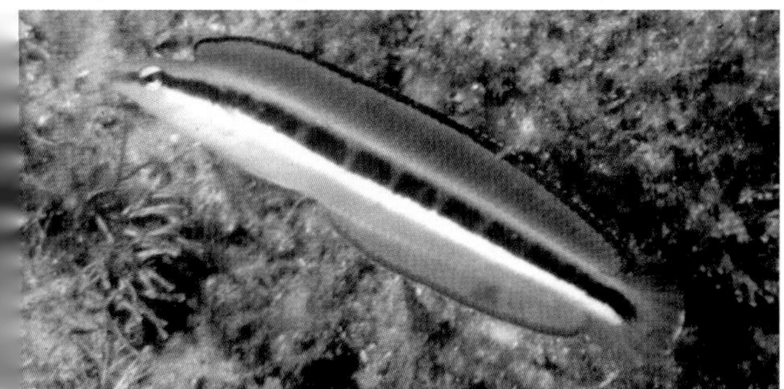

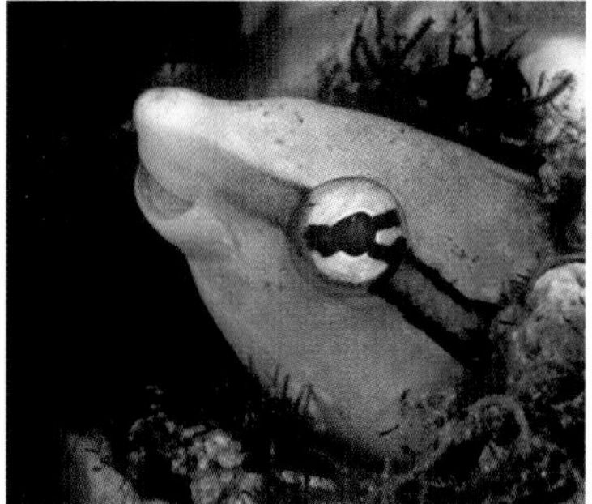

Crested Sabretooth Blenny
Petroscirtes mitratus

Only found on seagrass beds and reef with heavy algae or sargassum growth, but common in those habitats in the Maldives. Often rests against seagrass leaves and sometimes seen floating in the current, suspended in the water column with tail curled in. Recognised by tall dorsal fin close behind the head, and leafy bits above the eyes. Widespread Indo-Pacific. Length to 65 mm.

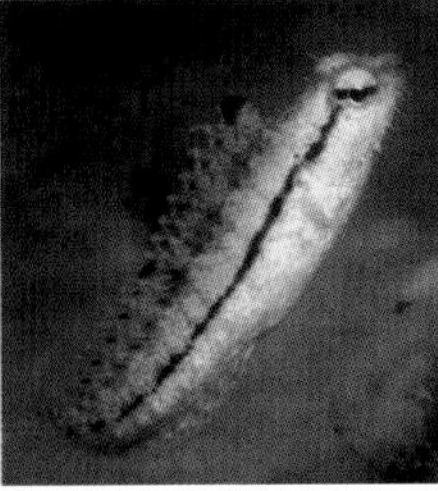

Bearded Sabretooth Blenny
Petroscirtes xestus

Mainly found on silty reefs and commonly occurs in harbours and lagoons on rubble reef, seeking refuge in small holes or crevices. Recognised by pale colour, thin dark line on sides, and leafy bits on the chin. Widespread Indo-Pacific. Length to 65 mm.

REEF BLENNIES
BLENNIIDAE-2

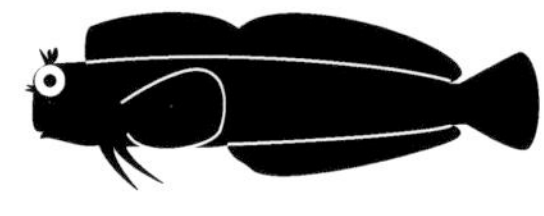

The largest group, these blennies are bottom dwellers in shallow coastal waters. Some species are intertidal and may be left high and dry for a short time as the water level drops from the swell or wave action. Most reef or rock blennies are territorial and, as they scrape algae for food off dead coral surfaces, each has its own little patch. Often they occur in spread out groups and males may allow some females nearby, but females often argue amongst themselves. There are many species-complexes that represent geographical forms, especially among the combtooth blennies. The similar species in such a group can be difficult to distinguish from each other. Amongst rock blennies, males may have different colour patterns from females, and in some species males develop a crest on the head.

Black-eared Eyelash Blenny
Cirripectes auritus

Inhabits clear water inner reef crests and slopes in rich coral habitat, usually shallow in 6 to 10 m depth. Pale creamy brown in colour and easily identified by the 'ear' spot. Moderately common in the Maldives. Widespread Indo-Pacific. Length to 9 cm.

Chestnut Eyelash Blenny
Cirripectes castaneus

Very common in the Maldives on inner and outer reef crests, rarely deeper than 6 m. Looks dusky and almost featureless with some indistinct barring, but tail fin is often yellowish. Widespread Indo-Pacific. Length to 12 cm.

Red-streaked Eyelash Blenny
Cirripectes stigmaticus

Inhabits reef crests with rich coral growth, especially large *Acropora* plate corals where males can sit boldly out in the open, but ready to dive for cover when approached, or by the first sign of trouble. Only males are easily identified by the red vertical streaks on their sides, females are plain dark. Widespread Indo-Pacific. Length to 10 cm.

Little Combtooth Blenny
Ecsenius minutus

Common on clear inner and outer reef slopes, usually found on corals or around the bases to about 10 m depth. Identified by the series of pale spots along the body. Only known from the Maldives. Belongs to a species-complex distributed throughout the Indo-Pacific. Length to 65 mm.

Two-colour Combtooth Blenny
Ecsenius bicolor

Found on clear water reef crests and slopes and in outer reef lagoons with coral bommies to about 20 m depth. There is two colour forms: half orange and half black, or a black top with white belly. Apparently the different colour forms are not sex related. Widespread Indo-Pacific. Length to 85 mm.

Lined Combtooth Blenny
Ecsenius lineatus

A common species in the Maldives, which occurs in various reef habitats, mainly sheltered deep lagoons on remote coral heads to depths of at least 30 m. Variable in colour from very dark banded, to the band broken up into a series of spots. The latter variation is common in the Maldives. Widespread Indo-Pacific. Length to 10 cm.

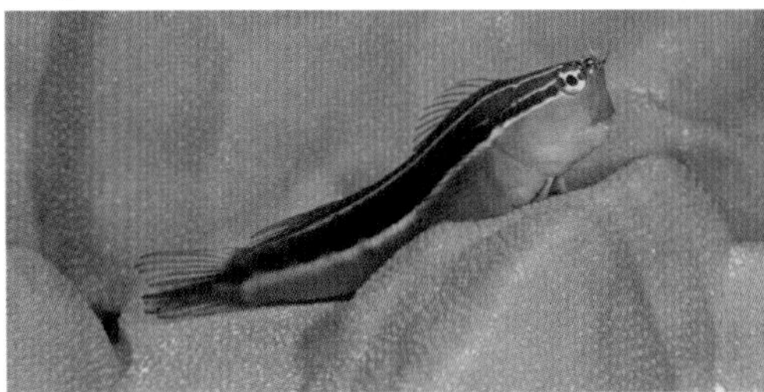

Lyre-tail Combtooth Blenny
Ecsenius midas

Inhabits inner to outer reef habitats on coral slopes in current prone areas. It has an unusual behaviour for its genus; it swims high above the bottom when current is running to feed on zooplankton. These blennies often mix with orange or yellow basslets and take on the same colour, becoming 'one of the pack'. They retreat to reefs and reverse themselves into small holes. Often seen with just the head at the entrance. Identified by shape and colour, the lyre-shaped tail is diagnostic. Widespread Indo-Pacific, with some colour variation in different areas. Length to 13 cm.

Leopard Blenny
Exallias brevis

Usually occurs in rich coral reef crests, sitting on top of *Acropora* thickets in depths of about 6 m, but quickly disappear when approached. Often seen in small loose groups but usually only the larger dominating one moves about openly. Males prepare a nesting site at the base of corals. Widespread Indo-Pacific. Length to 14 cm.

Jewelled Blenny
Salarias fasciatus

Not common in the Maldives; mainly found in calm, highly protected shallow reefs and harbours amongst dead coral rubble. Occurs elsewhere in coastal reef habitats to about 10 m depth. Appears to be deep-bodied because of the tall and long-based dorsal fins. It has a pattern of dark blotches and striations. Widespread Indo-Pacific with some geographical variations. Length to 14 cm.

Big-nose Blenny
Entomacrodus striatus

Inhabits silty reefs inshore, often on shallow beams below jetties near the surface. Occurs in small groups, dominated by the largest individuals. A large bushy tentacle above the eye and a broad rounded snout identifies it. Mainly bluish-grey in colour with dark mottling. Widespread Indo-Pacific. Length to 16 cm.

Orange-spotted Blenny
Blenniella chrysospilos

Occurs on very shallow reef flats, often in surge and high-energy zones on outer reefs, where it occupies the numerous small holes in the reefs. They are algae feeders that scrape dead coral from the base of corals, but quickly retreat to their narrow hideouts when approached. Readily identified by red spots that are prominent on the face. Widespread Indo-Pacific. Length to 12 cm.

Rippled Rockskipper
Istiblennius edentulus

Common in the intertidal zones in protected bays, including mangrove and harbour habitats. Only seen on high tide in a few metres depth. Identified by the regular banded pattern along the body. Widespread Indo-Pacific. Length to 16 cm, usually about 12 cm.

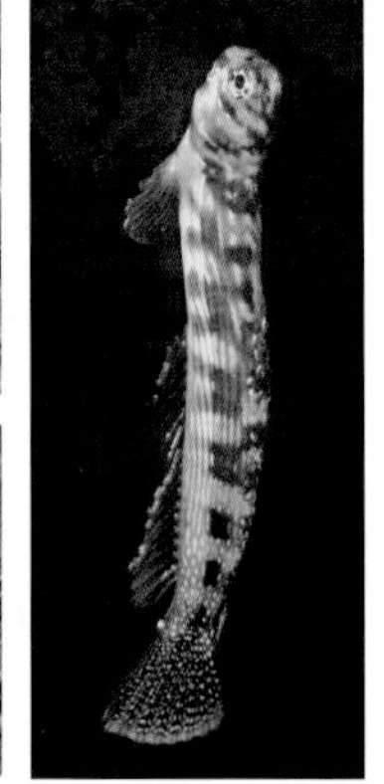

Thin-lined Rockskipper
Istiblennius lineatus

Found in intertidal zones, in exposed and surge zones. Seen hanging onto the reef and coming out of the water as the level drops from wave action. Scrapes algae off dead corals or rocks. Identified by the thin dark longitudinal lines along the sides. Males have a crest on the head. Widespread Indo-Pacific. Length to 15 cm.

DRAGONETS
CALLIONYMIDAE

A large, mainly tropical family with nine genera and about 125 species, but only one is commonly observed in the Maldives. Some other species are common in the Maldives, but these live on the sandy bottom and are coloured on top of their bodies accordingly, as well as being similar to each other. In all about 10 species can be found here, but apart from rarely being noticed, some are almost impossible to identify without collecting specimens. Most species occur in small groups of mixed sexes that are dominated by the largest male. Females are usually considerably smaller than fully-grown males. Males generally have extended rays in the dorsal fin or tail, which are erected to bare eye-like spots when they are displayed. Diet includes small creatures sucked from the sand or rubble with their small but extendable mouth.

Starry Dragonet
Synchiropus stellatus

Found on sheltered reefs, and along sand and rubble zones with mixed invertebrate and algae growth. They occur in spread out groups dominated by a large male. Females usually small, looking half the size of the male. Located in moderate depth in the Maldives, from about 10 to 40 m. Widespread Indian Ocean, with sibling species *S. moyeri* in West Pacific. Length to 8 cm.

Sand Dragonet
Callionymus sp.

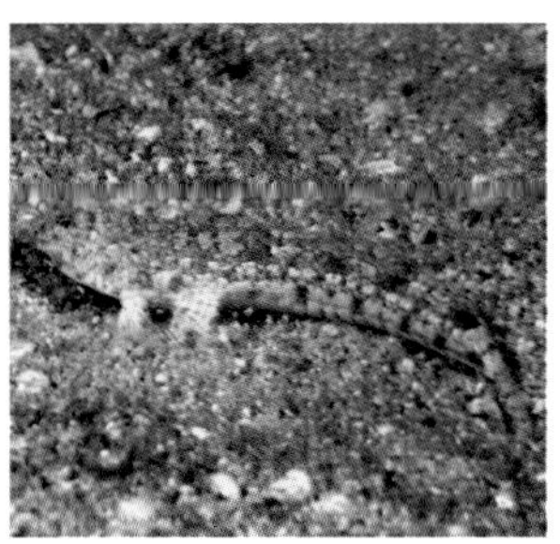

An undetermined species, possibly *C. delicatulus*. One of 5 very similar species reported from the Maldives. Mostly found on sand habitats in shallow lagoons and harbours, but one is known from depths over 70 m. Some are tiny, growing to only a few centimetres long, and usually occurring in small groups. Males have a tall first dorsal fin that is used for display. Identification is difficult without examining actual specimens.

GOBIES
GOBIIDAE

Gobies are the largest family of marine fishes with an estimated 200 genera and 1500 species worldwide. These comprise various distinctive groups and division of the family can be expected. They are well represented in the Maldives with about 30 genera and 80 species. The different groups are treated in this book separately.

SHRIMP GOBIES
GOBIIDAE-1

Some of the most interesting gobies live in a symbiotic relationship with snapping shrimps *Alpheus* spp. The shrimps are responsible for digging burrows and keeping them clean, whilst the goby stands guard at the entrance. The goby signals to the shrimp if it is safe to come out and dump material, or to work at the entrance. Adult gobies are nearly always in pairs but females are often in the burrow and only the male is visible. Adult shrimps are usually in pairs as well. Most gobies live with one particular species of shrimp, but there are many more goby than shrimp species. Shrimps are habitat specific and the various species are distributed over depth and bottom types. They inhabit shallow sandy flats, deep rubble slopes and coarse sand, while other species prefer fine mud. Gobies feed on small invertebrates, including zooplankton. The number of species in each genus is undetermined at this stage with many taxonomic problems.

Tall-fin Shrimp-goby
Vanderhorstia prealta

A spectacular species, usually found in moderately deep water from 20 to 40 m, on white sand with fine rubble. It lives with two types of snapping shrimps, *Alpheus randalli* and *A. ochrostriatus.* Readily identified by tall dorsal fin and dark colour. The dorsal fin of the male is considerably taller than that of the female. Only known from Western Indian Ocean. Length to 45 mm.

Twin-spotted Shrimp-goby
Vanderhorstia ambanoro

Inhabits fine sand or mud habitats, living with grey or brown snapping shrimps. Appears to be rare in the Maldives. Identified by pale colour and series of black spots, male with blue stripes along margin of ventral fin. Shallow to about 20 m depth. Widespread Indo-Pacific. Length to 12 cm.

Blue-barred Shrimp-goby
Vanderhorstia ornatissima

Commonly found along the edges of shallow seagrass beds and in silty lagoons amongst rubble in a few metres depth. It lives with a snapping shrimp species that is grey in colour with dark bands on its back. Adult fish and shrimp are usually undetermined in pairs. Recognised by the thin blue bars on the side and blue rings near the tail. Widespread Indo-Pacific. Length to 85 mm.

Dracula Shrimp-goby
Stonogobiops dracula

Inhabits open sand and rubble zones adjacent to reefs in moderate depths, usually in 20+ m, often in pairs. Lives with the red-banded snapping shrimp *Alpheus randalli.* Easily identified by white body and black-banded colour pattern. Large individuals develop additional narrow bars between broad ones. Only known from west Indian Ocean. Length to at least 7 cm.

Fan Shrimp-goby
Flabelligobius latruncularius

Inhabits open sand and rubble zones adjacent to reefs in moderate depths, usually in 20+ m, and mostly seen singly. Lives with the red-banded snapping shrimp *Alpheus randalli*. Identified by slender body with blotched pattern and large first dorsal fin, that develops filaments in males. Only known from Red Sea and west Indian Ocean. Length to 10 cm.

Black Shrimp-goby
Cryptocentrus fasciatus

Inhabits open sand flats and gentle slopes adjacent to reefs from about 10 m depth, often in pairs. Lives with banded snapping shrimps. Mostly black with fine pale spotting, or white saddles over the top of head and back. Sometimes yellow in colour. Widespread Indo-Pacific. Length to 10 cm.

Side-spot Shrimp-goby
Cryptocentrus strigilliceps

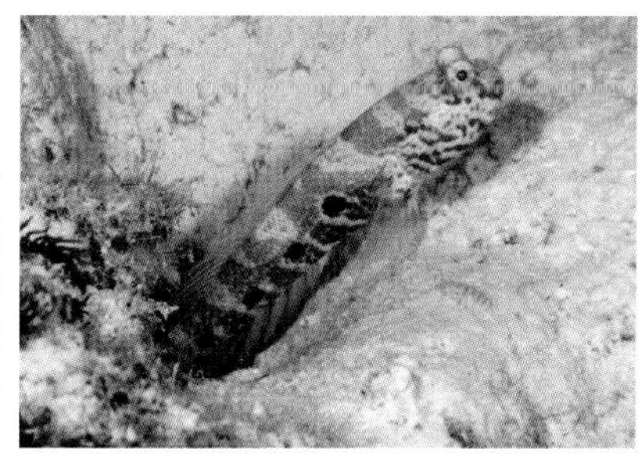

Inhabits shallow silty lagoons along reef walls and near bombies, in the deeper areas, to about 10 m depth. Identified by the series of round black spots located centrally along the sides, the first spot is the largest and often edged in white. It lives with grey or dusky snapping shrimps. Widespread Indo-Pacific. Length to 10 cm.

Pink-bar Shrimp-goby
Amblyeleotris aurora

Common in the Maldives, but usually in depths of about 30 m, occasionally shallower along the bases of outer reefs and lagoon channels on rubble and sand. Lives with the red-banded snapping shrimp *Alpheus randalli*. Widespread Indian Ocean, reported between 10 and 35 m. Length to 11 cm.

Diagonal Shrimp-goby
Amblyeleotris diagonalis

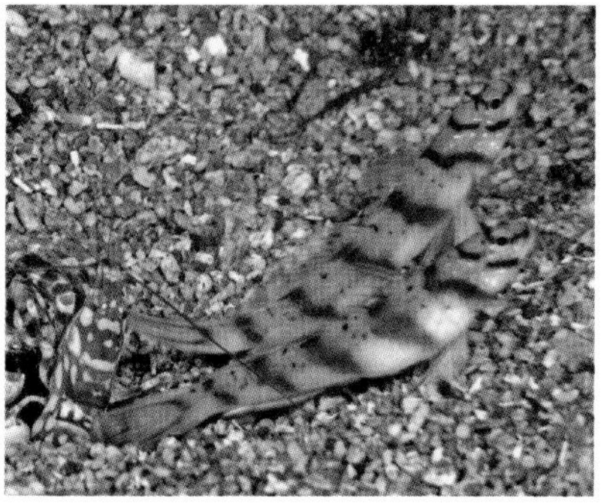

Occurs in various protected sand habitats, from shallow coarse sand and rubble slopes, to moderately deep rubble zones along deep reef bases, usually in pairs, living with the blotched snapping shrimp *Alpheus bellulus*. There are several similarly banded species, but the diagonal stripes on the head are diagnostic for this species. One of the most widespread Indo Pacific species. Length to 10 cm.

Broad-banded Shrimp-goby
Amblyeleotris periophthalma

Inhabits coarse sand and rubble patches on or near reef margins, usually seen singly, living with various grey or brown snapping shrimps, including *Alpheus djiboutensis*, which is often yellow. To about 20 m depth. Best identified by the combined spotted and banded patterns. Widespread Indo-Pacific. Length to 11 cm.

Steinitz's Shrimp-goby
Amblyeleotris steinitzi

Mainly common in clean white sand lagoons, often in sand patches surrounded by reef, in small spread out groups to about 10 m depth. Pale in colour in the Maldives and best identified by the occasionally black face and numerous small orange spots in the dorsal fins. Widespread Indo-Pacific, but with some geographical variations between the Indian and Pacific Oceans. Length to 12 cm.

Burgundy Shrimp-goby
Amblyeleotris wheeleri

Occurs on shallow reef flats and slopes in rubble, often in gutters or large open patches, including zones with moderate surge, ranging to about 40 m depth. Usually living with the snapping shrimp *Alpheus djiboutensis*. Strongly banded with dark, wine-red bars and mostly bluish spots. Widespread Indo-Pacific. Length to 10 cm.

Pale Shrimp-goby
Ctenogobiops feroculus

Commonly found on shallow white sand flats in sheltered lagoons and harbours, often in pairs, usually living with the snapping shrimp *Alpheus djiboutensis*. Identified by pale colour and a series of black spots and dashes along sides, and black eyes. Widespread Indo-Pacific. Length to 75 mm.

Crocus Shrimp-goby
Ctenogobiops crocineus

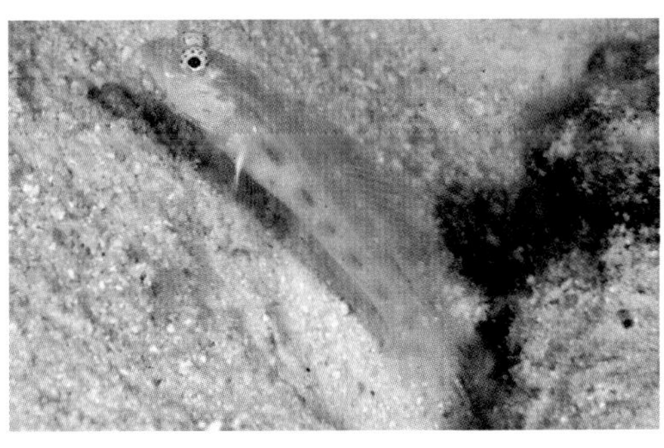

Moderately common in clear water lagoons on shallow sand flats with sparse rubble, usually in pairs when adult. Identified by the light colour and brown blotches along upper sides, and a series of diagonal orange spots over the head and behind the eye. Widespread Indo-Pacific. Length to 7 cm.

SAND GOBIES
GOBIIDAE-2

This group includes the gobies that are mainly found resting on the sand and that don't have symbiotic relationships with snapping shrimps. The species are usually similarly coloured and camouflaged with the type of bottom on which they live. They usually lack the bold colours found in reef fishes and are identified by the various spotted or speckled patterns, or by the shape of the head or fins. Food comprises small invertebrates, often filtered from the sand.

Silty Sand-goby
Gnatholepis anjerensis

A common species in shallow silty lagoons with seagrasses and in harbours with rubble piles on the sand. The genus, comprising about 9 species, is characterised by the thin vertical dark line below the eye. This species has small spots all over, including the fins, and is part of a species complex that occur throughout the Indo-Pacific. This species is widespread in the Indo-West Pacific, ranging north to Japan, but comprises several geographical colour variations. Length to 75 mm.

Eye-bar Sand-goby
Gnatholepis cauerensis

A common species on mixed rubble, sand and reef habitat, including lagoons and sheltered zones to about 20 m depth. Variable in colour from very pale with few markings, to dark with small black spots and some larger white spots over the back and along the sides usually to suit habitat. Has a distinct vertical black line through the eye. Widespread Indo-Pacific. Often wrongly identified as *G. scapulostigma*, a junior synonym. Length to 65 mm.

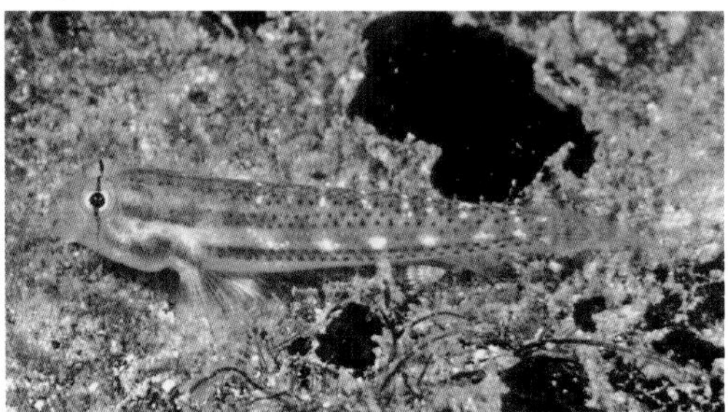

Bandit Goby
Gladiogobius rex

Moderately common but easily overlooked. Found in sandy lagoons, along edges of coral patches with rubble to about 10 m deep. Identified by raised eyes and a horizontal dark band that runs across them. Widespread Indo-Pacific. Length to 75 mm.

Mud-reef Goby
Exyrias belissimus

Occurs in silty habitat lagoons, along reef margins and usually below large branching corals that grow on mud and rubble bottoms. Identified by generally large size, big head, tall fins and filamentous tips on first dorsal fin. Tail becomes very elongated in large males. Widespread Indo-Pacific. Length to 15 cm.

Decorated Sand-goby
Istigobius decoratus

Inhabits most sand and rubble habitats. Several similar species in the Indo-Pacific are difficult to identify, but only one is so far known from the Maldives. Easily distinguished from other sand gobies by the strongly spotted fins. Other species could be discovered. Widespread Indo-Pacific. Length to 10 cm.

Big-toothed Goby
Macrodontogobius wilburi

Inhabits sand and rubble zones along reef edges in sheltered habitats to about 20 m depth. Identified by the combination of a series of small but distinctive spots along sides and black marking on cheeks. Usually found solitary with other sand gobies. Widespread Indo-Pacific. Length to 65 mm.

Orange-spotted Sand-goby
Fusigobius sp. 1

Commonly found on rubble reef habitat in the Maldives, but appears to be undescribed and one of an orange spotted species complex, found distributed throughout the Indo-Pacific. It has a small, but distinctive black or blue spot on the first dorsal fin. Probably occurs throughout the west Indian Ocean, but needs to be researched. Length to 50 mm.

Inner-spotted Sand-goby
Fusigobius inframaculatus

Occurs in clear sand and rubble habitat and on the bottom of caves, shallow to about 15 m depth. Identified by orange spotting and several dark blotches. First dorsal fin with an extended ray in adults.Restricted to west Indian Ocean. Length to 65 mm.

Double-spot Sand-goby
Fusigobius duospilus

Inhabits clear sand and rubble zones among reefs, or on the sandy bottom of large overhangs or caves along drop-offs and walls, to depths of at least 25 m. Usually in small loose groups. Adults are best identified by the double dark spot in the first dorsal fin, as shown in the photograph. Widespread Indo-Pacific. Length to 50 mm.

Fine-spotted Sand-goby
Fusigobius neophytus

Occurs inshore, mainly in protected lagoons and harbours on sand and rubble habitats in often silty conditions to a depth of about 10 m. Identified by the mixed pale and dark spotting and usually some short angular lines across the back. Widespread Indo-Pacific. Length to 45 mm.

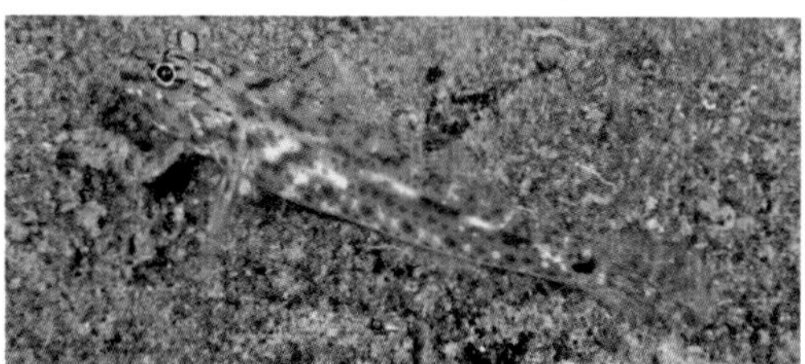

African Sand-goby
Fusigobius africanus (?)

Mainly found on reefs at the bottom of sandy caves or below large overhangs on slopes and drop-offs. The heavily pigmented pattern identifies this species. It appears to be synonymous with a species from the east African coast. Length to 45 mm

Pretty Lagoon-goby
Oplopomus oplopomus

Commonly occurs from a few metres depth in silty lagoons and harbours to very deep in some large lagoons with mud habitats. Deep bodied and ornamented with blue spots. Usually found near large crater-like holes in mud probably made by some invertebrates. It readily dives for cover when approached too closely. Widespread Indo-Pacific. Length to 10 cm.

Shy Lagoon-goby
Oplopomus caninoides

Seen on sand in current or tidal channels and in moderate depths of 20+ m. More slender than the Pretty Lagoon Goby, and with a larger spotted pattern. A flighty species, that swims away rather than diving into holes. Widespread Indo-Pacific. Length to 65 mm.

Sparsely-spotted Sand-goby
Oplopomops atherinoides

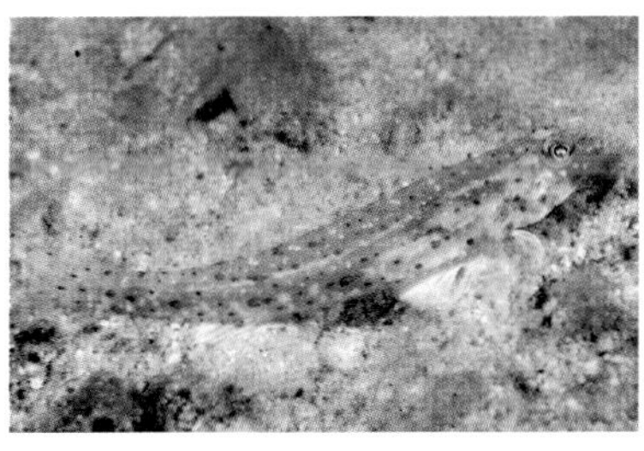

Occurs in shallow protected sand habitats in lagoons and harbours. Common in the Maldives, but easily overlooked, as it is well camouflaged on sand and hugs the bottom closely. Identified by the numerous small brown and white spots all over the body. Widespread Indo-Pacific. Length to 85 mm.

White Sand-goby
Hazeus maculipinnis

Occurs in clear white sand habitat to about 20 m depth. Originally described from the Maldives in 1993 on the basis of a single specimen in the genus *Opua*. Very plain and only have a few dark spots along the side and in the first dorsal fin. Eyes and pectoral fins are rather large. Length to about 50 mm.

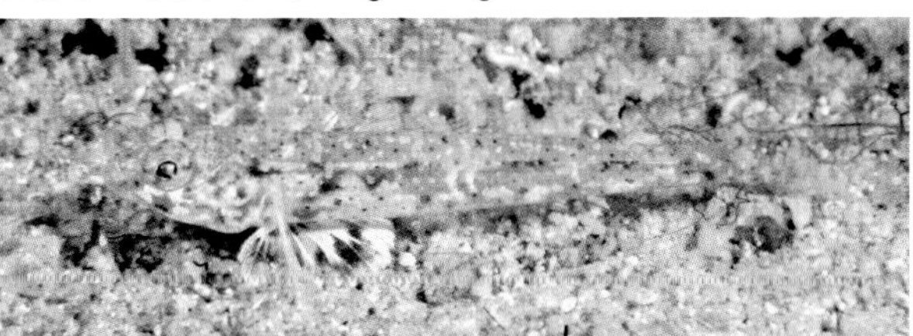

REEF GOBIES
GOBIIDAE-3

This is by far the largest group in the family, but also comprises the smallest species, many of which are living secretively in caves and reefs. These are the more colourful gobies and usually have distinctive colouration that easily identifies the species. Many of the small species are new to science and have not yet been named and more discoveries are expected, especially in places such as the Maldives, where large areas are yet to be explored. Some of the small species are free swimming over corals or in caves, and usually these are planktivores. Others feed on a variety of small invertebrates and also zooplankton.

Yellow Coral-goby
Gobiodon citrinus

This species lives exclusively in staghorn corals and is often common in lagoons where it forms colonies. Like other members in the genus, it has a slimy skin that is toxic. Readily identified by yellow colour with blue stripes on the side of the head, at the base of dorsal and anal fins, as well as habitat. Widespread in the Indo-Pacific. Length to 65 mm.

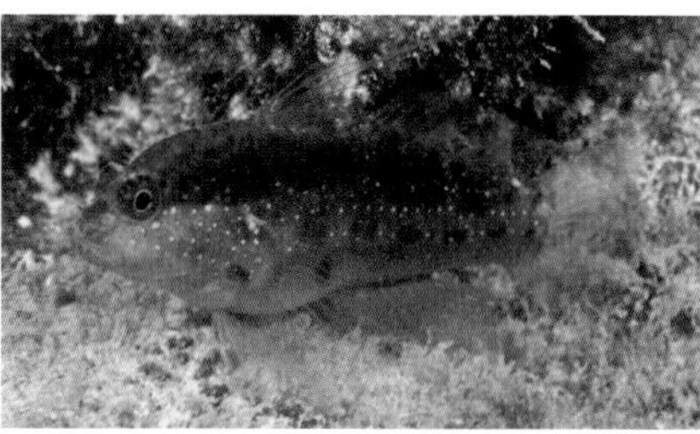

Starry Goby
Asterropteryx semipunctata

Common in the Maldives in lagoons and protected reef habitats with mixed rubble and silt. Usually found at the bases of large corals amongst rubble with small holes to escape danger, and often seen in small loose groups to about 10 m depth. Widespread Indo-Pacific. Length to 45 mm.

Full-Moon Reef-goby
Priolepis nocturna

Lives secretively in coral heads on sand. Easily recognized by the white body and black banding. Rare in the Maldives and only known from a few specimens in shallow sandy lagoons to about 10 m depth. Widespread Indo-Pacific, and recently found in Japan at 45 m depth. Length to 45 mm.

Banded Reef-goby
Priolepis cincta

A secretive but common species in reefs, usually observed when using a torch to inspect caves and crevices along reef slopes and walls. Depth ranges from almost intertidal to at least 50 m. Body distinctly banded and fins yellowish. Widespread Indo-Pacific, ranges into subtropical waters. Length to 70 mm but usually to 50 mm.

Orange-tail Reef-goby
Priolepis inhaca

Occurs in sheltered and silty habitats, lagoons and harbours. Secretive in rubble reef where seen living in pairs. Recognised by the reddish tail and dark edges on the scales. Only known from the west Indian Ocean. Length to 35 mm.

Sheppard's Pygmy-goby
Trimma sheppardi

Seen in caves and crevices, where secretive and often swims upside down on ceilings. Distinguished from similar species by the orange and white barring on the cheek. Widespread in the Indian Ocean and Red Sea. Length to 25 mm.

Red-lined Pygmy-goby
Trimma striatum

Occurs in lagoons and found in small caves or overhangs over sand in coral bommies, usually upside down on the ceilings to about 15 m depth. Easily recognised by the red lines on the face. Widespread Indo-Pacific. Length to 35 mm.

Red Pygmy-goby
Trimma naudei

Usually upside down on ceilings in caves and crevices to about 30 m depth. Identified by the large red blotches over the body, and some white spots variably present on the sides or back. Widespread Indo-Pacific. Length to 35 mm.

Orange-spotted Pygmy-goby
Trimma flammeum

Inhabits clear inner reef slopes and walls among rich coral growth mixed with sponges and ascidians, usually resting on ascidians in wait for zooplankton. Identified by the close set of orange spots over the head and body. Depth range about 10 to 30 m. Widespread west Indian Ocean. Length to 30 mm.

Red-spotted Pygmy-goby
Trimma sp. 1

Occurs on inner reef slopes, rich in mixed invertebrates and encrusting algae growth to about 20 m depth. Identified by the red spots over the head and body. An undetermined species, that appears to be undescribed. Length to 30 mm.

Sparsely-spotted Pygmy-goby
Trimma halonevum

Occurs on sheltered rubble and sand slopes with small coral heads or large rubble pieces, often in silty habitats. Identified by the red spots scattered over the head and following part of body. Ranges east to Flores, Indonesia. Length to 35 mm.

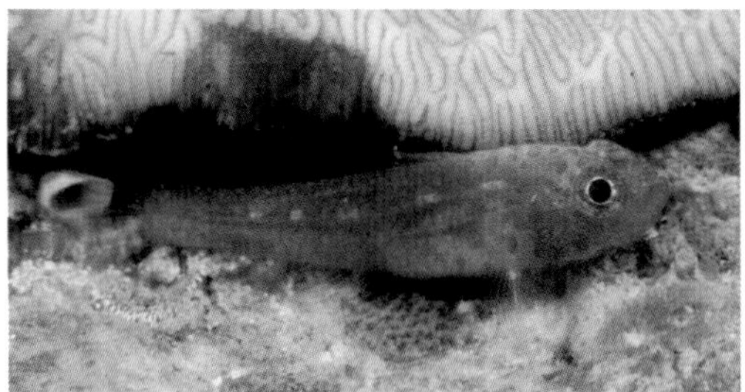

Yellow-spotted Pygmy-goby
Trimma sp. 2

Photographed on the shipwreck "Maldives Victory" at 20 m. An undetermined species, somewhat transparent, that shows white spots inside its body along vertebrate, and yellowish spots over the head and body. Length about 30 mm.

Filamentous Pygmy-goby
Trimma sp. 3

Inhabits steep slopes and walls in current prone areas, in caves with rich invertebrate growth and often on the ceiling upside down. An undetermined species showing little colour, but has a filamentous first dorsal fin and forked tail. Length, including long tail, 45 mm.

Sharp-eye Pygmy-goby
Trimma sp. 4

Occurs in various coral reef habitats, on bommies in lagoons to outer walls in 6 to 30 m depth. Moderately common and appears to be undescribed. Identified by bright blue in the eye shown in natural light. Length 25 mm.

Taylor's Pygmy-goby
Trimma taylori

Seen in caves along drop-offs and outer reef walls, usually in small groups that are free swimming when feeding on plankton, in depths of 20+ m. A light brownish species with numerous yellow spots and some fins with elongated rays. Widespread Indo-Pacific. Length to 40 mm.

Cave Pygmy-goby
Trimma tevegae

Seen in caves along inner reef drop-offs and outer reef walls, usually in small groups that are free swimming when feeding on plankton. Its depth range is 10 to 50 m. Recognised by the broad bluish grey stripe along upper sides and purplish tail. Widespread Indo-Pacific. Length to 35 mm.

White-line Pygmy-goby
Eviota mikiae

Commonly found on rich coral reef slopes away from strong surge but where moderate tidal currents run in depths from 6 to 25 m. Usually occurs in small groups on large coral heads. Readily identified by the obvious white line through the eye and extending along the body. Length to 35 mm.

Sebree's Pygmy-goby
Eviota sebreei

Occurs on clear water reef slopes and walls with rich coral growth. Usually found on rounded coral heads from 6 to 25 m depth. Identified by the series of internal white dashes showing along the back. Widespread and often common throughout the Indo-Pacific. Length to 30 mm.

White-spotted Pygmy-goby
Eviota zebrina

Photographed on inner reef slopes with rich invertebrate growth at about 20 m. Usually found in moderate depths, reported to 40 m. Identified by red to brownish head and body with a series of white spots, and black spot at tail fin base. Appears to be rare in the Maldives, reported from few specimens. West Indian Ocean. Length to 25 mm.

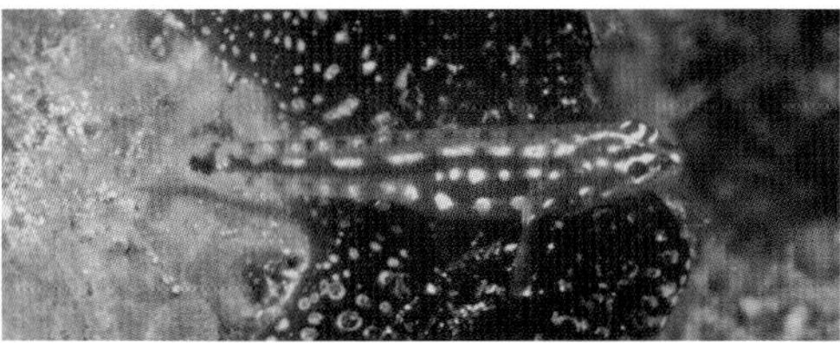

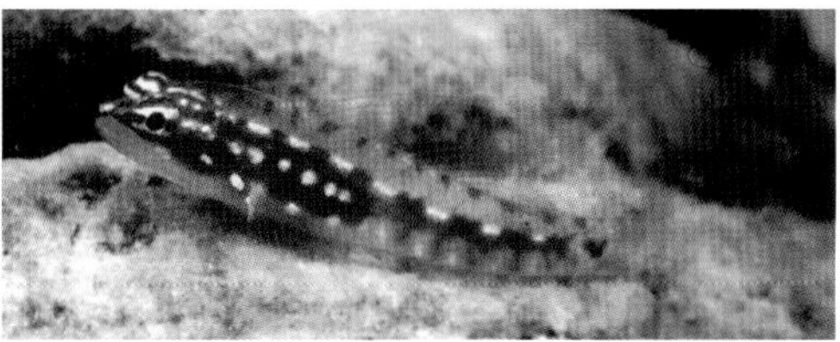

Belly-line Pygmy-goby
Eviota sigillata

Occurs in sheltered lagoons on rubble reef zones, usually shallow, to about 10 m depth. Semi-transparent body with distinctive black and white lines along the head and belly, and a series of short dark lines across the back. Widespread Indo-Pacific. Length about 20 mm.

Green Pygmy-goby
Eviota albolineata

A common shallow water species in mixed rubble, coral and short algae reef habitats, usually in shallow depths to about 15 m. Identified by the general greenish colour when seen in the wild. West Indian Ocean, with several very similar species elsewhere. Length to about 25 mm.

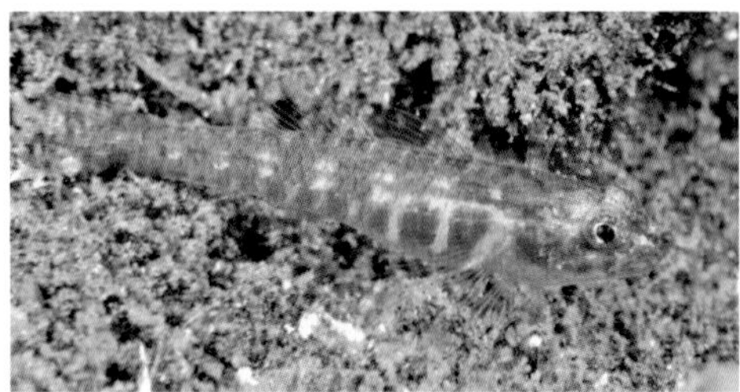

Red-blotched Pygmy-goby
Eviota guttata

Occurs in sheltered clear water reef habitat at coral bases and in caves with coralline algae growth. There are many similar species throughout the Indo-Pacific that are greenish with red spots or blotches. Length 20 mm.

Purple-eyed Goby
Bryaninops natans

Occurs in well-protected coral gardens in lagoons in small groups, to about 10 m depth. Usually swimming just above *Acropora* plate corals in slight currents to feed on zooplankton. Readily identified by the deep pink to purple eyes. Widespread Indo-Pacific. Length to 20 mm.

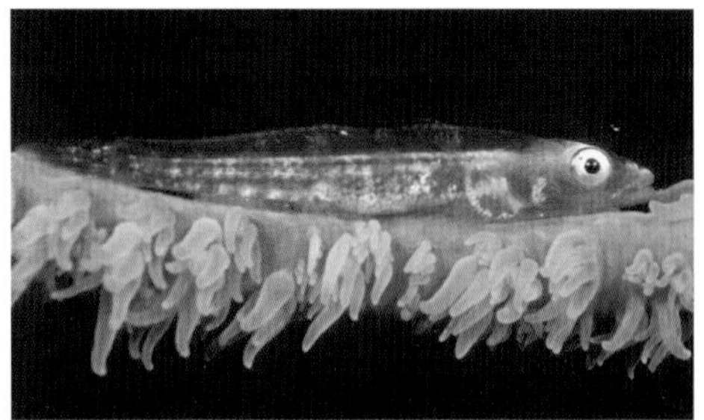

Loki Whip-goby
Bryaninops loki

This species is moderately common on seawhips and gorgonian corals, but only noticed by those purposely looking for them. Seawhips like current habitats and often stand on coral bommies in tidal channels. Gobies are usually present on the more remote whips. Widespread Indo-Pacific. Length to 30 mm.

Seawhip Goby
Bryaninops yongei

Lives mainly on seawhips in the genus *Cirrhipathes* and commonly occur in pairs. Sometimes juveniles are present on the same whip. Eggs are laid on a cleared section and guarded by the parents. Widespread Indo-Pacific. Length to 40 mm.

White-line Whip-goby
Bryaninops amplus

Lives on *Junceela* seawhips, which are in channels of deep lagoons in depths from about 6 m down. A very transparent species and has an internal white line and speckles along its spinal column. Widespread Indo-Pacific. Length to 40 mm.

Black-coral Goby
Bryaninops tigris

Lives on Black Coral bushes, Anthipathes sp. that grow on rubble ridges or remote patches on sand flats. The goby usually occurs in groups, which can get crowded in small bushes. Eggs are laid on cleared branches of the coral. Widespread Indo-Pacific. Length to 40 mm.

Slender Sponge-goby
Pleurosicya elongata

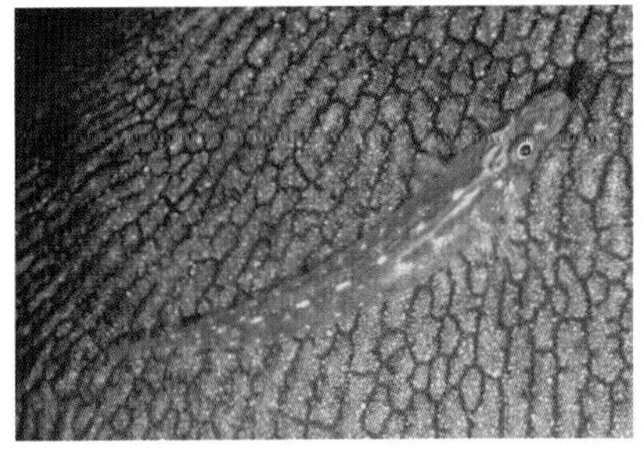

A common species, that lives on the underside of floppy sponges growing on shallow reef crests and slopes in 3 to 10 m depth. Finding the sponges usually reveals several of these gobies underneath, and more species can be expected by looking at differently coloured sponges. Widespread Indo-Pacific. Length to 40 mm.

Cling Goby
Pleurosicya micheli

Commonly found on corals and sponges on sheltered reef crests and slopes from intertidal to about 30 m depth, where it sits openly on reef. Recognised by semi-transparent body with a brown stripe from the tip of snout to eye, around eye and continuing along sides. Behind the eyes, the lines taper to a 'V'. Widespread Indo-Pacific. Length to 30 mm.

Many-host Goby
Pleurosicya mossambica

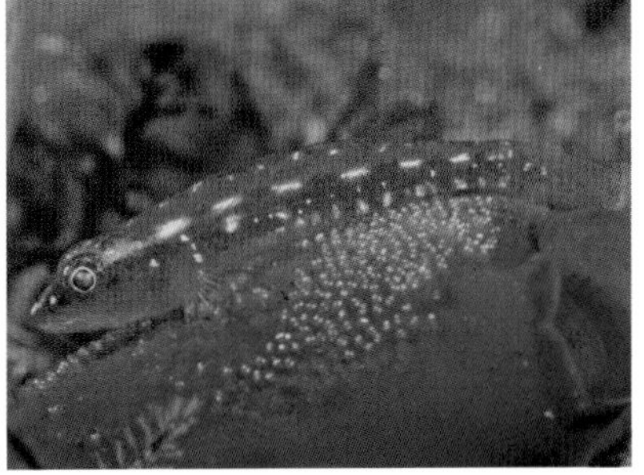

Occurs on sheltered inner reefs on sponges, ascidians and soft corals. It has red eyes and the body often has some white speckles. Males guard the eggs, which are laid directly on the host's side or near the base. The female may participate in guarding or is nearby. Widespread Indo-Pacific. Length to 26 mm.

SLEEPER GOBIES
GOBIIDAE-4

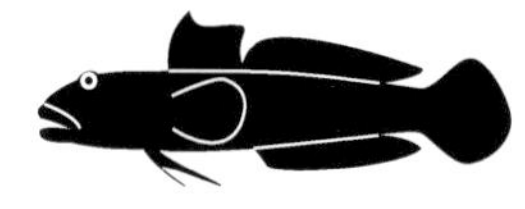

This group includes some of the largest gobies in the Maldives. Most species occur in pairs and live on the rubble bottom along reef margins. The genus *Valenciennea* makes large homes on the sand below solid objects and will often pile rubble and sand over the area, leaving a small entrance, which is covered at night. They feed by taking a mouthful of sand that is filtered through the gills for tiny creatures. Several similar species, originally thought to be just geographical variations, appear to be valid species.

Six-spot Sleeper-goby
Valenciennea sexguttata

Occurs in sheltered lagoons on white sand, often in semi-silty habitats, near reefs or bommies where they dig holes under sand covered coral pieces, rarely deeper than 10 m in the Maldives. Adults in pairs, juveniles may form small groups. Identified by the pale colour, blue spots on the cheek and a small black tip on the dorsal fin. Widespread Indo-Pacific. Length to 16 cm.

Black-chin Sleeper-goby
Valenciennea cf. *puellaris*

Inhabits clean white sand slopes, usually in depths of 20+ m. Adults are nearly always in pairs, swimming closely together near their hideouts. Easily recognised by the barred pattern over the back and the black chin. Only known from the west Indian Ocean and was thought to be the same as the spotted Pacific counterpart, *V. puellaris*, or the similar form from Samoa that lacks the black chin. Appears to be undescribed. Length to 20 cm.

Little Sleeper-goby
Valenciennea parva

Rare in the Maldives, known from North Malé Atoll. Occurs on sand flats along reef margins and in lagoons with rubble sand, singly or in pairs, to depth of about 15 m. Lacks any distinctive features in the Maldives due to the white sand. Widespread Indo-Pacific. Length to 10 cm.

Black-lined Sleeper-goby
Valenciennea helsdingenii

Usually found on deep sand flats in the Maldives at 30+ m depth, and on open substrate with rubble ridges or near small remote bommies. Readily identified by the two lines running parallel along the body and a black blotch in the dorsal fin. Widespread Indo-Pacific. There are some variations, with lines more black in Pacific populations. Length to 25 cm in sub-tropical waters, usually 20 cm in the Maldives.

Golden-head Sleeper-goby
Valenciennea strigata

Inhabits clear water reef slopes and crests, often in semi-exposed areas, in 6 to 25 m depth. Adults occur in pairs, while juveniles are solitary. Easily recognised by the golden-orange head and blue stripe on the cheek, but the orange is variable in colour and occasionally fades to a pale yellow. Widespread and common in the Indo-Pacific, but less numerous in the Maldives. Length to 18 cm.

Broad-barred Sleeper-goby
Valenciennea wardii

Usually seen at moderate depths on fine sand or mud slopes. Known depth range is 10 to 30 m, but is probably much deeper in the Maldives. Readily identified by the broad-banded colour pattern. Generally a rare species and included here based on two specimens in collections that came from the Maldives. Widespread Indo-Pacific. Length to 15 cm.

False Sleeper-goby
Amblygobius nocturna

Inhabits lagoons and harbours with fine sand, often silty habitats, usually in a few metres depth, ranging to about 10 m. Adults occur in pairs. Identified by the pale colour and stripe from tip of snout running through the eye and along the sides of the body, fading as it goes. On dark sand it has pink lines, but they are faint when on white sand. Widespread Indo-Pacific. Length to 10 cm.

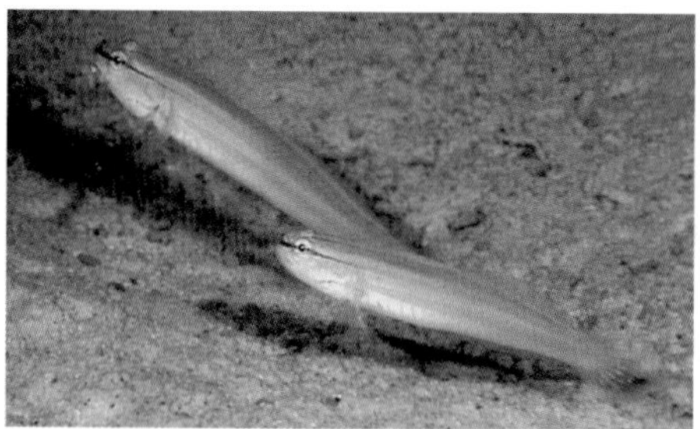

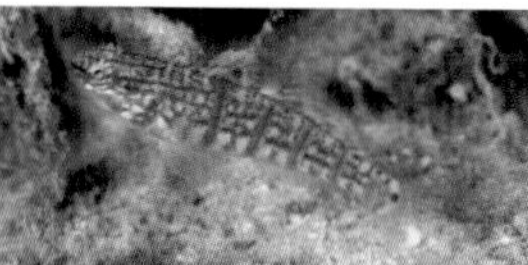

White-barred Reef-goby
Amblygobius semicinctus

Occurs inshore on seagrass beds, silty lagoons, harbours and reef slopes to about 20 m. Usually very shallow and is highly variable in colour according to its habitat, as shown in the photographs. Widespread Indian Ocean and ranges to Java, Indonesia, where it lives sympatrically with the very similar Pacific *A. phaleana*. Length to about 10 cm.

Hector's Reef-goby
Koumansetta hectori

Inhabits inner reefs and lagoons with rich coral growth, usually seen singly but may occur in pairs or small groups that are loosely distributed in its territory. Readily identified by its distinctive colour pattern. Widespread Indo-Pacific, but is mainly confined to continental regions from the Red Sea to Japan. Length to 65 mm.

DART GOBIES AND WORM GOBIES MICRODESMIDAE

This is a moderately large family with 12 genera and about 45 species, dividable into two distinct groups, presently regarded as subfamilies, MICRODESMINAE, the worm gobies and PTERELEOTRINAE, the dart gobies. Previously the latter was included in GOBIIDAE. Worm gobies are usually seen solitary on sand flats and slopes, quickly diving into holes when approached. Dart gobies occur in pairs or small groups. All are planktivores and live in habitats with moderate currents.

Red Fire-goby
Nemateleotris magnifica

Usually found on the bottom of sandy caves along outer reef walls in depths over 15 m. Nearly always found in pairs in the Maldives, but known to form small groups elsewhere. It swims close to the bottom near its burrow, feeding on zooplankton. Readily identified by the white body and dark tail, and tall dorsal fin. Common in the Maldives. Widespread Indo-Pacific. Length to 75 mm, usually 60 mm.

Purple Fire-goby
Nemateleotris decora

A deep-water species usually found along deep walls in depths of 40+ m, rarely shallower. Occurs singly, but the female is shy and often dives into the hole, whilst the male stays out longer and is usually noticed. Identified by the dark blue colours seen at depth. Widespread Indo-Pacific. Length to 75 mm, usually 60 mm.

Arrow Goby
Ptereleotris evides

Inhabits inner and outer reef slopes. Adults are usually seen in pairs. Juveniles form small schools in protected inshore habitats around coral heads in shallow depths. Identified by the tall fins, which is darkened in adults. Adults range to at least 30 m depth. Widespread Indo-Pacific. Length to 10 cm.

Zebra Dart-goby
Ptereleotris zebra

Found primarily on outer reef slopes in shallow surge zones to about 10 m depth. Often forms large but spread-out schools high above the bottom when food is abundant in currents. A shy species, that is difficult to approach at close range. Easily identified by the many dark-edged, pink bars along the body. Widespread Indo-Pacific. Length to 12 cm.

Tail-spot Dart-goby
Ptereleotris heteroptera

Usually found over sand and rubble bottom and often well away from reefs. Occurs in pairs and swims well above the bottom when feeding. In the Maldives, they are rather deep in depths over 20 m, and are more common in 30 m. Identified by the blue body and black spot in the tail. Widespread Indo-Pacific. Length to 10 cm.

Green-eyed Dart-goby
Ptereleotris microlepis

Occurs in shallow protected lagoons and harbours, usually over a silty, fine sand bottom to about 10 m depth. Found in pairs or small groups, swimming well above the bottom. It has no distinctive features, except green eyes. Widespread Indo-Pacific. Length to 12 cm.

Threadfin Dart-goby
Ptereleotris hanae (?)

Inhabits deep sand flats in 30+ m and is seen solitary or in pairs. It swims well above the bottom but readily dives into holes of shrimpgobies when approached too close. Recognised by the elongate filaments on the tail, similar to the Pacific *P. hanae* from Japan but there appears to be a species complex involved with at least one other undescribed species in Indonesia. Length to 10 cm.

Weeping Dart-goby
Ptereleotris lineopinnis

A rarely noticed species found on sand flats, usually seen in pairs at about 20 m depth. Identified by the black angular bar below eye. Widespread Indo-Pacific. Length to 10 cm.

Splendid Dart-goby
Ptereleotris grammica

Due to itsdeep water dwelling preference, this beautiful dart-goby is rarely seen in the Maldives. The colourful markings and elongate filaments on the first dorsal fin readily identify it. In the young, the mid-lateral line is often black. It usually occurs very deep in 50+ m. Widespread Indo-Pacific. Length to 9 cm.

Black-spot Worm-goby
Gunnellichthys monostigma

Mainly foundswimming just above the bottom in small spread-out groups on sand crests formed by tidal currents. The depth ranges from 1 to 15 m. The body is rather plain and is best identified by the small spot behind the head. Widespread Indo-Pacific. Length to 15 cm.

Neon Worm-goby
Gunnellichthys curiosus

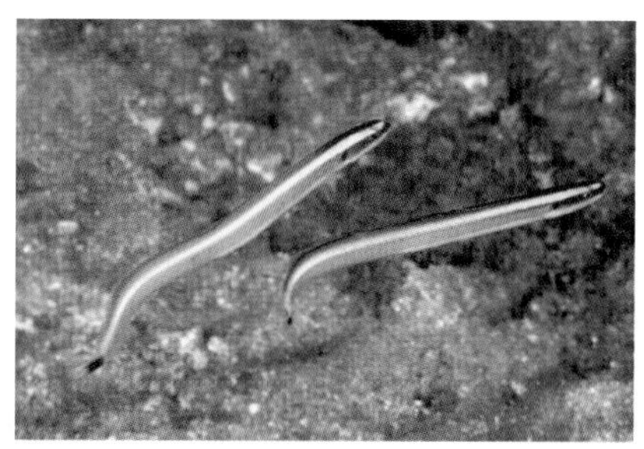

Not common in the Maldives and usually seen in pairs at depths over 20 m, in clear inner reef habitat over rubble zones adjacent to reefs. It swims around in search of food, rather than waiting for plankton. Identified by the broad orange and neon blue stripe. Widespread Indo-Pacific. Length 10 cm.

Orange-line Worm-goby
Gunnellichthys viridescens

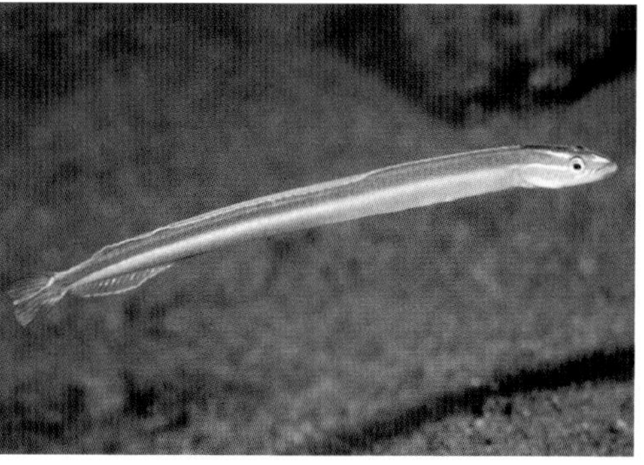

Rare in the Maldives, but populations are known to fluctuate greatly elsewhere, being common one year and absent the next. Found on inshore sand slopes and soft bottom with sparse seagrass and sponge growth in 10 to 30 m depth. Usually seen hovering in the current while remaining in the one place. Identified by the orange stripe. Widespread Indo-Pacific. Length to 12 cm.

MOORISH IDOLS
ZANCLIDAE

Represented by a single widespread species, that is closely related to surgeonfishes (the next family) but lacks the spines on the tail and has an almost circular, compressed body. The greatly elevated dorsal fin has a long banner-like filament.

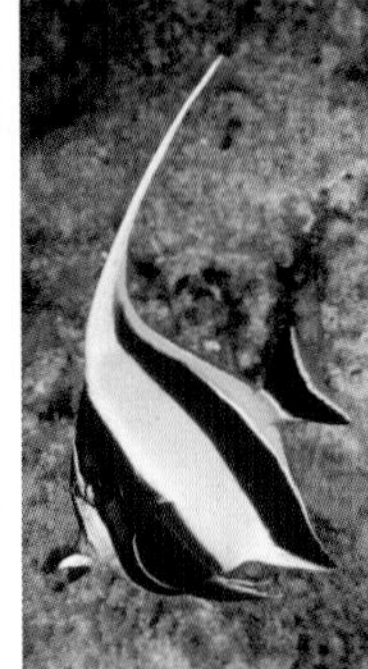

Moorish Idol
Zanclus cornutus

Occurs in most reef habitats from shallow flats to deep outer walls. It swims singly, or in pairs and occasionally forms schools to either feed or migrate to other areas. Readily identified by elongate snout, dorsal fin filament, shape and colour. Common in the Maldives. Widespread throughout the Indo-Pacific, ranges into subtropical waters. Length to 22 cm.

SURGEONFISHES
ACANTHURIDAE

A large family with 3 subfamilies: ACANTHURINAE, the surgeons, with four genera and about 50 species; NASINAE, the unicorns, with a single genus and 15 species; and PRIONURINAE, the sawtails with just a few species. The latter is subtropical, and is not represented in the Maldives, although one is found in Indonesia. There are 22 surgeonfishes and eight unicorns known from the Maldives. Surgeonfishes feature a sharp blade-like spine in a fold on the tail that points outwards when the tail is bent, that is used for defence or fighting. In some species it is armed with venom. Most species are readily identified by colour and shape, but a few large drab species are similar and may differ in minor, less obvious, detail. Juveniles are similar to adults in shape and colour, except for the caudal fin, which becomes strongly lunate in adults. Surgeonfishes commonly occur on reefs where they graze on algae from the reefs surface. Some form schools or swim in small groups. Juveniles are secretive and often live solitary. The unicorns have one or two hook-like spines that are external, while the sawtails have a series of keeled plates along the tail. Most surgeonfishes are herbivores but several combine their diet with many kinds of plankton. They are mostly plain coloured fishes, but may turn-on different colour-patterns for display. Some of the large species develop a long, horn- or hump-like, protrusion on the snout when adult, or male. Some species form large schools along outer reef walls.

Blue Tang

Paracanthurus hepatus

Not common in the Maldives and appears to be localised in only a few areas. Occurs on current-prone reef crests to about 20 m depth. The Indian Ocean population differs slightly in colour from Pacific fish when adult by having white instead of blue along the lower body. The two forms are probably subspecific. Juveniles form small groups and quickly dive for cover in small *Acropora* coral thickets. Widespread Indo-Pacific. Length to 20 cm.

Powder-blue Surgeonfish

Acanthurus leucosternon

A common and spectacular species that often forms large and dense schools in the Maldives. Readily identified by the black face, white chin, blue body and yellow dorsal fin. Found in most clear water reef habitats to about 20 m depth. Widespread Indian Ocean, ranging to Bali, Indonesia. Length to 20 cm.

Night Surgeonfish

Acanthurus thompsoni

Commonly found along outer reef walls, sometimes in schools well off the reef in open water, feeding on plankton. Easily recognised by the black body and white tail when in open water. May turn grey when sheltering in reefs or visiting cleaning stations. Occurs at various depths in pursuit of plankton, ranging to at least 50 m depth. Widespread Indo-Pacific. Length to 25 cm.

Pale Surgeonfish

Acanthurus mata

A common schooling species in the Maldives, often found along inner and outer reef slopes and walls, feeding away from the reef when currents are running. They sometimes congregate in large caves during the day when the currents stop running. Widespread Indo-Pacific. Length to 45 cm.

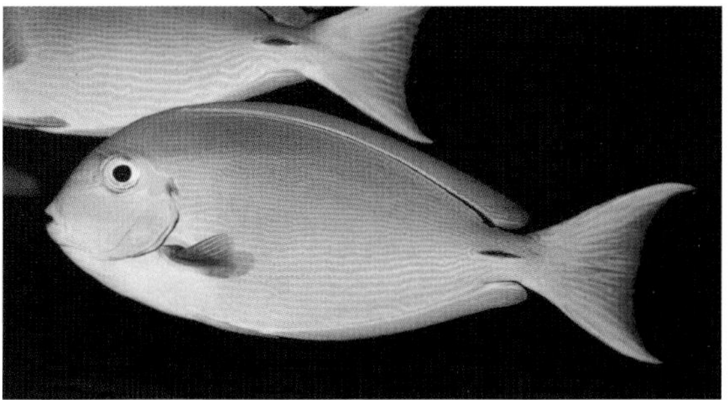

Yellow-fin Surgeonfish
Acanthurus xanthopterus

Common in the Maldives. Often forms schools in sandy lagoons and shows curiosity towards boats and divers. Grazes algae off sand surfaces and rubble and occurs in depths from intertidal zones to about 30 m. Identified by the large yellow pectoral fins on the sides. Juveniles have a lined pattern and are found inshore in silty habitats. Widespread Indo-Pacific. Length to 56 cm.

Pencilled Surgeonfish
Acanthurus dussumieri

Adults are usually found in protected habitats, often with shipwrecks, in moderate depths rarely less than 25 m. Juveniles often inshore on algae reefs in depths of a few metres, but gradually move to deeper water. Identified by the white spine and yellow mask over the eyes. Widespread Indo-Pacific. A large species, length to 50 cm.

Eye-spot Surgeonfish
Acanthurus bariene

Inhabits protected inner reefs with large caves or overhands in depths from 15 to 50 m, often seen on shipwrecks. Grazes algae from dead coral or flat surfaces of solid objects. Identified by the distinctive round spot closely behind the eye and yellow-orange dorsal fin. Tail fin with long lobes when adult. Widespread Indo-Pacific. Length to 40 cm.

Eye-line Surgeonfish
Acanthurus nigricauda

Mainly found on protected inner reefs, grazing algae on shallow crests and slopes. Identified by the dark stripe behind the eye and over the tail spine. Variable in colour from grey to almost black all over and often shows a white band on the tail. Widespread Indo-Pacific. Length to 45 cm.

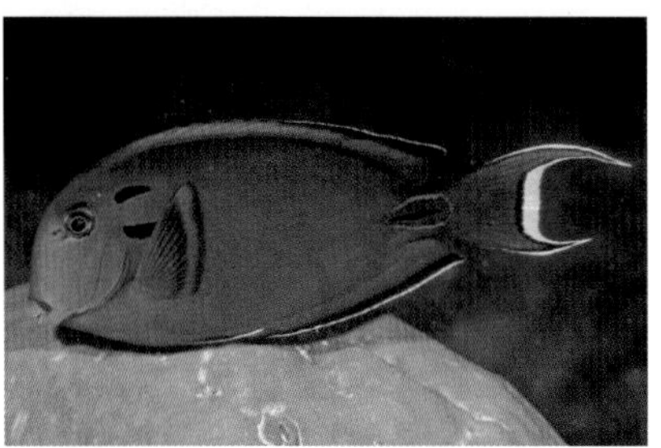

Lieutenant Surgeonfish
Acanthurus tennentii

Found on various reef flats and slopes from silty inshore to outer reefs, often in small groups, to about 15 m depth. Identified by the double stripe behind the head at eye level and blue line around tail spine in adults. Widespread Indian Ocean, ranging east to Bali, Indonesia. Length to 30 cm.

Ring-tail Surgeonfish
Acanthurus auranticavus

Inhabits shallow protected reef flats and slopes to outer reef walls. Often seen in small groups, and mixes with other similar species. Sometimes almost black with only a white band around the tail. Other features, such as orange border around the spine, are not always visible. Widespread Indo-Pacific. Length to 45 cm.

White-spine Surgeonfish
Acanthurus leucocheilus

Inhabits shallow protected reef flats and slopes to outer reef walls, to about 20 m depth, singly or in small groups. Large adults are almost black but the spine is distinctly white. A white or yellowish tail distinguishes juveniles and sometimes adults have a white band around the tail. Widespread Indo-Pacific. Length to 45 cm.

Spot-face Surgeonfish
Acanthurus maculiceps

Rare in the Maldives and only seen once on outer reef slopes in about 10 m depth, where several fish swam together on a shipwreck. Mainly west Pacific, Maldives represents the western known limit of range. Easily identified by the numerous yellow spots over the entire head, elongate spot behind gill cover at eye level and narrow band across tail base. Length to 40 cm.

Lined Surgeonfish
Acanthurus lineatus

Inhabits shallow reef flats and slopes that are usually exposed to surge and currents to about 10 m depth. Forms schools in gutters when adult. Small juveniles are secretive among boulder rubble. Easily identified by blue-lined patterns. Tail spine is venomous in this species. Widespread Indo-Pacific. Length to 35 cm.

Convict Surgeonfish
Acanthurus triostegus

Inhabits shallow protected lagoons and commonly found around jetties. Often forms large schools where freshwater runs over the reef, and found grazing on the rich algae growth in such areas. Easily identified by pale body with vertical black stripes. Widespread Indo-Pacific. Length to 20 cm.

White-spotted Surgeonfish
Acanthurus guttatus

Found schooling on inshore reefs in very shallow depths usually between 1 and 5 m. Mainly in surge zones near breaking waves in water filled with small air-bubbles. The white spotting on the body is thought to represent air-bubbles for camouflage. Widespread Indo-Pacific. Length to 26 cm.

Mimic Surgeonfish
Acanthurus tristis

Inhabits clear reef slopes and crests, and appears to be localised and common in some places in the Maldives. Adults are whitish on the head and around the eye, followed by black over the pectoral fin base. Juveniles mimic small angelfishes such as *Centropyge eibli*. There is also a non-mimic form in the Maldives that is yellow with orange speckles, and there could be additional mimic forms, yet to be discovered. Ranges east to Bali, Indonesia. Length to 20 cm.

Dusky Surgeonfish
Acanthurus nigrofuscus

Occurs on clear inner to outer reef slopes in channels and gutters. Grazes algae from rubble and dead coral bases, but also feeds on plankton at times. Identified by the black spots near the tail fin base and the tail fin, which looks purple or blue in natural light. Widespread Indo-Pacific. Length to 20 cm.

Fine-lined Bristletooth
Ctenochaetus striatus

Inhabits lagoons and forms schools along reef slopes with large rubble zones, such as storm-smashed staghorn corals, that have good algae cover. They graze in groups and prefer soft algae that grow on rubble as well as on sand. The numerous thin horizontal lines and spotting around the eye identify it. Widespread Indo-Pacific. Length to 25 cm.

Two-spot Bristletooth
Ctenochaetus binotatus

Occurs on protected reef slopes with rich invertebrate growth such as large soft corals and where encrusting algae covers rubble and coral bases. Identified by the brown body with numerous thin pale lines, spots on the face and two dark spots above and below the tail fin base. Juveniles have a bright yellow tail fin. Widespread Indo-Pacific. Length to 18 cm.

Gold-ring Bristletooth
Ctenochaetus truncatus

Inhabits clear inner reef crests and slopes. Usually seen singly or in small loose groups in reef gutters. Identified by the numerous small pale dots over the body and yellow around the eye. Small juveniles are sometimes all yellow with a blue eye. Widespread Indo-Pacific. Length to 18 cm.

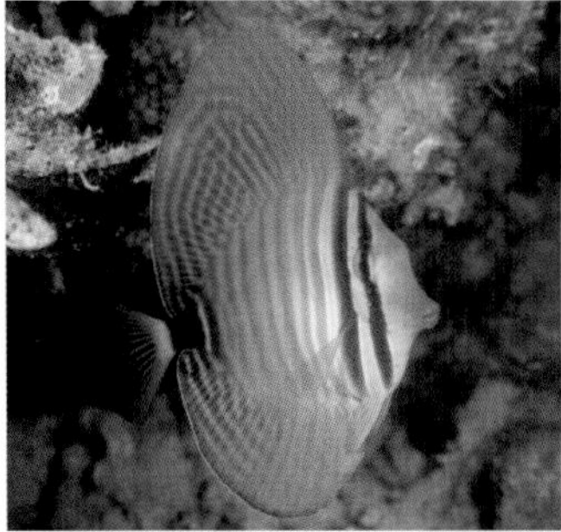

Sailfin Surgeonfish
Zebrasoma desjardinii

Inhabits protected inner reefs and large lagoons. Adults usually seen in pairs along rubble zones at shallow depths to about 25 m. Juveniles inshore, solitary, and seek protection among staghorn corals. This species has very large fins, which look particularly tall in small juveniles, when held erect. Widespread Indian Ocean, ranges to Java, Indonesia. Replaced by sibling species *Z. veliferum* in the West Pacific east from Java. Length to 40 cm.

Brown Tang
Zebrasoma scopas

Inhabits protected shallow reefs, often forming schools when feeding on slopes with good algae growth among the corals. Small juveniles are secretive in staghorn corals. Identified by dark colour, protruding snout, rounded body and white spine. Sometimes has a bright yellow, xanthic phase, and one such individual was seen in the Maldives by the author. Widespread Indo-Pacific. Length to 20 cm.

Yellow-tail Tang
Zebrasoma xanthurum

Rare in the Maldives, and those seen are possible strays from the mainland. Larval stages can be pelagic for a long time. Reported from North Malé Atoll. Mainly known from the Red Sea and Arabian Gulf where they form large schools in 2 to 20 m depth. Readily identified by the blue body and bright yellow tail. Length to 25 cm.

Orange-spine Unicornfish
Naso elegans

Inhabits shallow inner and outer reef crests and slopes, occasionally seen in deep water. Adults usually in pairs, sometimes forming schools in the Maldives. Identified by the bright orange spines on the tail. Widespread Indo-Pacific, but two forms are divided between Indian Ocean and Pacific. Both forms occur together in Bali, Indonesia, suggesting they are separate species. Length to 45 cm. Photo, lower, Indian Ocean form in Bali, showing scars from a fight. The Pacific form, *Naso lituratus*, which has a mostly black dorsal fin, is more common there and most likely inflicted the wound.

Big-nose Unicornfish
Naso vlamingii

Commonly occurs on clear water reefs along upper regions of deep drop-offs. Often seen in loose groups feeding on plankton well away from reefs in currents. Adults develop a small bump on the nose and thin trailing filaments on upper and lower tip of tail. Males often display with intensified blue colours that can quickly change to a very pale colour when visiting cleaning stations. Widespread Indo-Pacific. Length to 55 cm.

Spotted Unicornfish
Naso brevirostris

Very common in the Maldives on along upper part of reef slopes and drop-offs. Forms schools in pursuit of plankton at various depths. Seen with horns protruding from the surface while feeding. Males can quickly change colour, showing a broad bluish white band to impress other members of the species. Widespread Indo-Pacific. Length to 50 cm.

Blue-spine Unicornfish
Naso unicornis

Inhabits protected shallow reef habitats with good algae growth. Adults usually near moderately deep water and seen to about 40 m depth. Juveniles found inshore in algae rich reefs. Feeds on the bottom or loose floating weeds. Identified by the blue spines, juveniles lack the horny protrusion on the head. Widespread Indo-Pacific. Length to 70 cm.

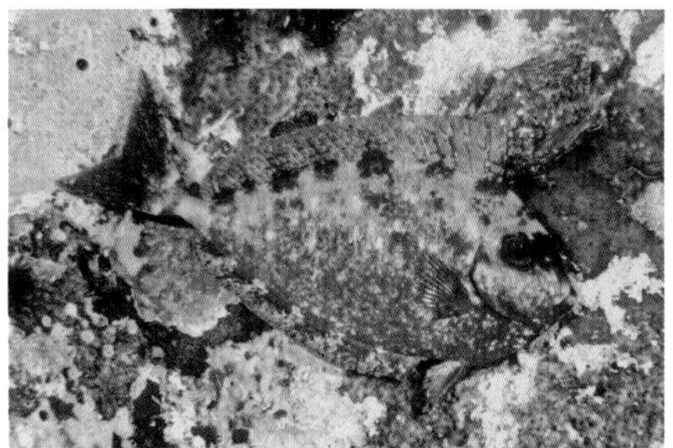

Humpback Unicornfish
Naso brachycentron

Usually seen on outer reef slopes or along deep walls where forming moderately large schools. Identified by the light grey colour and camel-like hump on the back. In addition, males have a thin protruding spine in front of the eyes. Widespread Indo-Pacific. Length to 70 cm.

Photos: upper juvenile, below left male, below right female.

Hump-nose Unicornfish
Naso mcdadei

Mainly seen along outer reef walls in shallow depths, either singular or in small groups. Young remain inshore on algae rich reefs. Males have a hump on their back and develop a large rounded snout, which extends well in front of the mouth. It feeds on algae and plankton. Western Indian Ocean. Previously confused with the Pacific *Naso tuberosus*. Length to 60 cm.

Horse-face Unicorn

Naso fageni

A widespread species in the Indo-West Pacific, originally named from the Philippines, but also occurs in the western Indian Ocean and may form large schools in oceanic locations such as the Seychelles, as well as the Maldives. The male develops a rounded short horn just above the mouth. Although plain grey in colour, it shows white spots at night or when visiting a cleaning station. Length to 80 cm.

Sleek Unicornfish

Naso hexacanthus

Common in the Maldives, found along drop-offs where they feed in schools on plankton. They have a great depth-range, reported to 135 m. Identified by the blue tail and are also known as the Blue-tail Unicorn. Widespread Indo-Pacific. Length to 75 cm, usually 50 cm.

One-spine Unicornfish

Naso thynnoides

Inhabits inner and outer reef slopes, forming large schools at times. They travel along at a steady pace near the reef edge in pursuit of plankton. A small species that is identified by the thin vertical lines along the back and the single spine on the tail, compared to two in similar species. Widespread Indo-Pacific. Length to 40 cm.

RABBITFISHES
SIGANIDAE

A tropical Indo-Pacific family, with a single genus comprising about 30 species, of which at least five species occur in the Maldives. Dividable into two subgenera, but the long-snouted species, subgenus *Lo*, does not occur in the Maldives. Rabbitfishes have some unusual features: a spine at both ends of the ventral fins, with three rays in between; and seven spines in the anal fin (three or less in most similar fishes). All fin spines are venomous and a stab causes agonising pain. Most species occur in pairs in the Maldives and usually associate with algae-rich reefs. There is one schooling species. Seagrass beds need to be investigated for other species as more than half of all the species associate with seagrasses and could potentially occur in the Maldives. A species seen in seagrass beds is probably *Siganus margaritiferus*, but this requires verification. All species feed on algae, weeds and seagrasses.

Starry Rabbitfish
Siganus laques

Large adults are usually seen in pairs along reef edges bordering onto sand and rubble in lagoons in inner reefs. Usually found shallow but ranges to about 35 m depth near outer reefs where filamentous algae grow at moderate depths. Identified by the numerous close-set dark spots all over the body. Widespread Indian Ocean, ranges to Java, Indonesia. Closely related to the yellow-tailed *Siganus stellatus* from the Red Sea and is often included with this species. Length to 40 cm.

Schooling Rabbitfish
Siganus argenteus (?)

Inhabits sheltered inner reef slopes with rich algae growth. Usually seen in pairs in the Maldives and appears to be different from the Indonesian schooling populations that have a forked tail and larger yellow spots. There are possibly two species in the Maldives. It is most similar to an undescribed species from Japan and is perhaps the same. *S. argenteus* is reported Widespread Indo-Pacific. Length to 30 cm.

Coral Rabbitfish
Siganus corallinus

Inhabits rich coral reef slopes, usually seen in pairs. There are two similar-looking yellow species in the Maldives. This species has blue spots on yellow background colour, is deep bodied and has a black area on the throat. Widespread Indian Ocean, ranging to Java, replaced by *S. tetrazona* further east, which is easilydistinguished by the lack of black on the throat. Length to 35 cm.

Chin-strap Rabbitfish
Siganus puelloides

Inhabits rich coral reef slopes, usually seen in pairs. A shy species, more slender than the Coral Rabbitfish and has a black mark on the chin, directly following the mouth, unlike the Coral Rabbitfish, which is further back on the throat. Distribution is uncertain, originally described from the Maldives and Similan Islands in the Andaman Sea. Length to 35 cm.

Sri Lankan Rabbitfish
Siganus cf. *lineatus*

Rare in the Maldives, this coastal species is common in Sri Lanka and near Indian coast. Recognised by the strong pattern of longitudinal lines along its entire body and yellow blotch near tail base. Replaced by similar *S. guttatus*, with spots instead of lines, in Indonesia and a sibling species *S. lineatus* further east, from eastern Australia to southern Japan. Length to about 25 cm.

Java Rabbitfish
Siganus javus

Occurs mainly in coastal habitats, estuaries and lagoons. A common mainland species not often seen in the Maldives. Easily recognised by the white spots or lines on the side and large black area in the caudal fin. Widespread Indo-Pacific. Length to 40 cm.

TUNAS & MACKERELS SCOMBRIDAE

A large commercially important family with 15 genera and nearly 50 species worldwide. The large tunas are oceanic and are occasionally seen along outer reef walls. They are targeted commercially and form the basis of the world's largest fishing industry. Few species visit reefs. Most family members are streamlined fast fishes that hunt other fish species and pelagic invertebrates, such as squid.

Dogtooth Tuna
Gymnosarda unicolor

A common species along deep outer reef walls, usually found singly but occasionally several found together. Often shows curiosity towards divers and makes a close pass. Feeds on other small pelagic fishes and reef planktivores venturing too far out. Distinguished from similar pelagic fishes by large teeth and eyes. Widespread Indo-Pacific. Length to about 2 m.

Mouth Mackerel
Rastrelliger kanagurta

Not common in the Maldives. Occurs in moderate to large schools along deep slopes and drop-offs to feed on zooplankton, but may target eggs of spawning fishes at specific times. Easily recognised when feeding by the large expanded mouth and silvery reflective gills. Widespread Indo-Pacific. Length to about 35 cm.

LEFT-EYED FLOUNDERS BOTHIDAE

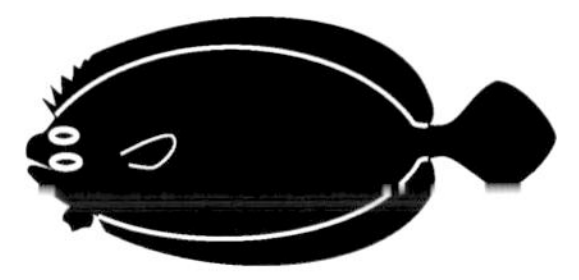

A very large family with about 15 genera and 90 species distributed in the Indo-Pacific, and double that worldwide. They are poorly represented away from continental waters, and only a few are recorded from the Maldives. No doubt more will turn up as many species have pelagic larvae that can travel long distances. These fishes have adapted to lying on their sides on the bottom. Both eyes are on one side (upperside) that faces upwards and is pigmented like the surroundings for camouflage, whilst the other (underside) is blind and often unpigmented. There are several other families that are closely related, but not yet known from the Maldives. The various families are either left or right-eyed, meaning that the eyes are on that particular side of the fish. They feed on various bottom creatures, including various invertebrates, worms and fishes.

Leopard Flounder
Bothus pantherinus

Inhabits clear water reef sand flats from shallow areas near reefs or deep open flats close to remote bommies with fine rubble patches. Identified by numerous pale flower-shaped spots all over upper sides and eyes highly elevated. Males with long filaments on upper pectoral fin that are used for display. Widespread Indo-Pacific. Length to 30 cm.

RIGHT-EYED FLOUNDERS PLEURONECTIDAE

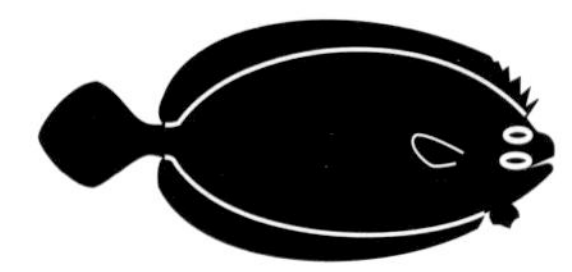

A large and very diverse family, with 45 genera and about 100 species. It comprises several sub-genera and only SAMARINAE is represented with a single species in the Maldives. It is one of the smallest species, amongst generally large fishes that are commercially harvested in many sub-tropical regions. They feed on a variety of invertebrates and fishes.

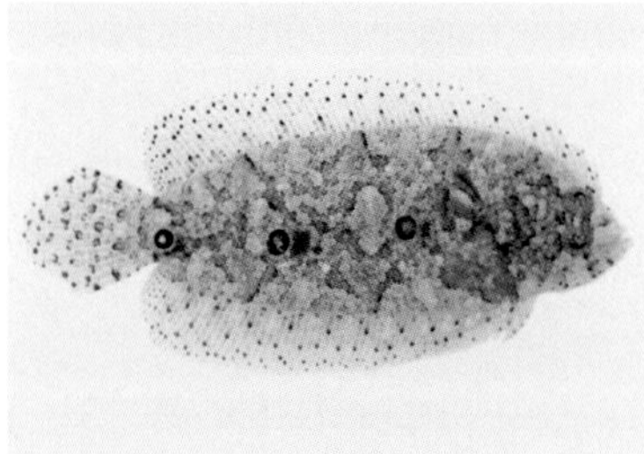

Three-eyed Flounder
Samariscus triocellatus

Inhabits clear water inner reef slopes to outer reef walls. Usually buries itself in sandy bottoms of large caves or below reef overhangs during the day and becomes active on dusk. It moves around like a slug sliding over the bottom, waving its upper pectoral fin in the process. Identified by small size, slender shape and a series of dark blotches located centrally along the upper side. Widespread Indo Pacific. Length to 10 cm.

SOLES SOLEIDAE

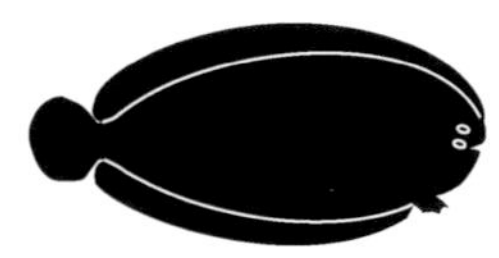

A large family of mostly small fishes, with 30 genera and over 100 species. Only recently one member was found in the Maldives. They generally prefer coastal and often muddy habitats. Both eyes are on theright hand side. During the day they are usually buried in the sand. Some have strong banded or spotted patterns on the pigmented sides, and some juveniles are brightly coloured, mimicking nudibranchs or flatworms.

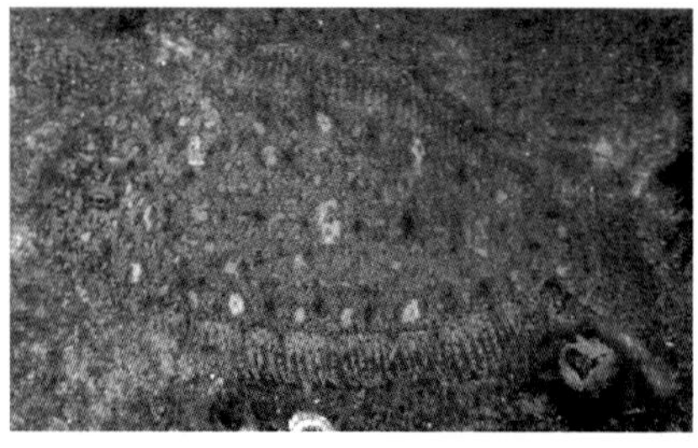

Pebble Sole
Pardachirus sp.

The members of this genus are usually found on sand along reef margins, usually where sand is mixed with slightly course reef particles. This species was recently photographed in a shallow lagoon at Ari Atoll and appears to be undescribed. Length to 20 cm.

FILEFISHES
MONACANTHIDAE

A large family with about 30 genera and over 100 species, of which eight genera and at least 11 species occur in the Maldives. Many more species occur in nearby continental waters and as they can have a long pelagic stage, more can be expected in the Maldives. More than half of all the species occur in Australian waters. They are similar to triggerfishes, but are generally more compressed with often-thin bodies, a dorsal fin that has a prominent separate single spine, and they are often armed with a series of downward facing spines on the sides. Maldives species associate with reefs and can be found in protected inner reefs and lagoons. Diet comprises various invertebrates and algae, but the larger species are also scavengers.

Long-nose Filefish
Oxymonacanthus longirostris

Also called Harlequin Filefish. Inhabits clear inner reef crests with rich coral growth, usually in *Acropora* thickets feeding on coral polyps. Juveniles form small groups and adults are usually seen in pairs. Readily identified by body shape, tube-like snout and orange spotted colour pattern. Widespread Indo-Pacific. Length to 10 cm.

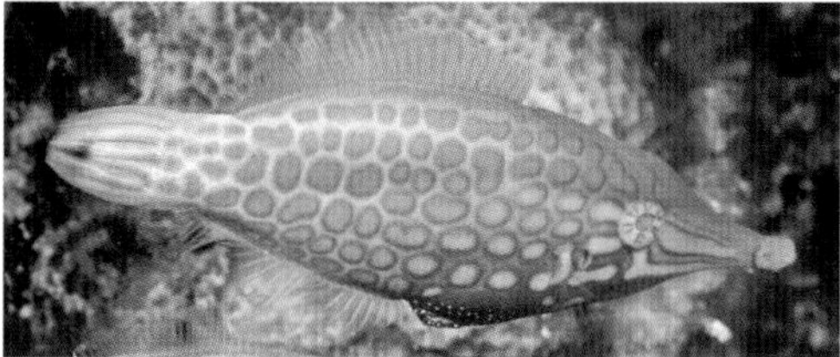

Mimic Filefish
Paraluteres prionurus

Inhabits sheltered reef habitats in mixed soft coral and algae, often deep in the Maldives along slopes at the bases of drop-offs of inner reefs between 20 to 40 m. A mimic of *Canthigaster* pufferfishes (see Fig. 8., page 19) mainly valentini, but there are some geographical variations. Maldives populations have a strong reticulated pattern in the white areas, and mimic not as convincingly as in the Pacific. They are likely to take on different forms where other *Canthigaster* pufferfishes occur. Widespread Indo-Pacific. Length to 10 cm.

Ear-spot Filefish
Pervagor janthinosoma

Occurs in various reef areas with rich coral and other invertebrate growth that provide good cover, on crests to about 20 m depth. Usually seen in the shade of overhanging corals, sometimes making a quick dash over short open spaces. It is territorial and occasionally seen fighting. Best recognised by the greenish colour and vertical blotch at the gill opening. Common in the Maldives. Widespread Indo-Pacific. Length to 13 cm.

Orange Filefish
Pervagor aspricaudus

Occurs in mainly semi-silty habitats, secretive on inner reef slopes with mixed soft coral, sponges, and algae reefs. Not often seen in the Maldives, and usually only when a torch is used to check darker areas in reefs. It looks pale orange with numerous small spots in natural light. Occurrence is sporadic in the Indo-Pacific. Length to 13 cm

---

Rhino Filefish
Pseudalutarius nasicornis

Usually seen on sand slopes with ridges of rubble with soft corals and seawhips. A pale coloured species identified by a pair of dark stripes along upper sides and dorsal spine placed in front of the eye. They often line up vertically with seawhips and hide behind them. Adults are found in pairs and usually in depths in excess of 15 m. Rare in the Maldives. Widespread Indo-Pacific, ranges to subtropical zones. Length to 18 cm.

Scribbled Leatherjacket
Aluterus scriptus

Adults inhabit deep water and swim along slopes and drop-offs, usually in 20+ m depth. Juveniles are pelagic to about 10 cm long and seen swimming with floating weeds or sheltering in large jellies. They settle inshore in sheltered often muddy habitats, before moving offshore. Best identified by the very large tail fin. Widespread in all tropical seas. The longest filefish, when including the extremely long tail in large individuals, reaching 1 m.

Broom Filefish
Amanses scopas

Inhabits clear water reef crests with mixed coral rubble and sand patches, semi-protected areas with shelter in gutters and uses coral coverage to hide. Rather shy in the Maldives, adults occur in pairs. Identified by the dark colour and brush-like patch of spines on the sides of males. Widespread Indo-Pacific. Length to 20 cm.

Barred Filefish
Cantherhines dumerilii

Inhabits clear water inner reef slopes with good coral growth, adults are usually seen in pairs. Identified by size and colour, males have yellow spines on sides of the tail fin base. A very shy species in the Maldives, that swims quickly out of sight or dives for cover under large corals. Small juveniles are spotted. Widespread Indo-Pacific. Length to 35 cm.

Spectacled Filefish
Cantherhines fronticinctus

Occurs in protected inner and outer reef habitats, adults usually in depths of 20+ m. Juveniles inshore and sometimes under jetties among large algae on pylons or with sponges. A secretive fish and often camouflaged. Identified by a white band around the tail base and dark stripes along the body. Widespread Indo-Pacific. Length to 23 cm.

Honeycomb Filefish
Cantherhines pardalis

Inhabits various reef habitats with rich algae and sargassum weed growth, including shallow outer reef zones exposed to surge. Juveniles often found in floating weeds until reaching reefs to settle. Variable in colour and best identified by the white saddle spot on top of the tail fin base. Widespread Indo-Pacific. Length to 25 cm.

TRIGGERFISHES
BALISTIDAE

A moderately large family, with 12 genera and over 40 species in tropical waters worldwide, of which 10 genera and 17 species are reported from the Maldives. They arebig-headed fishes with eyes placed high and well back on the head. The dorsal fin features a strong spine that can be locked in an upright position by a second smaller spine. The spine is used at night to wedge itself into sleeping crevices, so a predator cannot pull it out. The mouth is small but the strong jaws feature dog-like teeth that are used to crush hard-shelled snails or other invertebrates. Some large species favour urchins and have learned to manipulate them and bite away spines until the inside part can be attacked and eaten. A few species form large schools to feed on zooplankton.

Starry Triggerfish
Abalistes stellatus

Occurs mainly on moderately deep slopes and occasionally comes inshore, to an often-silty habitat. Adults often seen swimming high above the bottom over open substrate. Small juveniles are found in the same areas, but hide on solid matter, especially dead coral pieces or bits of wood with small holes. Has a very thin caudal peduncle and usually has several white saddles over the back. Widespread Indo-Pacific. Length to 25 cm.

Striped Triggerfish
Balistapus undulatus

Commonly found in various reef habitats in the Maldives, from sheltered shallow lagoons to outer reefs to at least 50 m depth. Readily identified by greenish colour and diagonal yellow to orange lines. Males lack stripes over top of the snout. Widespread Indo-Pacific. Length to 30 cm.

Clown Triggerfish
Balistoides conspicillum

Usually seen along steep slopes or walls, retreating into caves when approached. Adults swim openly about, usually afraid of divers. Juveniles are secretive in small caves with rich invertebrate growth often deep, usually in excess of 30 m. Readily identified by black body with large white spots on lower half of the body and yellow to orange mouth. Widespread Indo-Pacific. Length to 35 cm.

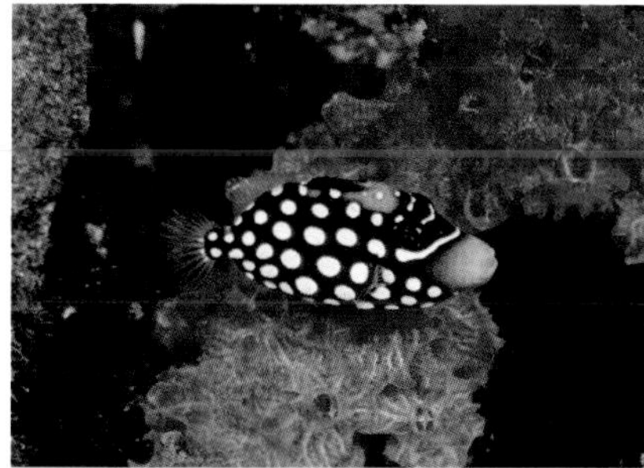

Titan Triggerfish
Balistoides viridescens

This is the largest triggerfish, also known as Giant Triggerfish. Usually seen on sheltered inner reef slopes adjacent to moderately deep water. Often aggressive towards divers, especially when caring for eggs, but may attack unprovoked by charging at great speed. A hit with their solid jaws with or without biting, either way, hurts. Widespread Indo-Pacific. Length to 75 cm.

Yellow-margin Triggerfish
Pseudobalistes flavimarginatus

An inshore species, adults often on shallow seagrass beds and juveniles usually with remote bommies on open sandy bottoms in silty habitats, sometimes in small groups. Large males congregate in loose groups over sand flats away from reefs to prepare nesting sites. Adults identified by short horizontal stripes behind the eye and yellow fin margins, juveniles by the numerous black spots. Widespread Indo-Pacific. Length to 60 cm.

Yellow-spotted Triggerfish
Pseudobalistes fuscus

Juveniles (above) typically occur solitary with small remote coral bommies on sand, in clear-water channels in depths of about 15 to 40 m. Adults generally deep and usually seen when spawning on deep sand flats adjacent to reefs in 30+ m depth. Widespread Indo-Pacific. Length to 55 cm, including pointed part of caudal fin, but excluding the filamentous parts.

Blue Triggerfish
Odonus niger

Occurs in schools in current channels, in entrances to lagoons and along reef walls. They feed on zooplankton in currents, often in massive schools that fill the entire water column. Easily recognised by the generally blue colour, when adult. Widespread Indo-Pacific, but different forms occur between the Indian and Pacific Oceans. Indian Ocean form has a longer stripe from the mouth that goes along entire head, compared to a short stripe in the Pacific form. Length to 40 cm includes long caudal fin lobes.

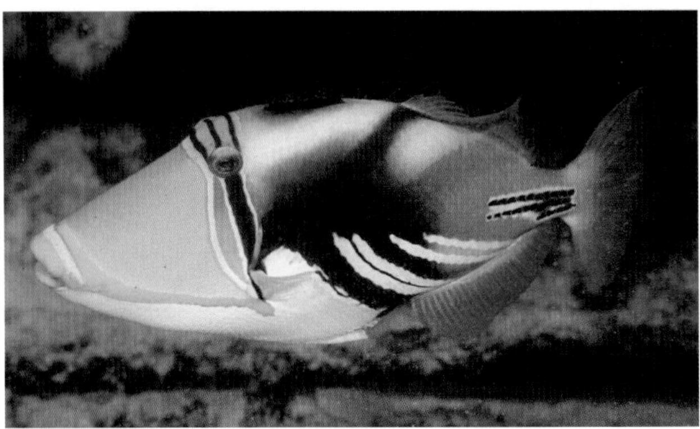

Picasso Triggerfish
Rhinecanthus aculeatus

Hawaiian Triggerfish. Occurs in shallow protected lagoons and harbours, often in silty habitats around rubble pieces or small bommies. They make shelters under solid objects by biting it and swimming fiercely to force away sand. Identified by the long snout and colour pattern. Widespread Indo-Pacific. Length to 25 cm.

Wedge-tail Triggerfish
Rhinecanthus rectangulus

Not common in the Maldives and mainly confined to shallow reef slopes exposed to surge on outer reefs. Sometimes seen openly swimming about, but a shy species that quickly runs for cover. Readily identified by long snout and large black markings. Widespread Indo-Pacific. Length to 25 cm.

Strickland's Triggerfish
Rhinecanthus cinereus

Little is known about this species and it appears to prefer clear outer reef conditions. The few specimens reported in the Maldives were at moderate depths, ranging to 25 m. Distinguished from similar species by the white semi-circle and white-edged black bar at tail fin base. Appears to be widespread Indian Ocean, but rare and only known from a few oceanic locations, including Mauritius and Andaman Sea. Length to 25 cm.

Bridled Triggerfish
Sufflamen fraenatum

Moderately common in the Maldives on deep open sand flats with remote patches of low reef and rubble at 30+ m depth. Identified by plain brown to yellowish colour all over, male with stripe along snout. Juveniles dark over the back and side pale with thin lines. Widespread Indo-Pacific. Length to 35 cm.

Photos: male left, juvenile right.

Boomerang Triggerfish
Sufflamen bursa

Occurs in clear inner reef and outer reef habitats with mixed invertebrate and algae habitat from surge zones to 90 m depth. The pale colour and boomerang-shaped stripe on the head, which passes through the back of the eye, identifies it.Widespread Indo-Pacific. Length to 30 cm.

Half-moon Triggerfish
Sufflamen chrysopterum

Inhabits inner reef crests and slopes and semi-exposed outer reef habitats with rubble and sand patches or borders of reef to about 35 m depth. Adults with distinctive tail fin pattern ending in a half-moon shaped white margin. Small juveniles are yellow on top and white from below eye level, separated by black stripe. Widespread Indo-Pacific. Length to 30 cm.

Black Triggerfish
Melichthys niger

Inhabits upper reef areas adjacent to deep water often feeding above on plankton. Males dominate females in loose groups in separate territories. Almost black with white along bases of the dorsal and anal fins. Tail lacks white and becomes lunate in large individuals. Widespread Indo-Pacific. Length to 30 cm.

Indian Triggerfish
Melichthys indicus

Occurs mainly on inner reef crests and slopes with mixed rich coral growth and rubble patches, to about 20 m depth. Digs holes below coral bases for shelter. Identified by general black colour and white lines at dorsal and anal fin bases Distinguished from the similar Black Triggerfish (above) by the rounded tail with a white edge. Widespread Indian Ocean, ranging to Java, Indonesia. Length to 24 cm.

Gilded Triggerfish
Xanthichthys auromarginatus

Occurs in moderate depths along outer reef walls, usually in 35+ m, where loose groups of mixed sexes gather in current areas to feed on zooplankton. Identified by shape and colour: females grey with series of small white spots along scale rows, males with additional orange fin margins and blue area from mouth to below eye. Widespread Indo-Pacific. Length to 22 cm.

Blue-line Triggerfish
Xanthichthys caeruleolineatus

Occurs deep along outer reefs, mainly known from depths over 100 m. May rise to shallower depth when feeding on zooplankton. Identified by mid-lateral blue line from behind the pectoral fin. Both sexes are similar, males with lines on cheek. Widespread Indo-Pacific. Length to 30 cm.

Oceanic Triggerfish
Canthidermis macrolepis

Adults are flighty and usually only seen when coming to deep sand flats to spawn. Juveniles found below floating weeds and adults school in oceanic waters. Identified by greyish colour, triangular dorsal and anal fins and large size. Known from the Red Sea and western Indian Ocean. Similar, but smaller-scaled Canthidermis maculata may also occasionally occur in the area. Length to 50 cm.

BOXFISHES
OSTRACIIDAE

A tropical family, with six genera and 20 species, with only one genus and two species commonly seen in the Maldives. Two other genera are reported from trawls or in the stomachs of pelagic predators, and may occur in deep water only. Boxfishes have a hard external skin made of fused scales that encloses much of the body, with holes for the movable parts: tail, fins, mouth, eyes and gills. In some species (not yet known from the Maldives) there are horn-like protrusions in front of the eyes or on the back. The skin or mucus may have poison that is released under stress. It can cause casualties when collecting aquarium fishes. Food comprises various invertebrates but most species favour worms from sandy bottoms.

Yellow Boxfish
Ostracion cubicus

A common species on most reef habitats but it changes habitat with growth. Large adults are mostly found on deep slopes and drop-offs on protected reefs to at least 40 m depth. Juveniles are often in shallow protected bays or harbours in holes and under ledges with urchins. Easily identified by the square yellow body and black spots when small. More elongate when adult. Widespread Indo-Pacific. Length to 45 cm.

Black Boxfish
Ostracion meleagris

Prefers clear water reefs with good coral cover on slopes and shallow drop-offs, usually in depths less than 20 m.Males recognised by the yellow spots and blue sides, and often swim openly about. Female is black with many small white spots over the body, and is more secretive in the reefs. Widespread Indo-Pacific. Length to 20 cm.

PUFFERFISHES
TETRAODONTIDAE

A large family, with about 20 genera and over 100 species, of which five genera and 18 species have been recorded from the Maldives. Dividable into subfamilies with the short-snouted TETRAODONTINAE, usually growing large, and long-snouted CANTHIGASTERINAE, that is mostly small. Pufferfishes are named for their ability to inflate themselves into balloon-like shapes. Any predator trying to eat them finds it gets more than it bargained for. In some cases this has killed not only the prey, but also the predator that couldn't let go. In addition, the skin and flesh is poisonous and can be fatal to humans if consumed. They are mostly bottom fishes that either live on reefs or on sand flats. Larvae are pelagic and a few species are completely pelagic. Food comprises a great variety of invertebrates, algae, and some are scavengers.

Saddled Pufferfish
Canthigaster valentini

Adults usually swim openly on reefs in pairs, juveniles are solitary and often shy in reefs. One of the best-known small pufferfish species and often noticed on reefs because of their distinctive colour pattern, a white body with black saddles and yellow tail. This serves as a warning to predators, "I'm poisonous", and there are a number of look-alikes that are not poisonous at all. The best example is the Mimic Filefish *Paraluteres prionurus* that will fool anybody that is not aware of it. Only the long transparent fins compared to the short paddle-like ones of the pufferfish will tell them apart (see Fig. 8., page 19). Sometimes the filefish swims near the pufferfish. Widespread Indo-Pacific. Length to 10 cm.

Crowned Pufferfish
Canthigaster coronata

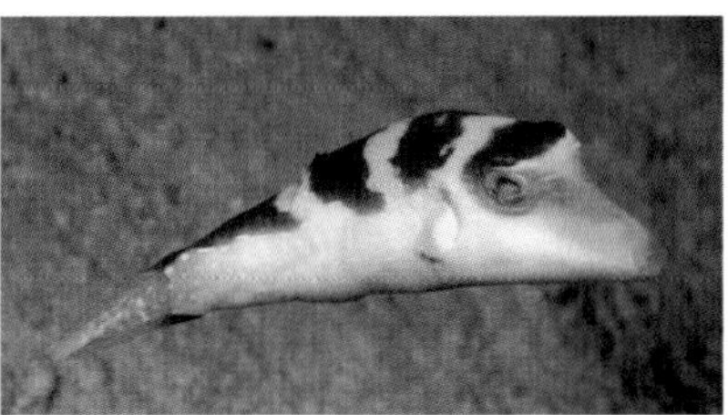

Usually seen deep on sand flats and slopes with patches or ridges with rich invertebrate growth such as seawhips and sponges, mostly in depths of 25+ m in the Maldives. Very similar to the saddled pufferfish but saddles are short. Maldives fish are very pale, probably because of the white sand, compared to the Pacific fish, which feature orange margins along black saddles and are ornamented with blue. Widespread Indo-Pacific, Indian Ocean and Pacific populations are slightly different and both forms occur in Bali, Indonesia. Length to 14 cm.

Smith's Pufferfish
Canthigaster smithae

Seen in clear inner reef habitat, usually solitary, often on slopes along bases of drop-offs or steep slopes, with mixed rubble and boulders in depths of about 30 m. Identified by dark top and white belly. West Indian Ocean only. Length to 13 cm.

Tyler's Pufferfish
Canthigaster tyleri

Seen in clear water on inner and outer reef walls, usually in large caves, swimming with belly towards vertical sides and often upside-down on ceilings. Adults are usually in loose pairs. Identified by pale side with close-set dark spots and scribbles on snout and over top of head. Widespread Indian Ocean, replaced by *C. leoparda* in Pacific. Length to 85 mm.

Ambon Pufferfish
Canthigaster amboinensis

Occurs on inner and outer reefs from shallow surge zones to about 15 m depth. A flighty species, it is secretive in small dark caves and crevices. Identified by light-blue spots over the body – whitish when juvenile – and lines radiating upward from behind the eyes. Widespread Indo-Pacific. Length to 12 cm.

False-eye Pufferfish

Canthigaster petersii

Occurs in shallow protected lagoons, harbours, and reef flats with rubble and sand mix. Adults usually seen in pairs, and variable in colour according to their habitat. Best identified by numerous small bluish-white spots and ring-like dark spot on the back, at the base of dorsal fin. Widespread western Indian Ocean. Length to 9 cm.

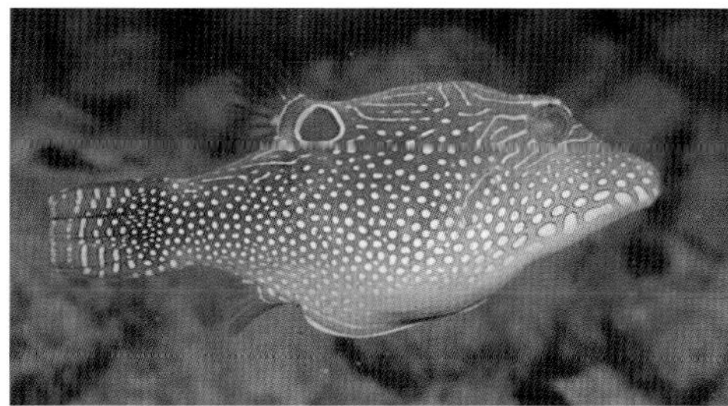

White-spotted Pufferfish

Canthigaster janthinoptera

Usually found on inner and outer reefs from shallow surge zones to at least 40 m depth, in rich coral algae mix habitat. A secretive species, found in small caves and crevices, or intertwining branching sponges. Identified by white spots over the body that increase in size below, and male develops short greenish lines radiating from the eyes. Widespread Indo-Pacific. Length to 8 cm.

Bennett's Pufferfish

Canthigaster bennetti

Occurs inshore often in silty habitats, algae reefs, harbours and protected weedy lagoons, to about 30 m depth. Adults usually in pairs and variable in colour according to their habitat. Identified by fine spots and a dark elongated spot on the back at base of dorsal fin. Widespread Indo-Pacific. Length to 9 cm.

Scribbled Pufferfish
Arothron mappa

Occurs in various clear water reef habitats with rich invertebrate growth. Often in caves during the day and adults are mainly active at night. Colour and spotting is highly variable, sometimes with numerous thin black lines. Usually short black lines radiate from the eyes, except very large individuals, which have lines encircling the eyes. Widespread Indo-Pacific. Length to 60 cm.

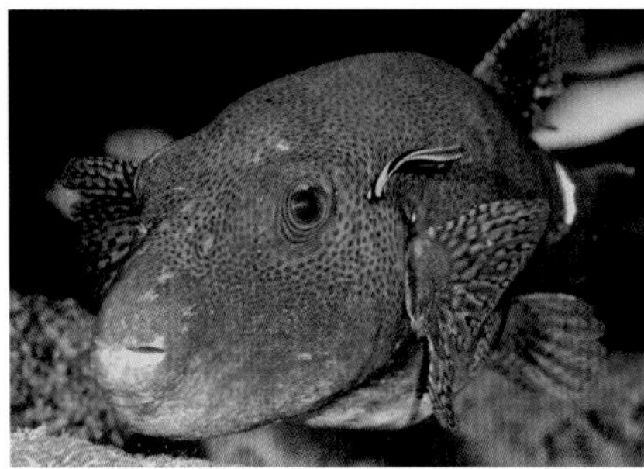

Guineafowl Pufferfish
Arothron meleagris

Occurs in protected inner reef habitats, usually at moderate depths but often shallow in the Maldives on reef crests in 6 m or just below, along top of drop-offs and slopes. Identified by numerous white spots all over the body, but sometimes has a bright yellow phase that may be completely yellow or with black blotches. Latter often confused with *A. nigropunctatus* but the black blotches feature tiny white spots. Sometimes found in pairs of different colour forms. Widespread Indo-Pacific. Length to 45 cm.

Black-spotted Pufferfish
Arothron nigropunctatus

Inhabits inner and outer reef slopes and crests with a mix of rich invertebrate growth and algae, often with sponges to depths of about 30 m. Highly variable in colour from grey to yellow-orange with few to many black spots, sometimes all yellow. Widespread Indo-Pacific. Length to 30 cm.

Yellow-eye Pufferfish
Arothron immaculatus

Occurs in mud and sand habitat, usually sleeping during the day in low depressions or partly buried. Active at night, feeding on invertebrates like sand-urchins. Identified by plain grey to brown colour, yellow eye and yellow to dark blotch around pectoral fin base. Widespread Indian Ocean, ranging to Australia and Indonesia, replaced by lined sibling *A. manilensis* in Pacific. Length to 30 cm.

Stars-and-Stripes Pufferfish
Arothron hispidus

Occurs in sheltered inshore habitats, coastal bays and deep open sand stretches between reefs with sparse growth, often semi silty habitats. Colour is highly variable, from grey to near black with white spots over back and lines along belly, and a black area around pectoral fin base. Widespread Indo-Pacific. Length to 50 cm.

Starry Pufferfish
Arothron stellatus

Occurs on deep slopes around inner and outer reefs, sometimes swimming in surface waters, juveniles inshore in silty habitats, often estuarine. Colour is highly variable, changing with growth from a fine zebra-lined pattern when a small juvenile, to small dark spots all over the body when adult. Widespread Indo-Pacific. Large species, length to 1 m.

PORCUPINEFISHES
DIODONTIDAE

A small family with six or seven genera and about 20 species worldwide, of which three genera and four species are reported from the Maldives. None are common and single individuals are usually sighted. Like the closely related pufferfishes, they quickly inflate themselves in defence when handled. The spines that normally lay flat, stand-up and project outwards so the whole fish becomes a prickly ball. Most species are active at night and shelter in caves during the day, usually at moderate depths. However, in the Maldives some large individuals can be seen hovering in the shallows above reefs, at times during the day, for no apparent reason. Diet comprises various hard-shelled invertebrates, but sometimes includes jellies.

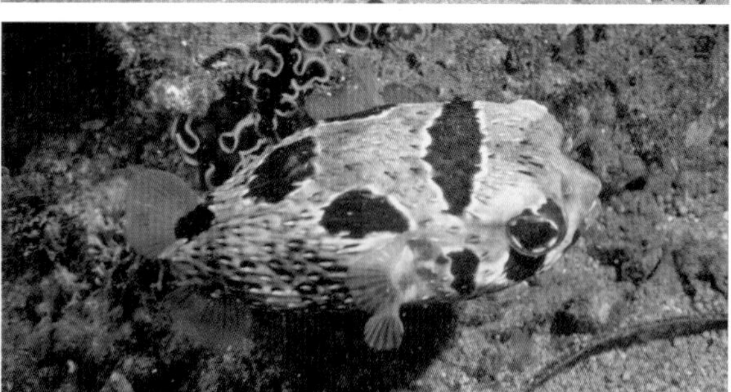

Blotched Porcupinefish
Diodon liturosus

Inhabits moderately deep inshore reefs to about 40 m depth. Hides during the day in crevices or below overhanging reefs, and is active at night, entering shallow sand flats, feeding onhard-shelled invertebrates. Identified by the large black blotches. Widespread Indo-Pacific. Length to 45 cm.

Black-spotted Porcupinefish
Diodon hystrix

Usually occurs on deep coastal reefs in caves during the day, but occasionally seen above in surface waters. Juveniles pelagic to moderate sizes and drift with weed rafts or other floating matter. Recognised by the numerous black spots over back and sides. Occurs widespread in all tropical seas. Length to 70 cm.

Few-spined Porcupinefish
Chilomycterus reticulatus

Occurs on deep coastal slopes, adults usually seen in depths of 20+ m, mainly entering shallow depths at night. Juveniles are pelagic to about 20 cm length and drift with floating weeds or objects. This species has few spines on the body, and fins have numerous small black spots. Widespread in all tropical seas, ranges into subtropical waters. Length to 55 cm.

Rounded Porcupinefish
Cyclichthys orbicularis

Inhabits clear protected reefs, slopes with sponge, and algal habitats. Often seen resting in large sponges during the day, active at night and feeds on the substrate on invertebrates. Mainly brownish, lacking black spots or blotches in the Maldives. Widespread Indo-Pacific. Small species, length to 20 cm.

INDEX TO FAMILIES AND SPECIES

ABOUT THE AUTHORS

Rudie H. Kuiter

Rudie H. Kuiter, author and principle photographer, has always had a passion for fishes. Dutch born, he started diving in Sydney, Australia, in 1964 and began drawing and photographing the various fish species, most of which were unknown at the time. As a research associate with the Australian Museum and Museum of Victoria, Rudie published scientific papers on biology and descriptions of new taxa. Articles on seahorses, seadragons and various other subjects of aquatic life have appeared in magazines around the world. He has dived temperate and tropical waters around Australia, and in many parts of the Indo-Pacific as far as Japan and the Maldives. He moved to Melbourne in 1980, working full time on fishes, and has published a number of books on fishes.

Tim Godfrey

Tim Godfrey, author for the sharks and rays, started diving while working as a journalist in Northwest Australia in 1983. He later travelled and worked on fishing boats and charter vessels in the Gulf of Carpentaria and Queensland and on abalone boats along Victoria's Southwest coast, before working as a dive instructor and guide on safari boats in the Maldives in 1986. In 1996 he started Atoll Editions and self-published Dive Maldives, A Guide to the Maldives Archipelago; Malways, Maldives Island Directory (later published as Atlas of the Maldives) and Maldives Divers and Travellers Map. He later published Photo Guide to Fishes of the Maldives, by Rudie Kuiter in 1998 and Marine Life of the Maldives, by Neville Coleman in 1999. He completed a Bachelor Science (Marine Biology) degree at James Cook University, Qld in 2013.